Teacher's Edition

Laboratory Manual

Prentice Hall

Physical Science

Concepts in Action

With Earth and Space Science

PEARSON

Prentice
Hall

Needham, Massachusetts
Upper Saddle River, New Jersey

CONTENTS

Laboratory Manual
Teacher's Edition

Prentice Hall *Physical Science: Concepts in Action*
With Earth and Space Science

ISBN 0-13-069985-3

1 2 3 4 5 6 7 8 9 10   07 06 05 04 03

PEARSON
Prentice
Hall

Introduction to the Teacher

Physical science is an exciting area of study for the high school student, and the Prentice Hall *Physical Science: Concepts in Action Laboratory Manual* is designed to capture this excitement through a variety of interesting and informative activities. In addition to reinforcing key concepts and scientific terms, these activities help students understand and appreciate the processes involved in scientific experimentation.

The Laboratory Manual contains 53 Laboratory Investigations directly related to the information presented in Prentice Hall *Physical Science: Concepts in Action*. It also contains 4 Laboratory Skills activities that give students an opportunity to practice and master specific laboratory skills, which include applying the scientific method and identifying errors. In addition, the Laboratory Manual includes worksheets for the end-of-chapter labs contained in Prentice Hall *Physical Science: Concepts in Action*.

The Laboratory Manual provides two Laboratory Investigations for each chapter of Prentice Hall *Physical Science: Concepts in Action*. The first investigation, designated Investigation A, is intended for use by average and above-average students. The second investigation, designated Investigation B, is meant for use by less-able students.

This Teacher's Edition provides the information you will need to perform the investigations and activities with your students. It includes answers to all investigations and activities, guidelines for laboratory safety and the use of animals in the classroom, comprehensive lists of laboratory equipment and materials, notes on the care and maintenance of live organisms, instructions on the preparation of specific chemical solutions, and a number of annotations that will help you organize and stock your biology laboratory and facilitate your teaching.

Laboratory Investigation Format

The investigations and activities in the Laboratory Manual are designed to strengthen students' laboratory, critical thinking, and science process skills and to provide a practical application of material presented in the student textbook. The easy-to-follow format of each Laboratory Investigation allows students to complete the investigations on their own, perhaps after an overview and brief explanation from you. This gives you an opportunity to provide the necessary help to those individuals or groups of students who require teacher assistance.

Each Laboratory Investigation has the following format:

Title A brief title presents the topic explored in the investigation. To the right of the title are teacher annotations regarding the time required for the investigation and the textbook pages in Prentice Hall *Physical Science: Concepts in Action*.

Background Information The Background Information section offers a short introduction that develops relevant concepts, or relates the Laboratory Investigation to specific concepts discussed in the student textbook. In a few cases, this section may also provide new concepts and terms specific to the investigation.

Problem Each Laboratory Investigation challenges the student by introducing a problem in the form of a question or series of questions. Students should be able to solve the problem(s) upon successful completion of the Laboratory Investigation.

Pre-Lab Discussion Asking them to identify the role of certain materials or the reasons for specific steps in the Procedure, questions in this section prepare students for the active understanding needed to take full advantage of the Laboratory Investigation. Questions in this section may also highlight safety procedures to which students should pay careful attention.

Materials This section lists all materials required to conduct the investigation. The quantity of material for each investigation is indicated for individual students, pairs of students, or groups of students. Teacher annotations on how to prepare materials specific to the investigation are found in or near the Materials section. The necessary equipment and materials for all of the Laboratory Investigations are listed alphabetically and by category on pages T9 to T16.

Safety If a Laboratory Investigation requires specific safety precautions, students are alerted to that fact in the special Safety section as well as in the Procedure. The Safety section is intended to make students aware of potential hazards before the investigation is begun, thereby decreasing the risk of accidents.

Procedure This section provides a detailed step-by-step outline of the Laboratory Investigation procedure. Diagrams are included where necessary to further explain a technique or illustrate an experimental setup.

The Procedure contains a number of symbols and instructions that guide students as the lab is performed. Safety symbols, which appear next to certain steps in the Procedure, signal students to begin following specific safety precautions for an indicated step in the procedure and all following steps. **CAUTION** statements within the steps of the Procedure warn students of possible hazards and indicate how accidents can be avoided. **Notes** in the Procedure direct students' attention to special directions or techniques. At the end of some steps in the Procedure, students may be instructed to record data or answer questions.

In keeping with the traditional scientific method, observations are recorded in each investigation. Observations are often recorded by filling in data tables, graphing data, labeling diagrams, and drawing observed structures, as well as answering general questions.

In the Teacher's Edition, annotations to the questions in Procedure and Analysis and Conclusions are printed in red on the pages corresponding to the student pages. These annotations include answers to objective questions, sample drawings and diagrams, and anticipated student data when these can be predicted.

Analysis and Conclusions Questions in this section are designed to assist students in answering the investigation's Problem, relating the investigation to concepts learned in the textbook, and drawing conclusions about the results of their investigation. Using data gathered during the investigation and knowledge gained from the textbook and Introduction, students are asked to analyze and interpret their experimental results. Many questions emphasize possible applications of the experiment and allow students to relate the investigation to real-life situations.

Go Further Each Laboratory Investigation concludes with a section entitled Go Further. This section suggests additional activities that may be used to enrich or supplement the investigation. The Go Further activities may also be used as alternatives to the Laboratory Investigation. Complete instructions are included so that individual students can perform the Go Further activities without additional teacher help.

Inquiry Labs Several of the investigations contained in the Laboratory Manual are Inquiry labs, which involve experiments designed to address a question that the students cannot answer before performing the lab.

Design Your Own Experiment Labs The Laboratory Manual also contains investigations that ask students to develop their own experiments. In these activities, the Pre-Lab Discussion helps guide students in planning their experiments. A list of **Suggested Materials** follows. In place of a set Procedure, a section titled **Design Your Experiment** leads students through the planning and performance of their own experiments.

Modifying the Laboratory Investigations

School schedules often do not permit extended laboratory periods. The Laboratory Manual provides a number of options to help you circumvent the difficulties associated with having limited laboratory time. First, most investigations require only 30 to 40 minutes and thus can be completed within a single class period. Second, the investigations are often divided into two or more parts. This provides flexibility by allowing you to select the parts of the investigation that best suit your needs, objectives, and laboratory situation. In addition, you can often schedule the parts of an investigation to be performed during different class periods, as your schedule permits. Finally, a number of the investigations have annotations that suggest specific ways in which the investigation may be modified for a shorter laboratory period.

Correlation Between Textbook Chapters and Laboratory Investigations

The Laboratory Manual is designed to accompany Prentice Hall *Physical Science: Concepts in Action* in the presentation of a comprehensive physical science program for high school students. When used in conjunction with the textbook, the Laboratory Manual reinforces, expands, and enhances the student's experiences of reading the textbook and participating in classroom discussions. Although the investigations are numbered to correspond to chapters in Prentice Hall *Physical Science: Concepts in Action*, they can be used with any high school physical science program.

Guidelines for Laboratory Safety

Safety should be an integral part of the planning, preparation, and implementation of a laboratory program. Both the science teacher and the student are responsible for creating and maintaining an enjoyable, instructional, and safe environment in the science laboratory.

A number of general safety concerns are discussed. You should also refer to pages x through xiii in the Student Edition of the Laboratory Manual for a detailed discussion of safety rules and procedures. You may want to expand or modify the safety guidelines, procedures, and rules suggested here according to local and state government regulations and policies, as well as school regulations and policies. The school administration should be able to provide you with specifics on local safety requirements.

General Safety Considerations

Emphasis on proper safety precautions for each laboratory investigation is an essential part of any pre-laboratory discussion. Prior to each investigation, demonstrate the proper use of the required equipment. Demonstrate any potentially hazardous procedure used in that investigation. Always wear the required safety protective devices during the demonstrations and the investigations. If students are required to wear safety goggles, you and any visitors to the class must also wear them.

During an investigation, move about the laboratory to keep constant watch for potentially dangerous situations. Behavior that is inappropriate to a laboratory situation should be curtailed immediately. Wild play and practical jokes are forbidden in the laboratory. Once students realize that the practice of safety is a required part of the course, they will accept a serious approach to laboratory work.

Any laboratory investigation a student performs should have your prior approval. Students should never work in the laboratory without adult supervision. At the conclusion of the lab investigation, cleanup should follow authorized guidelines for waste disposal. The laboratory should be restored to a safe condition for the next class.

Classroom Organization

Furniture and equipment in the laboratory should be arranged to minimize accidents. Assign students to laboratory stations. Each station should be equipped with a flat-topped table and laboratory bench. Do not use desks with slanted tops. Provide several locations where students can obtain needed supplies. Control traffic flow in the room to prevent collisions between students who are carrying or handling equipment. Tell students to leave their personal property in a designated location, away from the laboratory stations. Do not use the floor and benches for storage area. Stress that good housekeeping is important in maintaining safe laboratory conditions. Students should keep all laboratory work areas clean. Unnecessary papers, books, and equipment should be removed from working areas.

Be sure that water faucets, hot plates, gas outlets, and alcohol or Bunsen burners are turned off when not in use.

Safety Equipment

Any classroom where laboratory investigations are done should contain at least one each of the following pieces of safety equipment: (1) fire extinguisher, (2) fire blanket, (3) fire alarm, (4) phone or intercom to the office, (5) eyewash station, (6) safety shower, (7) safety hood, and (8) first-aid kit. If any of these basic pieces of safety equipment are not available, you may need to modify your laboratory program until the situation is remedied.

Make sure students know the location and proper use of all safety equipment. Where appropriate and practical, have students handle or operate the equipment so that they become familiar with it. Make sure all safety equipment is in good working order. All malfunctions should be promptly reported in writing to the proper school or district administrator.

Fire Equipment At the beginning of the school year, you may wish to give each student the opportunity to actually operate a fire extinguisher, as the sound and action of a CO_2 fire extinguisher can be quite alarming to those who never used one. You may also want to have students practice smothering imaginary flames on one another with the fire blanket.

Eyewash Station The eyewash station should be used if chemicals are splashed onto the face or eyes. The exposed area should be left in the running water for 15 minutes.

Safety Shower The shower is used when chemicals have been spilled on a student's body or clothing. The student should remove contaminated clothing and stand under the shower until the chemical is completely diluted. Have a bathrobe or some other type of replacement clothing handy in case the student's clothing must be removed.

You may want to set up one or two spill kits in your laboratory. The contents of a spill kit are used to neutralize chemicals such as acids and bases so that they can be cleaned up more easily. Baking soda (sodium bicarbonate) can be used to neutralize acids. Vinegar (acetic acid) can be used to neutralize bases. Commercial spill kits for acids, bases, and a number of other chemicals are available from supply houses.

Safety Hood Use a safety hood whenever students are working with volatile or noxious chemicals. Make sure that the room is well-ventilated when students are using any kind of chemicals or are working with preserved specimens. Warn students of the flammability and toxicity of various chemicals.

First-Aid Kit A typical first-aid kit contains an assortment of antiseptics, bandages, gauze pads, and scissors. Most also contain simple instructions for use. Be sure to read the instructions if you are not familiar with basic first-aid procedures. A first-aid kit should be taken on all field trips. For field trips, you may wish to add such items as a bee-sting kit, meat tenderizer, tweezers, and calamine lotion. Do not dispense medication (including aspirin).

Cleanup

Before beginning an investigation, instruct students in the proper cleanup procedures. Mark certain containers for the disposal of wastes and the collection of soiled glassware and equipment. Have students dispose of broken glassware in a separate trash container. Before the end of the laboratory period, have students unplug microscopes and other pieces of equipment and put them away in their proper location. Have students wash glassware, wipe up spills, and do whatever else is necessary to clean up their work area. At the conclusion of the laboratory investigation, the room should be restored to a clean and safe condition for the next class. You may wish to institute a policy of not dismissing the class until the laboratory area meets with your approval.

Preparations and the Storage Room

Reagents stored in the biology stockroom should be clearly labeled and stored safely. Take inventory of reagents frequently and keep up-to-date records of their use. Check local and state regulations for maximum permissible amounts of reagents allowed in school. In case of fire or vandalism, inform the authorities of possible hazards to the community. Keep all chemicals in a locked storage area that is accessible only to you or individuals under your direct supervision.

Some chemicals are incompatible and should be stored separately. Check local and state laws for regulations on storage of flammable liquids. The National Fire Protection Association recommends that flammable liquids be stored in vented, flame-resistant cabinets. Store large containers near floor level. Make sure that storage shelves have a raised lip at the front to prevent containers from sliding forward.

Hazardous Materials

Some reagents can be explosive and should not be on the premises. If found, they should be removed by trained fire or police bomb squads or by other qualified officials.

If you have doubts about the hazards of any reagent in the stockroom, contact an appropriate agency (NIOSH or a local health agency).

Known carcinogens commonly found in school science laboratories include the following: arsenic powder, arsenic trichloride, arsenic pentoxide, arsenic trioxide, asbestos, benzene, benzidine, chromium powder, formaldehyde, lead arsenate, sodium arsenate.

Probable carcinogens include the following: acrylonitrile, cadmium chloride, cadmium powder, cadmium sulfate, carbon tetrachloride, chloroform, ethylene oxide, nickel powder.

Exercise great care in using refrigerators. Never store flammable liquids in a refrigerator unless it is explosion-proof. Do not store food where microbial cultures are stored. Clean refrigerators frequently and safely discard old material.

Laboratory Glassware

Probably the most common school laboratory accidents involve cuts from chipped or broken glassware and burns from hot glassware. Discard any glassware that has a crack or chip. Use only borosilicate glassware. Fire-polish the ends of glass tubing. Allow hot glassware to cool on a hot pad for several minutes before picking it up. If an accident should happen, first aid for minor cuts and burns is immersion in cool running water. For cuts that are bleeding heavily, apply pressure with folded toweling or gauze. Call a health professional immediately.

To insert glass tubing into a stopper, lubricate the stopper hole and the tubing. Wrap the tubing in several layers of toweling and gently work the tubing into the stopper, using a twisting motion and keeping the hands as close together as possible. Wear heavy gloves. Remove the tubing in the same manner as soon as possible. Tubing that is stuck is nearly impossible to remove without cutting the stopper.

Measuring small amounts of liquids with pipettes is common in investigations. But never pipette by mouth. Use rubber suction bulbs designed for use with pipettes or pipette fillers.

Field Studies

Before taking the students on a field study, examine the area for possible safety hazards. Look for terrain or water hazards and poisonous plants and animals. Obtain the necessary written permission from parents and school authorities. Instruct students on proper dress and behavior. Make sure that students are thoroughly familiar with the investigations they are to conduct. If students are to form small groups, decide in advance when and where they will reassemble. Do not allow any student to travel alone.

Identify any students who have special health problems, especially allergies. Alert these students to potential hazards. Be sure they are adequately prepared to deal with emergencies.

Guidelines for Safe Disposal of Laboratory Wastes

Every effort should be made to recover, recycle, and reuse materials used in the laboratory. When disposal is required, however, specific procedures should be followed in order to ensure that your school complies with local, state, and federal regulations.

1. Discard only dry paper into ordinary wastebaskets.

2. Discard broken glass into a separate container clearly marked "For Broken Glass Only."

3. Acidic or basic solutions need to be neutralized before disposal. Slowly add dilute sodium hydroxide to acids and dilute hydrochloric acid to bases until pH paper shows that they are no longer strongly acidic or basic. Then flush the solutions down the drain with a lot of water.

4. Before each investigation, instruct your students concerning where and how they are to dispose of chemicals that are used or produced during the investigation. Specific teacher notes addressing disposal are provided on each lab as appropriate.

5. Keep each excess or used chemical in a separate container; do not mix them. This allows for possible recycling or reuse. It also eliminates unexpected reactions or the need for expensive separation by a contractor if the wastes must be disposed of professionally.

6. Only nonflammable, neutral, nontoxic, nonreactive, and water-soluble chemicals should be flushed down the drain.

Laboratory Procedures

The purpose of this section is to provide some general information about preparing solutions and making substitutions for pH indicators. For more specific information regarding the preparation and use of solutions in a particular Laboratory Investigation, consult the on-page annotations.

Solutions

General guidelines for preparing solutions and media include the following:

1. Prepare necessary solutions well in advance of the investigations in which they will be used. Each solution should be clearly labeled with its name, concentration, date of preparation, and any appropriate warnings such as toxic or flammable.

2. Always use clean glassware that has been washed with a low-sudsing laboratory soap. All glassware should be rinsed thoroughly in distilled water before use.

3. Mix each solution in a beaker or flask that holds 100 to 300 mL more than the amount of solution being prepared.

4. Use distilled water to make all preparations. Tap water may contain chemicals that alter the properties of solutions.

5. Pour concentrated acids and bases into water, stirring constantly. Never pour water into concentrated acids or bases.

6. Add solvents to solutes. Stir until solute is completely dissolved.

7. Store stains in dropper bottles.

Percentage Solutions: Volume/Volume To prepare a solution of a given percentage, dissolve the number of milliliters of solute equal to the percentage in enough solvent to make 100 mL of solution. For example, a 10% solution of hydrochloric acid (HCl) can be made by adding 10mL of concentrated HCl to enough distilled water to bring the volume to 100 mL.

Percentage Solutions: Mass/Volume To prepare a solution of a given percentage, dissolve the number of grams of solute equal to the percentage in enough solvent to make 100 mL of the solution. For example, a 3% solution of sodium chloride (NaCl) can be made by adding 3 g NaCl to a graduated cylinder and then adding enough distilled water to bring the volume to 100 mL.

Reducing the Concentration of a Solution To reduce the concentration of an existing solution, pour the number of milliliters of the existing solution that is equal to the percentage of the new concentration into a graduated cylinder. Add enough distilled water to bring the volume in milliliters to an amount equal to the percentage of the original solution. For example, to reduce an 80% glucose solution to 20%, pour 20 mL of 80% glucose solution into a graduated cylinder. Add enough distilled water to bring the volume to 80 mL of 20% glucose.

Indicator Substitutions

In the science laboratory, the pH indicators that are suggested for use can often be replaced by others that are equally effective. The following table lists some common indicators, the pH values at which they undergo a color change, and the expected color change.

Indicator	pH Value at Which Color Change Occurs	Color Change
thymol blue (acid)	1.5–2.5	red to yellow
bromphenol blue	3.0–4.5	yellow to blue
Congo red	3.0–5.0	blue to red
methyl orange	3.0–4.5	orange-red to yellow
litmus	4.5–8.5	red to blue
alizarin red	5.0–7.0	yellow to red
bromcresol purple	5.5–7.0	yellow to purple
bromthymol blue	6.0–7.5	yellow to blue
phenol red	6.5–8.0	yellow to red
neutral red	7.0–8.0	red to yellow
cresol red	7.0–9.0	yellow to red
thymol blue (alkaline)	8.0–10.0	yellow to blue
phenolpthalein	8.0–10.0	colorless to red
alizarin yellow	10.0–12.0	colorless to yellow

Laboratory Investigations Materials and Equipment

Note: Safety equipment has not been listed. A laboratory apron, safety goggles, and plastic or heat-resistant gloves should be worn when required.

Item	Quantity per Group	Laboratory Investigation
Alpha-radiation source, sealed	1	10B
Aluminum		
baking dish, large rectangle	1	23B
gum wrapper foil	1 piece	20B
foil	1 piece	2A, 20B
shot or turning	1	7A
Ammonium chloride	10 g	8B
Antacid tablets, 3 brands	3	8A
Baking soda	1 spoonful	24B
Balance	1	15A
triple-beam	1	2B, 7B, 8B
Ball		
plastic foam	2	4A
steel, 4-cm diameter	1	12B
Ball bearing, steel, 1.5-cm diameter	1	25A
Balloon	2	20B
Barium nitrate solution, 0.1 M	10 mL	5B
Beads	1 package	4A
Beaker		
150-mL	3	1B, 8B
250-mL	4	8A, 9B, 13A, 15A, 22B
500-mL	1	1A, 3, 9A
600-mL graduated	2	13B
1000-mL	1	16A
Benedict's solution	1 L	9A
Biuret reagent	24 drops	9A
Board or block, wooden		3A, 10B, 12A, 12B, 15A,
flat, 3-cm thick	1.5-m piece	15B, 17A, 25A
wedge	10-cm piece	14A
Book	3	12A, 12B, 15A, 25A
Bottle		
2-L plastic	2	3A, 24B
600-mL, plastic	1	15A
plastic with spray pump	1	22B
Box, transparent plastic with lid	1	23A
Brick, 8-cm height	4	15B
Bromthymol blue solution	10 mL	8A
Bunsen burner	1	3A, 6B, 7B, 16B
Buret, NaOH solution on ring stand	1	8A
Calcium carbonate chip	1	2A
Calcium nitrate solution, 0.1 M	10 mL	5B
Calculator	1	11A, 12B, 25B
Candle holder	1	2A
Capacitor		
4600-microfarads	1	10A
6000-microfarads	1	10A
Carbon grains	0.5 cup	20A

Item	Quantity per Group	Laboratory Investigation
Cardboard		
box, small	1	11B
flat piece	1-m piece	11B, 17B, 20B, 25B, 26B
tube	2	18B, 25A
Chlorophyll solution	15 mL	18A
Clamp	1	12A
utility	1	13B
Clay triangle	1	6B
Clips, alligator	4	10A, 20A
Coat hanger	2	4A
Compass	1	19B, 21A, 21B
drawing	1	26A
Container		
cylindrical, plastic	3 different diameters	16A
square, transparent, 7 cm × 7 cm	1	19A
Contour map, enlarged copy	1	23A
Copper		
strips	2	20A
powder	1	7B
uninsulated wire	1-cm piece	7A
Copper sulfate		
solution	0.1 M	2A
Cornstarch	1 spoonful	9A
Cork, strip or disk	3-cm piece	21B
Crucibles	2	6B
DC voltmeter	1	10A
DC power source	1	10A
Denatured ethanol		
(ethyl alcohol)	50 mL	2B
Dropper pipet	2	8A, 9A, 10B
Drum	1	17A
Dry cell, 1.5-V	1	20A
Egg		
white	1	9A
yolk	1	9A
Evaporating dish	1	7B
Felt, black	1 piece	10B
File	1	21B
triangular	1	19B
Film canister	1	13A
Fishing line	2-m piece	4A, 12A, 14B
Fishing weight	1	15B
Flashlight, powerful	1	10B
Flask		
250-mL	2	3A
Funnel	1	24B
Game die	1	4B
Gauze		
metal	1	3A
wire	1	7B, 13B, 16B

Item	Quantity per Group	Laboratory Investigation
Gelatin		
powdered	5 mL	9A
sugar-free mix	20 mL	9B
Glucose	1 spoonful	9A
Glue, fast-drying	few drops	10B
Graduated cylinder	2	19B, 22B, 24A
10-mL	3	7A, 8A, 9A
25-mL	1	24B
50-mL	1	1A, 8A
100-mL	2	1B, 2B, 3A, 3B, 8B, 16A
250-mL	2	3B
Hand lens	1	8B, 22A
Hot plate	1	8B, 9A, 9B, 16A
Hydrochloric acid	1 M	7A, 8A
0.1 M	100 mL	8A
1 M	25 mL	7A
dilute	10 mL	22A
Ice		
crushed	1	3A
cube	1	1B
dry	1	10B
Index card		
lined	25	5A, 26A
unlined	100	6A
Iodine solution	16 drops	9A
Iron, nail or pellet	1	7A
Isopropyl alcohol, 95%	100 mL	3B, 10B
Jar		
gallon pickle	1	24A
large glass w/screw-on lid	1	10B, 20B
Lamp		
with incandescent bulb	1	18A, 24B
1.5-V with socket	1	20A
Light source, bright	1	18B
Magnesium, ribbon	1-cm length	7A
Magnesium chloride solution, 0.1 M	10 mL	2A
Magnesium nitrate solution, 0.2 M	10 mL	5B
Magnet		
alnico	1	25A
bar	1	21A, 21B
Margarine	1 pat	9A
Mass	1 kg	14B
with hook	500 g	14A
Matches	1	2A, 16B
safety	1	24A
Meter stick	1	1A, 11A, 11B, 12A, 12B, 14A, 15A, 15B, 17A, 23A, 25A, 26A
wooden	1	17B

Item	Quantity per Group	Laboratory Investigation
Measuring rope	1	17A
Milk		
skim	10 mL	9A
whole	10 mL	9A
Mirror, small	1	19A
Mirror support	1	19A
Modeling clay	1 lump	23A
Needle	2	21B
Orange juice	10 mL	9A
Paper cup	3	9B, 16B
Paper towel	1	2B, 8B, 9A, 15A, 18B, 22A, 22B
Paper		
blotting, thick	1 piece	10B
graph	1 sheet	3A, 4B, 8B, 10A, 16A, 18B
newspaper	1 sheet	23B
notebook	3 sheets	5B, 25B
strip, 60 cm × 40 cm	1 piece	25A
unlined	1 sheet	19A
Paraffin	1 spoonful	6B
Paraffin candle	1	2A
Pebbles	2 cups	22B, 23B
Pen, nonpermanent	1	23A
Pencil	1	25A
colored	3	16A, 18A, 25B
glass-marking	1	1B, 2A, 6B, 7A, 8A, 9A
grease	1	16A, 21B
red	1	4B, 18B
with eraser	1	26B
Pennies	10	1A
Periodic table	1	5A
Petri dish	1	21B
Phenolphthalein-solution		
hydroxide solution	15 mL	18A
Pie tin, metal	1	16B
Pipe cleaners	1	4A
Plastic cup	1	15A, 20A
Plastic tubing	2 40-cm pieces	3A, 22B
Polarizing filters, square 2 cm × 2 cm	2	18B
Potassium carbonate solution, 0.2 M	10 mL	5B
Potassium chromate solution, 0.2 M	10 mL	5B
Potassium permanganate solution	15 mL	18A
Potassium sulfate solution, 0.2 M	10 mL	5B
Potato, minced	1	9A
Protractor	1	19A, 19B
Pulley		
double	2	14B
single	2	14B
Pushpins	2 pins	25B, 26B
green	1 package	4A
red	1 package	4A

Item	Quantity per Group	Laboratory Investigation
Reflector, from flashlight	1	19B
Ring		
iron	1	3A, 6B, 7B, 13B, 14B
support	1	16B
Ring stand	1	3A, 6B, 7B, 12A, 12B, 13B, 14B, 16B, 19B
Rod		
glass	1	20B
metal	1-m piece	12A, 17B
Rocks		
igneous (basalt, granite)	several	22A
metamorphic (marble, slate)	several	22A
sedimentary (sandstone, limestone)	several	22A
Rubber band, 15-cm circ.; 0.5 cm width	1	24A
Rubber stopper		
2-hole for flask	1	3A
1-hole with Celsius non-mercury thermometer	2	24B
Ruler		
metric	1	4B, 10A, 13A, 18B, 23B, 25B, 26A
30-cm	1	19A, 26B
Sand	200 mL	3B, 23B
Salt water	100 mL	2B, 3A
Salt		
rock	10 g	8B
table	10 g	8B
Scoop	2	7B, 8B
Scissors	1	4A, 10B, 11B, 14A, 18B, 20B
Silk	1 piece	20B
Sodium carbonate solution, 0.1 M	10 mL	2A
Sodium chloride	1 spoonful	6B
Sodium hydroxide solution		
0.1 M	200 mL	8A
0.5 M	5 mL	8A
Spatula	4	6B, 9A
Spectroscope	1	18A
Spherical object	2	11B
Spoon	3	8A, 8B
measuring, SI units	1	9B
plastic	1	24B
Spot plate	1	5B
Splints, wooden	3	9B
Spring scale, 10–20 N	1	14A, 14B
Stirring rod, glass	3	3B, 8A, 8B
Storage bag, plastic freezer, 26 cm × 26 cm	1	24A
String	1-m piece	11A, 14A, 15B, 20B, 25B
Strontium nitrate solution, 0.1 M	10 mL	5B
Stopwatch	1	11B, 12B, 17A
Straight pin	4	19A
Sugar	1 spoonful	6B

Item	Quantity per Group	Laboratory Investigation
Sugar solution		
20%	10 mL	18B
30%	10 mL	18B
40%	10 mL	18B
unknown	10 mL	18B
Sundan IV dye	1 spoonful	9A
Switch	1	10A
Tap water		
cold	80 mL	22B, 23B, 24A
hot (50°C)	600 mL	16A, 22B, 24B
Tape	1 roll	19B, 25B, 26A
duct	1 roll	18B
masking	1 roll	3A, 4B, 11A, 11B, 13A, 15B, 20B, 25A, 26B
transparent	1 roll	18B
Test tube	5	2A, 6B, 7A, 19B
medium	8	9A
stoppers	8	6B, 9A
Test-tube clamp	2	19B
Test-tube rack	1	2A, 6B, 7A, 9A
Thermometer		
Celsius	3	1A, 1B, 8B, 16A, 16B, 19B
Celsius, non-mercury	1	3A
Thermometer clamp	1	16B
Tongs	1	6B, 7B, 9A
Tray, plastic	1	10B
Tubing, flexible	40-cm piece	13B
Vegetable oil	200 mL	9A, 22B
Vial, glass with cap	1	18B
Vinegar	20 mL	24B
Watch or clock	1	1B, 2A, 6B, 7B, 8B, 9A, 10B, 13B, 16A, 22B
with secondhand	1	10A, 17B, 26B
Weights, identical small	2	26B
White vinegar (acetic acid solution)	1	2A
Wire	15-cm piece	14A
connecting	4-m piece	20A, 21A
insulated	5	10A
thick	1 piece	20B
Wool flannel	1 piece	20B
Zinc, mossy	1	7A

Materials Inventory

Equipment

Aluminum
    gum wrapper foil
    foil
    shot or turning

Baking dish
Balance, triple beam
Ball
    plastic
    steel
Ball bearing, steel
Balloon
Beads
Board or block, wooden
Book
Bottle
    2-L plastic
    600-mL plastic
    plastic with spray pump
Box, transparent plastic w/lid
Brick
Bunsen burner

Calculator
Candle holder
Capacitor
    4600-microfarads
    6000-microfarads
Cardboard
    box, small
    flat piece
    tube
Clamp, utility
Clay triangle
Clips, alligator
Coat hanger
Compass
Container
    cylindrical, plastic
    square, transparent
Contour map, enlarged copy
Copper
    strips
    uninsulated wire
Cork, strip or disk
Crucibles

DC voltmeter
DC power source
Drum
Dry cell, 1.5-V

Evaporating dish

Felt, black
File, triangular
Film canister
Fishing line
Fishing weight
Flashlight
Funnel

Game die
Gauze, wire
Glue, fast-drying

Hand lens
Hot plate

Index card
    lined
    unlined
Iron, nail or pellet

Lamp
    with incandescent bulb
    1.5-V with socket
Light source, bright

Magnet
    alnico
    bar
Mass
    with hook
Matches
    safety
Meter stick
    wooden
Measuring rope
Mirror, small
Mirror support
Modeling clay

Needle

Paper cup
Paper towel
Paper
    blotting, thick
    graph
    newspaper
    notebook
    strip
    unlined
Paraffin candle

Pebbles
Pen, nonpermanent
Pencil
    colored
    glass-marking
    grease
Pennies
Periodic table
Pie tin, metal
Pipe cleaners
Plastic cup
Plastic tubing
Polarizing filters
Protractor
Pulley
    double
    single
Pushpins
    green
    red

Reflector, from flashlight
Ring
    iron
    support
Ring stand
Rod
    glass
    metal
Rocks
    igneous
    metamorphic
    sedimentary
Rubber band
Rubber stopper
    2-hole for flask
    1-hole with Celsius non-
    mercury thermometer
Ruler
    Metric
    30-cm

Sand
Scoop
Scissors
Silk
Spatula
Spectroscope
Spoon
    measuring
    plastic
Spot plate

Splints, wooden
Spring scale, 10-20 N
Stirring rod, glass
Storage bag, plastic freezer
String
Stopwatch
Straight pin
Switch

Tape
  duct
  masking
  transparent
Test-tube clamp
Test-tube rack
Thermometer, Celsius
Thermometer clamp
Tongs
Tray, plastic
Tubing, flexible

Watch or clock
  with secondhand
Weights, identical small
Wire
  connecting
  insulated
Wool, flannel

Glassware

Beaker
  150-mL
  250-mL
  500-mL
  600-mL, graduated
  1000-mL
Buret

Dropper pipets

Flask
  250-mL

Graduated cylinder
  10-mL
  25-mL
  50-mL
  100-mL
  250-mL

Jar
  large glass w/screw-on lid
  gallon pickle

Petri dish

Test tubes, medium

Vial, glass with cap

Chemical Supplies

Alpha-radiation source
Ammonium chloride

Barium nitrate solution
Benedict's solution
Biuret reagent
Bromthymol blue solution

Calcium carbonate chip
Calcium nitrate solution
Carbon grains
Chlorophyll solution
Copper powder
Copper sulfate solution

Denatured ethanol

Glucose

Hydrochloric acid

Iodine solution
Isopropyl alcohol, 95%

Magnesium, ribbon
Magnesium chloride solution
Magnesium nitrate solution

Paraffin
Phenolphthalein solution
Potassium chromate solution
Potassium nitrate solution
Potassium sulfate solution

Salt
  rock
  table
Sodium carbonate solution
Sodium chloride
Sodium hydroxide solution
Strontium nitrate solution
Sugar solution
Sundan IV dye

Zinc, mossy

Consumables

Antacid tablets

Baking soda

Dry ice

Egg

Gelatin

Ice

Margarine

Milk
  skim
  whole

Orange juice

Potato, minced

Sugar

Tap water
  cold
  hot (50°C)

Vegetable oil
Vinegar

White vinegar
  (acetic acid solution)

Suppliers of Laboratory Materials and Equipment

Arbor Scientific
P.O. Box 2750
Ann Arbor, MI 48106
www.arborsci.com

Carolina Biological Supply
    Company
2700 York Road
Burlington, NC 27215
336-584-0381
carolina@carolina.com

Central Scientific Company
11222 Melrose Ave.
Franklin Park, IL 60131
847-451-0150
cenconet.com

Delta Biologicals
P.O. Box 26664
Tucson, AZ 85726-6664
520-745-7878
deltabio@flash.net

Edmund Scientific Company
101 E. Gloucester Pike
Barrington, NJ 08007
609-547-3488
edsci.com

Fisher Scientific Educational
    Materials Division
485 S Frontage Road
Burr Ridge, IL 60521
800-955-1177
fisheredu.com

Frey Scientific Company
905 Hickory Lane
Mansfield, OH 44905
419-589-1900
beckleycardy.com

Hubbard Scientific
1120 Halbleib
Chippewa Falls, WI 54729
800-289-9299
amep.com

Lab-Aids, Inc.
17 Colt
Ronkonkoma, NY 11779
516-737-1133

Lab Safety Supply Inc.
401 S. Wright Rd.
Janesville, WI 53546-8729
800-356-0783
labsafety.com

901 Janesville Ave.
Fort Atkinson, WI 53538
800-558-9595
nascota.com

Nasco West Inc.
P.O. Box 3837
Modesto, CA 95352-3837
800-558-9595
nascota.com

Nebraska Scientific
A Division of Cygus
    Company Inc.
3823 Leavenworth Street
Omaha, NE 68105
402-346-7214
nebraskascientific.com

Sargent-Welch Scientific Co.
911 Commerce Ct.
Buffalo Grove, IL 60089
800-727-4368
sargentwelch.com

Science Kit and Boreal
    Laboratories
777 East Park Drive
Tonawanda, NY 14150
1-800-828-7777
sciencekit.com

Ward's Natural Science
    Establishment Inc.
5100 West Henrietta Road
Henrietta, NY 14467
716-359-2502
customer_service@wardsci.com

Laboratory Manual

Prentice Hall
Physical Science
Concepts in Action
With Earth and Space Science

PEARSON

Prentice Hall

Needham, Massachusetts
Upper Saddle River, New Jersey

Laboratory Manual

Prentice Hall
Physical Science
Concepts in Action
With Earth and Space Science

FIELD TESTERS

Robert W. Arts
Pikeville College
Pikeville, Kentucky

Peggy Lynn Bondurant
Mesquite High School
Gilbert, Arizona

Teresa Casal
Felix Varela Senior High School
Miami, Florida

Richelle Lee Dull
Vance High School
Charlotte, North Carolina

Yvonne Favaro
Englewood Cliffs, New Jersey

Mary Louise Freitas
Peoria High School
Peoria, Arizona

Karen S. Garner
Rutherford County Schools
Murfreesboro, Tennessee

Margaret A. Holzer
Chatham High School
Somerset, New Jersey

Susan McCullen
Big Rapids High School
Big Rapids, Michigan

David Petro
Cardinal Carter Secondary
  School
Leamington, Ontario, Canada

A. Marie Pool
Clinton High School
Clinton, Oklahoma

Alan Seidman
Margaretville Central School
Margaretville, New York

Evan P. Silberstein
Spring Valley High School
Spring Valley, New York

Lesia Thaisz
Gloversville High School
Gloversville, New York

James R. White
Southside High School
Chocowinity, North Carolina

John P. Wilbur
Caledonia-Mumford Schools
Caledonia, New York

SAFETY REVIEWER
Dr. Kenneth R. Roy
Glastonbury Public Schools
Glastonbury, Connecticut

ISBN 0-13-069975-6

1 2 3 4 5 6 7 8 9 10   07 06 05 04 03

Contents

Student Safety Manual

The symbol 🔍 denotes Inquiry Lab

The symbol ⚗ denotes Design Your Own Experiment Lab

Laboratory Investigations

Chapter 1   Science Skills

Chemistry

Physics

Chapter 11   Motion

Chapter 12   Forces and Motion

Chapter 13   Forces in Fluids

Chapter 14   Work, Power, and Machines

Chapter 15   Energy

Chapter 16   Thermal Energy and Heat

Chapter 17   Mechanical Waves and Sound

Chapter 18   The Electromagnetic Spectrum and Light

Chapter 19   Optics

Chapter 20   Electricity

Chapter 21   Magnetism

Earth and Space Science

Student Edition Lab Worksheets

(continued)

SI Units and Conversion Table

COMMON SI UNITS

Measurement	Unit	Symbol	Equivalents
Length	1 millimeter	mm	1,000 micrometers (μm)
	1 centimeter	cm	10 millimeters (mm)
	1 meter	m	100 centimeters (cm)
	1 kilometer	km	1,000 meters (m)
Area	1 square meter	m^2	10,000 square centimeters (cm^2)
	1 square kilometer	km^2	1,000,000 square meters (m^2)
Volume	1 milliliter	mL	1 cubic centimeter (cm^3 or cc)
	1 liter	L	1,000 milliliters (mL)
Mass	1 gram	g	1,000 milligrams (mg)
	1 kilogram	kg	1,000 grams (g)
	1 ton	t	1,000 kilograms (kg) = 1 metric ton
Time	1 second	s	
Temperature	1 Kelvin	K	1 degree Celsius (°C)

METRIC CONVERSION TABLES

When You Know	Multiply by	To Find			
		When You Know	Multiply by	To Find	
inches	2.54	centimeters	0.394	inches	
feet	0.3048	meters	3.281	feet	
yards	0.914	meters	1.0936	yards	
miles	1.609	kilometers	0.62	miles	
square inches	6.45	square centimeters	0.155	square inches	
square feet	0.093	square meters	10.76	square feet	
square yards	0.836	square meters	1.196	square yards	
acres	0.405	hectares	2.471	acres	
square miles	2.59	square kilometers	0.386	square miles	
cubic inches	16.387	cubic centimeters	0.061	cubic inches	
cubic feet	0.028	cubic meters	35.315	cubic feet	
cubic yards	0.765	cubic meters	1.31	cubic yards	
fluid ounces	29.57	milliliters	0.0338	fluid ounces	
quarts	0.946	liters	1.057	quarts	
gallons	3.785	liters	0.264	gallons	
ounces	28.35	grams	0.0353	ounces	
pounds	0.4536	kilograms	2.2046	pounds	
tons	0.907	metric tons	1.102	tons	

When You Know		
Fahrenheit	subtract 32; then divide by 1.8	to find Celsius
Celsius	multiply by 1.8; then add 32	to find Fahrenheit

Science Safety Rules

To prepare yourself to work safely in the laboratory, read over the following safety rules. Then read them a second time. Make sure you understand and follow each rule. Ask your teacher to explain any rules you do not understand.

Dress Code

1. To protect yourself from injuring your eyes, wear safety goggles whenever you work with chemicals, flames, glassware, or any substance that might get into your eyes. If you wear contact lenses, notify your teacher.
2. Wear an apron or coat whenever you work with corrosive chemicals or substances that can stain.
3. Tie back long hair to keep it away from any chemicals, flames, or equipment.
4. Remove or tie back any article of clothing or jewelry that can hang down and touch chemicals, flames, or equipment. Roll up or secure long sleeves.
5. Never wear open shoes or sandals.

General Precautions

6. Read all directions for an experiment several times before beginning the activity. Carefully follow all written and oral instructions. If you are in doubt about any part of the experiment, ask your teacher for assistance.
7. Never perform activities that are not assigned or authorized by your teacher. Obtain permission before "experimenting" on your own. Never handle any equipment unless you have specific permission.
8. Never perform lab activities without direct supervision.
9. Never eat or drink in the laboratory.
10. Keep work areas clean and tidy at all times. Bring only notebooks and lab manuals or written lab procedures to the work area. All other items, such as purses and backpacks, should be left in a designated area.
11. Do not engage in horseplay.

First Aid

12. Always report all accidents or injuries to your teacher, no matter how minor. Notify your teacher immediately about any fires.
13. Learn what to do in case of specific accidents, such as getting acid in your eyes or on your skin. (Rinse acids from your body with plenty of water.)
14. Be aware of the location of the first-aid kit, but do not use it unless instructed by your teacher. In case of injury, your teacher should administer first aid. Your teacher may also send you to the school nurse or call a physician.
15. Know the location of the emergency equipment such as fire extinguisher and fire blanket.
16. Know the location of the nearest telephone and whom to contact in an emergency.

Heating and Fire Safety

17. Never use a heat source, such as a candle, burner, or hot plate, without wearing safety goggles.
18. Never heat anything unless instructed to do so. A chemical that is harmless when cool may be dangerous when heated.
19. Keep all combustible materials away from flames. Never use a flame or spark near a combustible chemical.
20. Never reach across a flame.
21. Before using a laboratory burner, make sure you know proper procedures for lighting and adjusting the burner, as demonstrated by your teacher. Do not touch the burner. It may be hot. Never

leave a lighted burner unattended. Turn off the burner when not in use.

22. Chemicals can splash or boil out of a heated test tube. When heating a substance in a test tube, make sure that the mouth of the tube is not pointed at you or anyone else.

23. Never heat a liquid in a closed container. The expanding gases produced may shatter the container.

24. Before picking up a container that has been heated, first hold the back of your hand near it. If you can feel heat on the back of your hand, the container is too hot to handle. Use an oven mitt to pick up a container that has been heated.

Using Chemicals Safely

25. Never mix chemicals "for the fun of it." You might produce a dangerous, possibly explosive substance.

26. Never put your face near the mouth of a container that holds chemicals. Many chemicals are poisonous. Never touch, taste, or smell a chemical unless you are instructed by your teacher to do so.

27. Use only those chemicals needed in the activity. Read and double-check labels on supply bottles before removing any chemicals. Take only as much as you need. Keep all containers closed when chemicals are not being used.

28. Dispose of all chemicals as instructed by your teacher. To avoid contamination, never return chemicals to their original containers. Never pour untreated chemicals or other substances into the sink or trash containers.

29. Be extra careful when working with acids or bases. Pour all chemicals over the sink or a container, not over your work surface.

30. If you are instructed to test for odors, use a wafting motion to direct the odors to your nose. Do not inhale the fumes directly from the container.

31. When mixing an acid and water, always pour the water into the container first then add the acid to the water. Never pour water into an acid.

32. Take extreme care not to spill any material in the laboratory. Wash chemical spills and splashes immediately with plenty of water. Immediately begin rinsing with water any acids that get on your skin or clothing, and notify your teacher of any acid spill at the same time.

Using Glassware Safely

33. Never force glass tubing or a thermometer into a rubber stopper or rubber tubing. Have your teacher insert the glass tubing or thermometer if required for an activity.

34. If you are using a laboratory burner, use a wire screen to protect glassware from any flame. Never heat glassware that is not thoroughly dry on the outside.

35. Keep in mind that hot glassware looks cool. Never pick up glassware without first checking to see if it is hot. Use an oven mitt. See rule 24.

36. Never use broken or chipped glassware. If glassware breaks, notify your teacher and dispose of the glassware in the proper broken-glassware container.

37. Never eat or drink from glassware.

38. Thoroughly clean glassware before putting it away.

Using Sharp Instruments

39. Handle scalpels or other sharp instruments with extreme care. Never cut material toward you; cut away from you.

40. Immediately notify your teacher if you cut your skil while working in the laboratory.

Field Safety

41. When leaving the classroom or in the field, do not disrupt the activities of others. Do not leave your group unless you notify a teacher first.

42. Your teacher will instruct you as to how to conduct your research or experiment outside the classroom.

43. Never touch any animals or plants that you encounter in the field unless your teacher instructs you in the proper handling of that species.

44. Clean your hands thoroughly after handling anything in the field.

End-of-Experiment Rules

45. After an experiment has been completed, turn off all burners or hot plates. If you used a gas burner, check that the gas-line valve to the burner is off. Unplug hot plates.

46. Turn off and unplug any other electrical equipment that you used.

47 Clean up your work area and return all equipment to its proper place.

48. Dispose of waste materials as instructed by your teacher.

49. Wash your hands after every experiment.

Safety Symbols

These symbols alert you to possible dangers in the laboratory and remind you to work carefully.

General Safety Awareness You may see this symbol when none of the symbols described below appears. In this case, follow the specific instructions provided. You may also see this symbol when you are asked to develop your own procedure in a lab. Have the teacher approve your plan before you go further.

Physical Safety When an experiment involves physical activity, take precautions to avoid injuring yourself or others. Follow instructions from the teacher. Alert the teacher if there is any reason you should not participate in the activity.

Safety Goggles Always wear safety goggles to protect your eyes in any activity involving chemicals, flames or heating, or the possibility of broken glassware.

Lab Apron Wear a laboratory apron to protect your skin and clothing from damage.

Plastic Gloves Wear disposable plastic gloves to protect yourself from chemicals or organisms that could be harmful. Keep your hands away from your face. Dispose of the gloves according to your teacher's instructions at the end of the activity.

Heating Use a clamp or tongs to pick up hot glassware. Do not touch hot objects with your bare hands.

Heat-Resistant Gloves Use an oven mitt or other hand protection when handling hot materials. Hot plates, hot glassware, or hot water can cause burns. Do not touch hot objects with your bare hands.

Flames You may be working with flames from a lab burner, candle, or matches. Tie back loose hair and clothing. Follow instructions from the teacher about lighting and extinguishing flames.

No Flames Flammable materials may be present. Make sure there are no flames, sparks, or other exposed heat sources present.

Electric Shock Avoid the possibility of electric shock. Never use electrical equipment around water, or when the equipment is wet or your hands are wet. Be sure cords are untangled and cannot trip anyone. Disconnect the equipment when it is not in use.

Breakage You are working with materials that may be breakable, such as glass containers, glass tubing, thermometers, or funnels. Handle breakable materials with care. Do not touch broken glassware.

Corrosive Chemical You are working with an acid or another corrosive chemical. Avoid getting it on your skin or clothing, or in your eyes. Do not inhale the vapors. Wash your hands when you are finished with the activity.

Poison Do not let any poisonous chemical come in contact with your skin, and do not inhale its vapors. Wash your hands when you are finished with the activity.

Fumes When poisonous or unpleasant vapors may be involved, work in a ventilated area. Avoid inhaling vapors directly. Only test an odor when directed to do so by the teacher, and use a wafting motion to direct the vapor toward your nose.

Sharp Object Pointed-tip scissors, scalpels, knives, needles, pins, or tacks are sharp. They can cut or puncture your skin. Always direct a sharp edge or point away from yourself and others. Use sharp instruments only as instructed.

Disposal Chemicals and other laboratory materials used in the activity must be disposed of safely. Follow the instructions from the teacher.

Hand Washing Wash your hands thoroughly when finished with the activity. Use antibacterial soap and warm water. Lather both sides of your hands and between your fingers. Rinse well.

LABORATORY SAFETY CONTRACT

I, _____ , have read the Science Safety Rules
and Safety Symbols sections on pages x–xiii of this manual, understand
their contents completely, and agree to demonstrate compliance with all
safety rules and guidelines that have been established in each of the
following categories:

(please check)

☐ Dress Code   ☐ Using Glassware Safely

☐ General Precautions   ☐ Using Sharp Instruments

☐ First Aid   ☐ Field Safety

☐ Heating and Fire Safety   ☐ End-of-Experiment Rules

☐ Using Chemicals Safely

Signature _____

Date _____

Recognizing Laboratory Safety

Pre-Lab Discussion

An important part of your study of science will be working in a laboratory. In the laboratory, you and your classmates will learn about the natural world by conducting experiments. Working directly with household objects, laboratory equipment, and even living things will help you to better understand the concepts you read about in your textbook or in class.

Most of the laboratory work you will do is quite safe. However, some laboratory equipment, chemicals, and specimens can be dangerous if handled improperly. Laboratory accidents do not just happen. They are caused by carelessness, improper handling of equipment, or inappropriate behavior.

In this investigation, you will learn how to prevent accidents and thus work safely in a laboratory. You will review some safety guidelines and become acquainted with the location and proper use of safety equipment in your classroom laboratory.

Problem

What are the proper practices for working safely in a science laboratory?

Materials *(per group)*

Be sure to show the location of all safety equipment in your laboratory. Also give instructions on its proper use. Guidelines pertaining to the use of special equipment, fire-drill procedures, or penalties for misbehavior in the lab might also be discussed at this time.

Science textbook

Laboratory safety equipment (for demonstration)

Procedure

Part A: Reviewing Laboratory Safety Rules and Symbols

1. Carefully read the list of laboratory safety rules listed on pages x – xii of this lab manual.
2. Special symbols are used throughout this lab book to call attention to investigations that require extra caution. Use pages xii and xiii as a reference to describe what each symbol means in numbers l through 7 of Observations.

Part B: Location of Safety Equipment in Your Science Laboratory

1. The teacher will point out the location of the safety equipment in your classroom laboratory. Pay special attention to instructions for using such equipment as fire extinguishers, eyewash fountains, fire blankets, safety showers, and items in first-aid kits. Use the space provided in Part B under Observations to list the location of all safety equipment in your laboratory.

RECOGNIZING LABORATORY SAFETY (continued)

Observations

Part A

1. Student is working with materials that can easily be broken, such as glass containers or thermometers. They should be handled carefully, and broken glassware should not be touched.

2. Student is working with a flame and should tie back loose hair and clothing.

3. Student should use oven mitts or other hand protection to avoid burning hands.

4. Student is working with poisonous chemicals and should not let the chemical touch the skin or inhale its vapors. Student should wash hands after the lab.

5. Student is performing an experiment in which the eyes and face should be protected by safety goggles.

6. Student is working with a sharp instrument and should direct the sharp edge or point away from himself or herself and others.

7. Student is using electricity in the laboratory and should avoid the possibility of electric shock. Electrical equipment should not be used around water, cords should not be tangled, and equipment should be disconnected when not in use.

RECOGNIZING LABORATORY SAFETY (continued)

Part B

Student responses will depend on the specific safety features of your classroom
laboratory. Locations might include such directions as above the sink, to the right of
the goggles case, near the door, and so on.

_____

_____

Analyze and Conclude

Look at each of the following drawings and explain why the
laboratory activities pictured are unsafe.

1. Safety goggles should always be worn whenever a
person is working with chemicals, lab burners, or any
substance that might get into the eye.

_____

_____

_____

2. When diluting an acid, pour the acid into water. Never
pour water into the acid. Also, safety goggles and a lab
apron should be worn when working with chemicals.

_____

_____

_____

3. Never heat a liquid in a closed container. The
expanding gases produced may shatter the container.

_____

_____

_____

_____

RECOGNIZING LABORATORY SAFETY (continued)

Critical Thinking and Applications

In each of the following situations, write yes if the proper safety procedures are being followed and no if they are not. Then give a reason for your answer.

1. Gina is thirsty. She rinses a beaker with water, refills it with water, and takes a drink.

   No; you should never drink from laboratory glassware. The last substance in it may

   have been poisonous and traces of the poison may remain.

2. Bram notices that the electrical cord on his microscope is frayed near the plug. He takes the microscope to his teacher and asks for permission to use another one.

   Yes; electrical appliances with frayed cords or broken insulation may present a hazard

   and should not be used.

3. The printed directions in the lab book tell a student to pour a small amount of hydrochloric acid into a beaker. Jamal puts on safety goggles before pouring the acid into the beaker.

   Yes; safety goggles should always be worn when working with dangerous chemicals.

4. It is rather warm in the laboratory during a late spring day. Anna slips off her shoes and walks barefoot to the sink to clean her glassware.

   No; shoes should always be kept on while working in the laboratory in case glassware

   breaks or chemicals are spilled onto the floor.

5. While washing glassware, Mike splashes some water on Evon. To get even, Evon splashes him back.

   No; misbehaving is never acceptable in a laboratory.

6. During an experiment, Lindsey decides to mix two chemicals that the lab procedure does not say to mix, because she is curious about what will happen.

   No; never mix chemicals unless directed to do so. The mixing might produce an explosive

   substance.

Laboratory Skills Checkup 1

Defining Elements of a Scientific Method

Laboratory activities and experiments involve the use of the scientific method. Listed in the left column are the names of parts of this method. The right column contains definitions. Next to each word in the left column, write the letter of the definition that best matches that word.

__A__ **1.** Hypothesis

__E__ **2.** Manipulated Variable

__B__ **3.** Responding Variable

__G__ **4.** Controlling Variables

__F__ **5.** Observation

__C__ **6.** Data

__D__ **7.** Conclusion

A. Prediction about the outcome of an experiment

B. What you measure or observe to obtain your results

C. Measurements and other observations

D. Statement that sums up what you learn from an experiment

E. Factor that is changed in an experiment

F. What the person performing the activity sees, hears, feels, smells, or tastes

G. Keeping all variables the same except the manipulated variable

Laboratory Skills Checkup 2

Analyzing Elements of a Scientific Method

Read the following statements and then answer the questions.

1. You and your friend are walking along a beach in Maine on January 15, at 8:00 am.
2. You notice a thermometer on a nearby building that reads −1°C.
3. You also notice that there is snow on the roof of the building and icicles hanging from the roof.
4. You further notice a pool of sea water in the sand near the ocean.
5. Your friend looks at the icicles and the pool and says, "How come the water on the roof is frozen and the sea water is not?"
6. You answer, "I think that the salt in the sea water keeps it from freezing at −1°C."
7. You go on to say, "And I think under the same conditions, the same thing will happen tomorrow."
8. Your friend asks, "How can you be sure?" You answer, "I'm going to get some fresh water and some salt water and expose them to a temperature of −1°C and see what happens."

Questions

A. In which statement is a prediction made?

  7 _____

B. Which statement states a problem?

  5 _____

C. In which statement is an experiment described?

  8 _____

D. Which statement contains a hypothesis?

  6 _____

E. Which statements contain data?

  1, 2, 3, 4 _____

F. Which statements describe observations?

  2, 3, 4 _____

Laboratory Skills Checkup 3

Performing an Experiment

Read the following statements and then answer the questions.

1. A scientist wants to find out why sea water freezes at a lower temperature than fresh water.

2. The scientist goes to the library and reads a number of articles about the physical properties of solutions.

3. The scientist also reads about the composition of sea water.

4. The scientist travels to a nearby beach and observes the conditions there. The scientist notes the taste of the sea water and other factors such as waves, wind, air pressure, temperature, and humidity.

5. After considering all this information, the scientist sits at a desk and writes, "If sea water has salt in it, it will freeze at a lower temperature than fresh water."

6. The scientist goes back to the laboratory and does the following:
   a. Fills each of two beakers with 1 liter of fresh water.
   b. Dissolves 35 grams of table salt in one of the beakers.
   c. Places both beakers in a freezer at a temperature of $-1°C$.
   d. Leaves the beakers in the freezer for 24 hours.

7. After 24 hours, the scientist examines both beakers and finds the fresh water to be frozen. The salt water is still liquid.

8. The scientist writes in a notebook, "It appears that salt water freezes at a lower temperature than fresh water does."

9. The scientist continues, "I suggest that the reason sea water freezes at a lower temperature is that sea water contains dissolved salts, while fresh water does not."

Questions

A. Which statement(s) contain conclusions? _____ 8, 9 _____

B. Which statement(s) contains a hypothesis? _____ 5 _____

C. Which statement(s) contain observations? _____ 4, 7 _____

D. Which statement(s) describe an experiment? _____ 6 a–d _____

E. In which statement is the problem described? _____ 1 _____

F. Which statement(s) contain data? _____ 4, 6 a–d, 7 _____

G. Which is the manipulated variable in the experiment? __the amount of salt in water__

H. What is the responding variable in the experiment? __the temperature at which water freezes__

Laboratory Skills Checkup 4

Identifying Errors

Read the following paragraph and then answer the questions.

Andrew arrived at school and went directly to his earth science class. He took off his cap and coat and sat down at his desk. His teacher gave him a large rock and asked him to find its density. Realizing that the rock was too large to work with, Andrew got a hammer from the supply cabinet and hit the rock several times until he broke off a chip small enough to work with. He partly filled a graduated cylinder with water and suspended the rock in the water. The water level rose 2 cm. Andrew committed this measurement to memory. He next weighed the rock on a balance. The rock weighed 4 oz. Andrew then calculated the density of the rock as follows: He divided 2 cm by 4 oz. He then reported to his teacher that the density of the rock was 0.5 cm/oz.

Questions

1. What safety rule(s) did Andrew break?

He didn't put on his safety goggles. Also, he didn't obtain permission from his teacher before

obtaining the hammer and breaking the rock.

2. What mistake did Andrew make using measurement units?

He used linear units (centimeters) instead of volumetric units (milliliters).

3. What should Andrew have done with his data rather than commit them to memory?

He should have kept a written record.

4. What is wrong with the statement "He next weighed the rock on a balance"?

A balance is used to determine mass, not weight.

5. Why is "4 oz" an inappropriate measurement in a science experiment?

Metric units (grams) should be used.

6. What mistake did Andrew make in calculating density?

Density is expressed in mass per unit volume (g/mL), not length per unit weight.

Some Common Laboratory Equipment

test tube

test-tube rack

test-tube holder

spatula

scoop

rubber stoppers

tongs

forceps

well plates
(24- and 96-well)

spring scale

magnetic
compass

stopwatch

magnifying
glass

triple-beam balance

SOME COMMON LABORATORY EQUIPMENT (continued)

wire gauze

pipe-stem triangle

evaporating dish

crucible and cover

iron ring

buret clamp

utility clamp

Bunsen burner

ring stand

funnel

dropper pipet

hot plate

graduated cylinders

watch glass

flask

beakers

thermometer

buret

How to Use a Balance

SKILLS FOCUS: Observing, Measuring, Calculating, Evaluating and Revising **TIME REQUIRED:** 40 minutes

Background Information

The ability to measure accurately the mass of an object is an important skill in the science laboratory. You can use a triple-beam balance to measure mass. As you can see in Figure 1, the balance has several parts. The pan is the flat surface on which you place the object to be measured. The three beams show the mass of the object. Notice that each beam has a different scale. The scale of the middle beam is from 0–500 grams and measures an object to the nearest 100 grams. The scale of the beam in back is from 0–100 grams and measures an object to the nearest 10 grams. The scale of the beam in front is from 0–10 grams and measures an object to the nearest tenth of a gram.

Figure 1

Notice that each beam carries a weight called a rider. You find the mass of an object by placing it on the pan and moving the riders until the pointer on the right of the balance stays pointed to zero.

There are three ways you can use the triple-beam balance to find mass:

Method 1. Measure mass directly. Place the object on the pan and move the riders until the pointer points to zero. Add up the numbers on the beams where the riders are positioned to find mass.

Method 2. Find mass by difference. How could you find the mass of a liquid? First, measure the mass of an empty container that can hold the liquid. Then, measure the combined mass of the container and the liquid. Finally, subtract the mass of the container from the combined mass.

Method 3. Measure out a chemical substance. Suppose you need to obtain 50 g of a powdered chemical. How could you do it? First find the mass of a piece of paper or empty container that will hold the chemical. Then, add this amount to the desired mass of the chemical and preset the riders to this number. Finally, add the chemical to the paper a little at a time until the pointer points to zero.

In this investigation, you will learn how to measure accurately the mass of various objects by using the three methods described above.

Problem

What is the proper way to use the triple-beam balance to measure the mass of different objects?

Pre-Lab Discussion

Read the entire investigation. Then, work with a partner to answer the following questions.

1. What does it mean when the pointer of the balance reads "zero"?

   When the balance pointer reads "zero," it means that the mass of the object being measured

   and the mass of the riders are equal.

2. Suppose a rock is balanced on a triple-beam balance. The riders on the three beams point to 60 g, 300 g, and 3.5 g. What is the mass of the rock?

   363.5 g

Materials *(per group)*

triple-beam balance

100-mL graduated cylinder

3 different small, solid objects

weighing paper

small scoop

table salt

200-mL beaker

Have triple-beam balances set up at student stations.

Any small object can be measured, such as a coin, a paper clip, or a rubber stopper.

Inform students that chemicals should never be placed directly on a balance pan. Therefore, it is necessary to use paper or a container as described in Method 3.

Safety ⚠

Review the safety guidelines in the front of your lab book. Note all safety alert symbols next to the steps in the Procedure and review the meaning of each symbol by referring to the Safety Symbols on page xiii.

Procedure

Before you measure the mass of any object, be sure that the riders are moved all the way to the left and that the pointer rests on zero. If necessary, slowly turn the adjustment knob until the pointer rests on zero. This is called zeroing the balance.

Part A: Measuring Mass Directly

1. Place a small, solid object on the balance pan. The beams will rise and the pointer will point above zero.

2. Move the rider on the middle beam on notch at a time until the pointer drops and stays below zero. Move the rider back one notch.

3. Move the rider on the back beam one notch at a time until the pointer again drops and stays below zero. Move the rider back one notch.

4. Slide the rider along the front beam until the pointer stops at zero. The mass of the object is equal to the sum of the readings on the three beams.

5. Record the mass to the nearest tenth of a gram in Data Table 1.

6. Remove this object and repeat Steps 1–5 twice, using two other solid objects.

Have students measure some objects with a standard weight as a check of their measuring accuracy.

Part B: Finding Mass by Difference

7. Find the mass of an empty 250-mL beaker. Record the mass in Data Table 2.

8. Using the graduated cylinder, obtain 50 mL of water.

9. Pour the water into the beaker and find the mass of the beaker and water. Record the mass in Data Table 2.

Part C: Measuring Out a Chemical Substance

10. Place a piece of weighing paper on the balance pan and find its mass. Record the mass in Data Table 3.
    Filter paper may be used as weighing paper. It can be folded in quarters and then opened to form a "cup" before placing it on the pan.

11. Add 5 g to the mass of the weighing paper and move the riders to this number.

12. Obtain a sample of table salt from the teacher. Using the scoop, add a small amount of salt at a time to the paper on the balance until the pointer rests on zero. Record the total mass of the weighing paper and salt in Data Table 3.

13. Dispose of the table salt in the container provided by the teacher.
    Caution students not to put solids into the sink.

Observations   Sample data are shown.

DATA TABLE 1

Object	Mass (g)
Nickel	5.0
Large paper clip	1.3
Rubber stopper	12.5

DATA TABLE 2

Mass of Empty Beaker (g)	Mass of Beaker with 50 mL of Water (g)
103.7	153.7

DATA TABLE 3

Mass of Weighing Paper (g)	Mass of Weighing Paper and Table Salt (g)
0.5	5.5

Analyze and Conclude

1. What is the mass of 50 mL of water? How did you find this mass?

   50 g; by subtracting the mass of the empty beaker from the mass of the beaker with 50 mL

   of water in it

2. Which rider on the balance should always be moved first when finding the mass of an object? Why?

   The middle (heaviest) rider should be moved first. This rider measures the largest unit of mass used.

3. What is the mass of the largest object your balance is able to measure?

   Answer may vary. Generally, 610 g is the largest mass that can be measured using a

   standard triple-beam balance.

4. What is the mass of the smallest object your balance is able to measure accurately?

The smallest mass that can be measured accurately is 0.1 g.

5. After using your balance, how should it always be left?

All the riders should be to the left, which should bring the pointer to zero.

6. Suppose you did not zero the balance before finding the mass of an object. How might that affect your measurement?

The reading would be inaccurate because you would be starting from a point below or above zero.

7. In this lab, you found the mass of 50 mL of water. Calculate the mass of 1 mL of water. (Do not use the balance.)

By dividing the mass of 50 mL of water by 50 g, students will find that the mass of 1 mL of

water is 1 g.

8. Describe how you could find the mass of a certain quantity of milk that you poured into a drinking glass.

First find the mass of the empty drinking glass. Then, pour in the milk and find the combined mass.

Subtract the mass of the empty glass from the combined mass.

9. If you were baking a dessert and the recipe called for 250 g of sugar, how could you use the triple-beam balance to obtain this amount?

Place a piece of paper or a light food container on the balance and find its mass. Add 250 g to the

mass of this object and set the riders for that amount. Slowly add sugar until the pointer balances

on zero.

Go Further

Design a balance that finds mass by comparing the mass of a known object to the mass of an unknown object. Study the triple-beam balance used in this activity and think about how you could balance two or more objects. Construct your balance and use it to find the mass of an object. How could you improve your balance?

Student designs will vary, but they should mimic the action of a double-pan balance. Two holding devices may be attached to a lever that is balanced on a fulcrum, like a seesaw, or suspended from a fixed point, using string. For example, cans can be placed on the far ends of a ruler, The ruler must be positioned on a fulcrum at the ruler's midpoint. Or two pieces of identical cloth can be cupped to fold objects. These cloth holders can be suspended from a fixed hanger at an equal distance from the midpoint. Objects of known mass can be placed in one holding device, while small objects such as pennies or paper clips can be placed in the other device. When the two holders and their contents are level, both sides have equal mass. Specific suggestions for improvement may include using hanging devices with less friction or using holding devices that are equal in mass.

Chapter 1   Science Skills   Investigation 1A

Evaluating Precision

Refer students to pages 14–20 in their textbooks for a discussion of measurement, precision, and accuracy.
SKILLS FOCUS: Measuring, Evaluating **CLASS TIME:** 30 minutes

Background Information

When an object is measured more than once, the measurements may vary. The closeness of a set of measured values to each other is called **precision.** Many people confuse precision with accuracy. **Accuracy** is a measure of how close the values are to the actual value. A set of values can be in close agreement, or precise, without being accurate.

For example, suppose you repeatedly measure the mass of a 4.00-g object by using a balance that reads too low by 3.00 g every time. You might get nearly identical readings—for example, 1.00 g, 1.01 g, and 0.99 g. These readings are quite precise because they are close together. However, they differ from the actual value by a large amount. Therefore, the measurements are very inaccurate.

In this investigation, you will make several measurements of length, temperature, and volume. Then, you will evaluate the precision of your measurements by comparing them to measurements made by your classmates.

Problem

How can you determine the precision and accuracy of measurements?

Pre-Lab Discussion

Read the entire investigation. Then, work with a partner to answer the following questions.

1. **Applying Concepts** Use the example of a series of repeated length measurements to explain the meaning of precision.

   The precision of a series of repeated measurements describes how closely the individual

   measurements agree. For example, if a meter stick is used to measure the length of a desk three

   times, the measurements 75 cm, 74 cm, and 76 cm are more precise than measurements of 70 cm,

   75 cm, and 80 cm.

   _____

   _____

2. **Inferring** What information would you need to determine the accuracy of a measurement?

   You would need a reliable measurement to which you could compare your measurement.

   _____

   _____

   _____

   _____

3. **Drawing Conclusions** In this investigation, you will compare measurements that you make to measurements that your classmates make. Will you do this to determine the accuracy or the precision of your measurements?

Comparing measurements made by different students can determine precision, but not accuracy.

_____

_____

_____

4. **Designing Experiments** Identify the manipulated, responding, and controlled variables in this investigation.

   a. Manipulated variable

   Teams making the measurements

   _____

   _____

   b. Responding variable

   Precision of measurements

   _____

   _____

   c. Controlled variables

   Devices for measuring length, temperature, and volume; the objects whose properties are

   being measured

   _____

5. **Analyzing Data** Two students measure the mass of a wooden disk, using the same balance. The first student repeats the weighing three times and obtains mass readings of 47 g, 52 g, and 51 g. The second student obtains mass readings of 45 g, 55 g, and 50 g. Explain which set of measurements is more precise. Can you tell if the measurements are accurate? Why or why not?

The first student's measurements are more precise because the values are closer together. Although

both sets of measurements suggest that the disk has a mass of nearly 50 g, this may not be true.

The balance may not be properly calibrated, and so it could be providing consistently inaccurate

measurements.

_____

_____

_____

_____

Name _____ Class _____ Date _____

Materials (per group)

meter stick
Celsius thermometer   Provide only non-mercury thermometers.
500-mL beaker filled with room-temperature water   Fill a 500-mL beaker with water and allow it
10 pennies   to sit at room temperature for at least 1 hour
before class.
50-mL graduated cylinder

Safety 🔲🧤🔲🔲

Put on safety goggles and a lab apron. Be careful to avoid breakage
when working with glassware. Note all safety alert symbols next to
the steps in the Procedure and review the meaning of each symbol by
referring to the Safety Symbols on page xiii. You may wish to start with one lab group measuring
length, a second group measuring temperature, and a
third group measuring volume, and then rotate the
groups to minimize waiting time between measurements.

Procedure

1. You and your partner make up a team. Your team and two   In any case, make
other teams will make up a group of six. Your teacher will tell   sure all students within
you and your partner whether you are Team A, B, or C of your   a group use the same
group. The three teams in your group will measure the same   measuring devices.
objects separately. You will not share your measurements with
the other teams in your group until you complete the
procedure.

🧤 2. Working with your partner, use the meter stick to measure the length
of a desk indicated by your teacher. Measure as carefully as possible,
to the nearest millimeter. Record the length of the desk in the data
table. (*Hint:* Do not reveal the measurements you make to the other
teams in your group. They must make the same measurements and
must not be influenced by your results.)

🔲 3. Use the thermometer to measure the temperature of the
🔲 beaker of room-temperature water. **CAUTION:** *Do not let the
thermometer hit the beaker.* Record this measurement in the
data table.

4. Place 25 mL of tap water in the graduated cylinder. Measure the
volume of the water. Record this volume in the data table to the   You may need to
nearest 0.1 mL. (*Hint:* Remember to read the volume at the   show students
bottom of the meniscus.)   how to read a
liquid volume at
5. Add the 10 pennies to the graduated cylinder. Read the volume   the bottom of the
of the water and pennies. Record this volume in the data table   meniscus.
to the nearest 0.1 mL.

6. Subtract the volume of the water from the volume of the water
and pennies. The result is a measurement of the volume of the
pennies. Record this value in the data table.

7. After all three teams in your group have finished measuring the
same objects for length, temperature, and volume, share your
results with the other two teams. Record their measurements in
the data table.

Observations Sample data are shown.

DATA TABLE

Measurement	Team A	Team B	Team C
Length of desk (mm)			
Temperature of water (°C)	18.0–21.0		
Volume of water (mL)	24.5–25.5		
Volume of water and pennies (mL)	27.5–29.0		
Volume of pennies (mL)	3.0–3.5		

Analysis and Conclusions

1. **Calculating** Average the three length measurements you compared by adding them together and dividing the result by 3. Find the range of values by calculating the difference between the largest and smallest values. Record the results of your calculations in the space below.

   Calculations should be correctly carried out. Actual results will depend on student data.

   a. Average of length measurements (mm)

   _____

   b. Range of length measurements (mm)

   _____

2. **Making Generalizations** Would it be correct to use the range of values you calculated in Question 1 to describe the precision of the measurements? The accuracy of the measurements? Explain your answer.

The range of values can be used to describe the precision of the measurements. The narrower the

range is, the more precise the measurements are. The range cannot be used to describe the accuracy

of the measurements, which depends on the difference between the measurements and the actual

value.

3. **Analyzing Data** Which of the three sets of measurements had the least spread among the measurements? Suggest reasons for the precision of these measurements.

Answers may vary for each group. Reasons for good precision in a set of measurements depend on

the smaller units with which the measuring instrument can be read, consistency of technique in

making and reading measurements, and the care that the conditions under which the measurements

are made are kept the same.

4. **Applying Concepts** Figure 1 shows the results of three people's attempts to shoot as many bull's-eyes as possible. Below Figure 1, label each of the results as *accurate* or *not accurate*, and as *precise* or *not precise*.

Figure 1

| Precise | Not Accurate | Accurate |
| Not Accurate | Not Precise | Precise |

5. **Evaluating and Revising** Discuss the reasons for the differences among the teams' measurements with the members of your group. Describe these reasons and explain how the measurements could be made more precise.

Students may cite skill and care of measurement and the limited precision of the measuring

instruments as factors that limited the precision of the measurements. Students may suggest

having one person make all the measurements or using more precise instruments.

_____

_____

_____

_____

_____

Go Further

Design an experiment to compare the precision of two or more measuring instruments. Is the precision of each instrument the same throughout its range of measurements? Write a procedure you would follow to answer these questions. After your teacher approves your procedure, carry out the experiment and report your results.

Measuring instruments differ in precision. For example, a micrometer is more precise than a ruler. The precision of a well-made measuring instrument is nearly the same throughout its range of measurements except for a decline in precision for values near zero. At very low values, the precision declines as the size of the measurement approaches the sensitivity of the instrument, which is the smallest nonzero value it can measure.

Measuring Volume and Temperature

Background Information

Refer students to pages 14–20 in their textbooks for a discussion of measurement. **SKILLS FOCUS:** Measuring **CLASS TIME:** 40 minutes

The amount of space an object takes up is called its volume. A commonly used unit of volume is the liter (L). Smaller volumes can be measured in milliliters (mL). One milliliter is equal to 1/1000 of a liter. In the laboratory, the graduated cylinder is often used to measure the volume of liquids.

Temperature is measured with a thermometer. The unit of measurement for temperature is the degree Celsius (°C).

In this investigation, you will practice making measurements of the volume and temperature of a liquid.

Problem

How can you accurately measure the volume and temperature of a liquid?

Pre-Lab Discussion

Read the entire investigation. Then, work with a partner to answer the following questions.

1. **Measuring** How many significant figures are there in the measurement shown in Figure 1?

   Three significant figures

2. **Inferring** Why is it important to read the volume of water in a graduated cylinder by using the bottom of the meniscus?

   Because water curves upward at the edges of the cylinder wall, the bottom of the meniscus is nearer

   to being the true top of the water column. By using this same point each time a measurement is

   made, the measurement is less likely to be in error.

3. **Designing Experiments** Why should you leave the thermometer in beaker B when you add ice?

   Removing the thermometer from the water would expose the thermometer bulb to the air. The

   resulting change in the thermometer reading would be because of a temperature change other than

   that caused by the ice melting in the water.

4. **Measuring** If each mark on a thermometer represents 1°C, which part of a temperature measurement will be the estimated digit?

   Tenths of a degree

Materials *(per group)*

2 150-mL beakers Provide beakers with volume graduations.

100-mL graduated cylinder

glass-marking pencil

2 Celsius thermometers Provide only non-mercury thermometers.

watch or clock

ice cube

Safety 🥽 🧥 🧤

Put on safety goggles and a lab apron. Be careful to avoid breakage when working with glassware. Note all safety alert symbols next to the steps in the Procedure and review the meaning of each symbol by referring to the Safety Symbols on page xiii.

Procedure

Part A: Measuring the Volume of a Liquid

🧤 1. Fill a beaker halfway with water.

2. Pour the water in the beaker into the graduated cylinder.

3. Measure the amount of water in the graduated cylinder. To accurately measure the volume, your eye must be at the same level as the bottom of the meniscus, as shown in Figure 1. The meniscus is the curved surface of the water.

Figure 1

4. Estimate the volume of water to the nearest 0.1 mL. Record this volume in Data Table 1.

5. Repeat Steps 1 through 4, but this time fill the beaker only one-fourth full of water.

Part B: Measuring the Temperature of a Liquid

6. Use the glass-marking pencil to label the beakers *A* and *B*.

7. Use the graduated cylinder to put 50 mL of water in each beaker.

8. Place a thermometer in each beaker. In Data Table 2, record the temperature of the water in each beaker.

Tell students not to stir the water with the thermometer.

9. Carefully add one ice cube to the water in beaker B. Note and record the time.

10. After 1 minute, observe the temperature of the water in each beaker. Record these temperatures in Data Table 2.

11. After 5 minutes, observe the temperature of the water in each beaker. Record these temperatures in Data Table 2.

12. After the ice in beaker B has melted, use the graduated cylinder to find the volume of water in each beaker. Record these volumes in Data Table 3.

Observations Sample data are shown.

DATA TABLE 1

Measurement	Volume of Water (mL)
Half-filled beaker	47.0–53.0
One-fourth filled beaker	22.0–28.0

DATA TABLE 2

Beaker	Temperature at Beginning	(°C) Temperature After 1 Minute (°C)	Temperature After 5 Minutes (°C)
A	18.0–20.0	18.0–20.0	18.0–20.0
B	18.0–20.0	15.0–17.0	8.0–14.0

DATA TABLE 3

Beaker	Volume of Water at Beginning (mL)	Volume of Water at End (mL)
A	50.0	50.0
B	50.0	58.0–68.0

Analysis and Conclusions

1. **Observing** What is the largest volume of a liquid that the graduated cylinder is able to measure? What is the smallest volume that the graduated cylinder is able to measure?

   100 mL; 1 mL

2. **Analyzing Data** Describe how the temperature of the water in beakers A and B changed during the investigation.

   The temperature of the water in beaker A did not change. The temperature of the water in beaker B decreased after the ice cube was added.

3. **Analyzing Data** How did the volume of water in beakers A and B change during the investigation? What do you think caused this change?

   The volume of water in beaker A did not change. The volume of water in beaker B increased because the melted ice added to the total amount of liquid water.

4. **Applying Concepts** Would you use a 100-mL graduated cylinder, a 25-mL graduated cylinder, or 10-mL graduated cylinder to measure 8 mL of a liquid? Explain your answer.

   To measure 8 mL of liquid, it is best to use a 10-mL graduated cylinder because it has the finest graduations and provides the most precise measurement.

Go Further

Some liquids do not form a meniscus in a graduated cylinder as water does. Use a 10-mL graduated cylinder to measure 8.0 mL each of water, isopropyl (rubbing) alcohol, and vegetable oil. Observe and draw the meniscus of each liquid. Label your drawings to show how you think the volume of each liquid should be measured. Explain why you think that the volumes should be measured in this way.

Vegetable oil and alcohol form a convex meniscus in a clean glass container. The volumes of these liquids are read at the top of the meniscus because most of the surface of these liquids is near the top of the meniscus (unlike water, whose surface is mostly near the bottom of the meniscus).

Recognizing Chemical and Physical Changes

Refer students to pages 51 and 56–58 in their textbooks for a discussion of physical and chemical changes. **SKILLS FOCUS:** Observing, Classifying
CLASS TIME: 40 minutes

Background Information

Some chemical and physical changes are easy to recognize. Other changes may be easy to observe, but difficult to classify as a chemical or a physical change just by observation. Many events that occur in nature, such as volcanic eruptions, include both chemical and physical changes. When you observe a complicated event, you may need more information before you can identify the chemical and physical changes that have occurred.

In this investigation, you will observe several events and identify the chemical and physical changes involved in each.

Problem

How can you identify chemical and physical changes?

Pre-Lab Discussion

Read the entire investigation. Then, work with a partner to answer the following questions.

1. **Observing** What evidence of chemical changes will you look for in this investigation?

   Evidence of chemical changes includes formation of a precipitate, production of a gas,

   and changes in color.

   _____

2. **Inferring** What are some examples of physical changes that you might observe in this investigation?

   Changes in shape, melting

   _____

3. **Predicting** In which step of this investigation is a physical change most likely to occur? Explain your answer.

   Step 8, because the paraffin is likely to melt when it is heated

   _____

4. **Predicting** In which step of this investigation is a chemical change most likely to occur? Explain your answer.

   Step 8, because chemical changes occur during burning

   _____

   _____

Materials *(per group)*

4 test tubes

glass-marking pencil

test-tube rack

magnesium chloride solution

sodium carbonate solution

copper sulfate solution

white vinegar (acetic acid solution)

aluminum foil

calcium carbonate chip

paraffin candle

matches

clock or watch

Prepare 0.1 M solutions of magnesium chloride, sodium carbonate, and copper(II) sulfate by dissolving 20.3 g $MgCl_2 \cdot 6H_2O$, 10.6 g Na_2CO_3, and 25.0 g $CuSO_4 \cdot 5H_2O$, respectively, in 1 L of water.

Place candles in holders or melt the non-wick ends and attach them to sturdy, nonflammable bases.

Review with students the safety information in the MSDS for each chemical before performing this investigation. Used solutions may be flushed down the drain with at least 10 volumes of water. If your school is served by a septic system, do not dispose of chemical waste in this way. Instead, allow the used solutions to evaporate and dispose of them as dry chemical waste.

Safety 🥽🧤🔥✋☠️🔥🗑️🧪

Put on safety goggles and a lab apron. Be careful to avoid breakage when working with glassware. Always use caution when working with laboratory chemicals, as they may irritate the skin or stain skin or clothing. Never touch or taste any chemical unless instructed to do so. Be careful when using matches. Tie back loose hair and clothing when working with flames. Do not reach over an open flame. Wash your hands thoroughly after carrying out this investigation. Note all safety alert symbols next to the steps in the Procedure and review the meaning of each symbol by referring to the Safety Symbols on page xiii.

Procedure

🔥 1. Use the glass-marking pencil to label the test tubes *1* to *4*. Place the test tubes in a test-tube rack.

✋ 2. Fill each test tube one-third full with the solution indicated in
☠️   Data Table 1.

3. Observe each of the solutions and record your observations in Data Table 1.

4. Observe the appearance of the aluminum foil, the calcium carbonate chip, and the paraffin candle. Record your observations in Data Table 1.

5. Pour the sodium carbonate solution from test tube 2 into the magnesium chloride solution in test tube 1. Observe what happens and record your observations in Data Table 2.

6. Crumple up the aluminum foil and drop it into the copper sulfate solution in test tube 3. Observe test tube 3 every 2 minutes for 10 minutes. Record your observations in Data Table 2.

Students can continue to work on the following steps as they observe test tube 3.

7. Carefully drop the calcium carbonate chip into the vinegar (acetic acid solution) in test tube 4. Record your observations in Data Table 2.

8. Use a match to light the paraffin candle. Observe what happens to the candle for 5 minutes. In Data Table 3, record what happens to the candle. **CAUTION:** *Be careful not to burn yourself or others.*

9. Complete Data Tables 2 and 3, identifying each change you observed as chemical or physical.

10. Follow your teacher's instructions for disposing of the used chemicals. Wash your hands thoroughly with warm water and soap or detergent before leaving the laboratory.

Observations   Sample data are shown.

DATA TABLE 1

Material	Observations
Test tube 1: magnesium chloride solution	Clear solution
Test tube 2: sodium carbonate solution	Clear solution
Test tube 3: copper sulfate solution	Blue solution
Test tube 4: vinegar (acetic acid solution)	Clear or slightly yellow solution
Aluminum foil	Flexible, shiny, silvery solid
Calcium carbonate	Hard, brittle, white solid
Paraffin candle	Soft, white solid

DATA TABLE 2

Materials	Observations	Type of Change (chemical or physical)
Magnesium chloride and sodium carbonate solutions	White precipitate forms.	Chemical
Copper sulfate solution and aluminum foil	Aluminum turns reddish, and eventually darkens until it is black. Solution turns reddish brown. Bubbles form.	Chemical Chemical Chemical
Calcium carbonate and vinegar	Bubbles form.	Chemical

DATA TABLE 3

Observation	Type of Change (chemical or physical)
Flame	Chemical
Smoke produced.	Chemical
Wick chars.	Chemical
Wax melts.	Physical

Analysis and Conclusions

1. **Inferring** What type of change occurred when you mixed the magnesium chloride solution with the sodium carbonate solution? Explain your answer.

   After the solutions were mixed, a white precipitate formed. Formation of a precipitate is often

   evidence of a chemical change.

   _____

   _____

2. **Inferring** What type of change occurred in the copper sulfate solution when you placed the aluminum foil in it? Explain your answer.

   The copper sulfate solution was initially a clear blue liquid, which turned reddish brown when the

   aluminum foil was added. A color change is often evidence of a chemical change.

   _____

   _____

   _____

3. **Inferring** What type of change occurred in the acetic acid solution when you placed the calcium carbonate chip in it? Explain your answer.

   Gas bubbles formed. Formation of a gas is often evidence of a chemical change.

   _____

   _____

   _____

   _____

4. **Evaluating** What evidence was there that new substances formed as the candle burned?

   Evidence included the formation of solid black particles and the presence of a flame.

   _____

   _____

   _____

5. **Evaluating** What evidence of a physical change did you observe as the candle burned?

   Melting of the candle was evidence of a physical change.

   _____

   _____

   _____

6. **Drawing Conclusions** What signs of chemical changes did you observe in this investigation?

The formation of a precipitate, color changes, and formation of gas

7. **Evaluating and Revising** Formation of a solid, formation of a gas, and a color change can also occur during some physical changes. Give examples of physical changes that could produce these clues. What evidence suggests that the changes you observed in test tubes 1–3 were, in fact, chemical changes?

Sample answer: A solid may form when a liquid is cooled. A gas may form when a liquid is heated.

A solid may change color when it is heated. During the procedure, the test tubes were not heated or

cooled. In test tube 1, the change occurred after two liquids were mixed. In test tubes 2 and 3,

changes occurred after solids were added to liquids.

Go Further

Many activities that people do at home on a regular basis can involve both physical and chemical changes. Examples include cooking or gardening. Pick an activity that you participate in at home and make a list of tasks for that activity. Divide the list into tasks during which a physical change occurs and tasks during which a chemical change occurs. Give reasons for your classifications.

Sample answers: For cooking, physical changes occur when food is sliced, ingredients are mixed, or ingredients melt or freeze; chemical changes usually occur when the color or texture of the food changes. For gardening, physical changes occur when a lawn is mowed, shrubs are pruned, or soil is tilled; chemical changes occur when fertilizer is added to soil, when fruit ripens, or materials are composted.

Chapter 2   Properties of Matter   Investigation 2B

Determining the Densities of Liquids
Refer students to page 47 in their textbooks for a discussion of density. **SKILLS FOCUS:**

Background Information
Measuring, Calculating **CLASS TIME:** 40 minutes

Mass and volume are properties of all matter. **Density** is the ratio of an object's mass to its volume. The density of a specific kind of matter helps to identify it and distinguish it from other kinds of matter. It is possible to determine the densities of liquids in grams per milliliter (g/mL).

In this investigation, you will determine the densities of several liquids by measuring their masses and volumes.

Problem

How can you determine the densities of liquids?

Pre-Lab Discussion

Read the entire investigation. Then, work with a partner to answer the following questions.

1. Formulating Hypotheses For identical volumes, what will the relationship be between the mass and the density of a sample?

For identical volumes, as mass increases, the density will increase.
_____

_____

_____

2. Controlling Variables What are the manipulated and responding variables in this investigation?

The type of liquid used is the manipulated variable, and the mass of the liquid is the responding

variable.
_____

_____

_____

3. Controlling Variables What is the controlled variable in this investigation?

Volume
_____

4. Calculating Why is it necessary to know the mass of the graduated cylinder in order to find the mass of the liquid?

The mass of the cylinder must be subtracted from the mass of the cylinder and liquid to determine

the mass of the liquid.
_____

_____

_____

5. Predicting Predict which liquid will be the most dense and which will be the least dense.

Salt water will be the most dense, and ethanol will be the least dense.

_____

_____

Materials *(per group)*

2 100-mL graduated cylinders

triple-beam balance

50 mL denatured ethanol (ethyl alcohol)

50 mL salt water

paper towels

To prepare this solution, add 100 g of NaCl to enough water to make 1 L of solution.

Safety

Put on safety goggles and a lab apron. Be careful to avoid breakage when working with glassware. Always use caution when working with laboratory chemicals, as they may irritate the skin or stain skin or clothing. Never touch or taste any chemical unless instructed to do so. Keep alcohol away from any open flame. Wash your hands thoroughly after carrying out this investigation. Note all safety alert symbols next to the steps in the Procedure and review the meaning of each symbol by referring to the Safety Symbols on page xiii.

Review with students the safety information in the MSDS for denatured ethyl alcohol before performing this investigation.

Procedure

1. Place a clean graduated cylinder on the laboratory balance. In the data table, record the mass of the graduated cylinder.

2. Place about 50 mL of water in the graduated cylinder. Record the exact volume to the nearest tenth of a milliliter. Use a paper towel to wipe any water from the outside of the cylinder. Find the mass of the graduated cylinder and the water. Record this mass in the data table. **CAUTION:** *Wipe up any spilled liquids immediately to avoid slips and falls.*

3. Calculate the mass of the water by subtracting the mass of the graduated cylinder from the mass of the graduated cylinder and water. Record your answer in the data table.

4. Calculate the density of water, using the following equation. Record the density of water in the data table.

$$\text{Density} = \frac{\text{Mass}}{\text{Volume}}$$

 5. Repeat Steps 1 through 4. This time, use a clean graduated cylinder and denatured ethanol instead of water. **CAUTION:** *Denatured ethanol is poisonous and flammable. Do not drink it. Do not use denatured ethanol near an open flame.*

6. Empty the graduated cylinder containing water and dry it thoroughly with a paper towel. Repeat Steps 1 through 4, using this graduated cylinder and the sample of salt water.

Name _____ Class _____ Date _____

Observations Sample data are shown.

DATA TABLE

Liquid	Mass of Graduated Cylinder (g)	Mass of Graduated Cylinder and Liquid (g)	Mass of Liquid (g)	Volume of Liquid (mL)	Density of Liquid (g/mL)
Water			49.5–50.5	49.5–50.5	0.98–1.02
Ethanol			40.0–41.0	49.5–50.5	0.79–0.83
Salt water			54.0–55.0	49.5–50.5	1.07–1.11

Analysis and Conclusions

1. **Analyzing Data** List the three liquids you studied in order of increasing density.

   Denatured ethanol, water, salt water _____

   _____

   _____

2. **Comparing and Contrasting** Which has the greater mass—1 L of water or 1 L of denatured ethanol? Explain your answer.

   1 L of water because water is denser than ethanol. A given volume of ethanol would have less

   mass than an equal volume of water. _____

   _____

   _____

   _____

3. **Comparing and Contrasting** Which has a greater volume—1000 g of water or 1000 g of denatured ethanol? Explain your answer.

   1000 g of denatured ethanol because ethanol is less dense than water. A given mass of

   denatured ethanol would have a greater volume than an equal mass of water.

   _____

   _____

   _____

4. **Inferring** Which is more dense—1 mL of water or 50 L of water? Explain your answer.

They have equal density because the density of a substance is a property that does not

change, regardless of the quantity of the sample.

_____

_____

_____

_____

5. **Predicting** Predict what would happen to the density of the salt solution if more salt was dissolved in a given volume of solution. Explain your answer.

The mass of the solution would increase. Therefore, the density of the solution would increase.

_____

_____

_____

_____

_____

Go Further

Use your data to predict the position of a small wooden dowel (or small pencil) placed in samples of the liquids used in this investigation. Would more or less of the dowel be visible above the surface of the liquid in each case? Plan a new investigation to test your predictions. Show your plan to your teacher. If your teacher approves your plan, carry out your experiment and report your results.

Students should carefully place a small wooden dowel or small pencil (about 10 cm in length) in a graduated cylinder of water, noting how high the rod or pencil floats. Students could remove the rod, dry it completely, and repeat the procedure with salt water and then with denatured ethanol. The higher the density of the liquids, the higher the rod or pencil should float.

Desalinization by Distillation

Refer students to pages 84–91 in their textbooks for a discussion of phase changes. **SKILLS FOCUS:** Observing, Designing Experiments **CLASS TIME:** Part A, 30 minutes; Part B, 20 minutes setup, 1–2 weeks for completion

Background Information

"Water, water everywhere, but not a drop to drink." This quotation is from *The Rime of the Ancient Mariner* by Samuel Coleridge, a poem that describes the fate of sailors in a boat that is stranded in the middle of the Pacific Ocean. The sailors are surrounded by water that they cannot drink. Both fresh water and seawater contain dissolved salts. But the amount of dissolved salts in a liter of seawater is much larger. Drinking seawater causes water to flow out of cells in the body, which increases dehydration. This effect is the exact opposite of the desired effect of drinking water.

In regions where the supply of fresh water is limited, seawater can be treated to make it safe to drink. The general name for processes that remove salts from water is desalinization. One method for separating dissolved salts from water is called distillation. During a distillation process, a liquid undergoes phase changes—vaporization followed by condensation.

Temperature and pressure affect the rate of vaporization. At atmospheric pressure, the rate of vaporization will be most rapid when a liquid is at a temperature equal to its boiling point. The container in which the hot vapor is collected must be chilled so that the vapor will rapidly condense. Distilling a liquid at its boiling point requires heat-resistant containers and a source of energy to heat the liquid, such as a gas burner. Sunlight can be used as the source of energy for distillation, but the process will take more time.

In Part A of this investigation, you will distill salt water by heating and boiling the salt water. In Part B of this investigation, you will use sunlight to vaporize the water.

Problem

How is the desalinization of salt water accomplished by distillation?

Pre-Lab Discussion

Read the entire investigation. Then, work with a partner to answer the following questions.

1. **Predicting** In Part A, how will the contents of the cooled flask differ from the contents of the heated flask?

   The liquid in the heated flask contains dissolved salts. The liquid in the cooled flask will not contain

   dissolved salts.

2. **Measuring** In Part A, are you measuring the temperature of the liquid in the flask or the vapor? Explain your answer.

   Because the bulb of the thermometer is located in the space above the liquid, the thermometer

   records the temperature of the vapor.

_____

3. **Designing Experiments** In Part B, why is it important to keep the clear bottle away from direct sunlight?

The temperature of the clear bottle must be kept low enough so that the water

vapor will condense.

4. **Formulating Hypotheses** In Part B, why is the bottle containing the salt water placed on a board? (*Hint:* Assume that some water vapor condenses in the plastic tubing.)

If the bottles were at the same height, the tube would be level and any condensed water vapor

could flow back into the black-painted bottle, which would defeat the goal of the distillation.

5. **Inferring** Differences in what physical property are used to separate the table salt from the water in the salt-water mixture?

Differences in boiling point are used to separate the dissolved table salt from water.

Materials *(per group)*

2 250-mL flasks
100-mL graduated cylinder
500-mL beaker
Lab burner
2-hole rubber stopper with glass tubing and non-mercury thermometer inserted
2 40-cm pieces of clear plastic tubing

ring stand and ring
wire gauze
salt water
crushed ice
2 2-L plastic bottles
electrical or masking tape
wooden board, at least 3 cm thick
glass marking pencil
graph paper

Wrap the tubing in a thick towel for your protection when gently inserting it in the stopper. Use a lubricant such as glycerol. **CAUTION:** Inserting glass through a stopper can cause the glass to break. Then, gently insert the thermometer until the thermometer bulb is 2 to 4 cm below the bottom of the stopper. To reduce the risk of breakage, you may wish to attach the plastic tubing to the right-angle glass tubing in advance. Prepare the mixture by dissolving 50 g of salt for each liter of tap water. Paint half of the plastic bottles black under a fume hood or outside.

Safety 🥽🧤🔪🧥🔥🔥🔥

Put on safety goggles and a lab apron. Be careful to avoid breakage when working with glassware. Never touch or taste any chemical unless instructed to do so. Use extreme care when working with heated equipment or materials to avoid burns. Observe proper laboratory procedures when using electrical equipment. Tie back loose hair and clothing when working with flames. Be careful when using matches. Do not reach over an open flame. Note all safety alert symbols next to the steps in the Procedure and review the meaning of each symbol by referring to the Safety Symbols on page xiii.

Procedure
Part A: Distillation of Salt Water By Boiling

1. Set up the apparatus, as shown in Figure 1. **CAUTION:** *Be sure that all glassware used in this investigation is heat-resistant.*

2. Place 100 mL of the salt-water solution in the flask to be heated.

3. Gently push one end of the rubber tubing onto the right-angle glass tubing. Place the stopper containing the right-angle glass tubing and thermometer firmly on the flask of salt water. The bulb of the thermometer should be near the top of the flask and not in the liquid. If necessary, ask your teacher to adjust the position of the thermometer.

4. Fill the beaker with crushed ice and set it away from the burner. Place the second flask in the crushed ice. Insert the open end of the plastic tubing in the middle of the flask, making sure that the tubing does not touch the bottom of the flask.

If you are using a hot plate instead of a Bunsen burner, use a flat-bottomed (Erlenmeyer) flask for the salt-water solution. Have students begin with the hot plate set to a high setting, and reset to a lower setting once the liquid begins to boil.

Figure 1

⚒ 🔥 5. Observe the temperature in the flask containing salt water. Record this temperature in the data table. Turn on the burner. Note and record the temperature at 2-minute intervals as you complete Steps 6 and 7. Attach a separate sheet of paper if you need more space to record the temperature.

6. When the temperature stops rising, you should notice a liquid beginning to collect in the flask in the beaker of crushed ice. Circle the temperature at this time in the data table. **CAUTION:** *Do not allow the plastic tubing to touch the liquid being collected.*

7. Continue collecting liquid in the cooled flask until about three-fourths of the liquid in the heated flask has been vaporized. Turn off the burner.

8. Observe the appearance of the contents of the cooled flask and the heated flask.

9. Allow the heated flask to cool. **CAUTION:** *Be careful in handling equipment that has been heated. Hot glass looks like cold glass. Do not touch the heated flask or burner.*

10. When the flask has cooled enough to handle, pour both of the solutions down the drain. Instead of disposing of the distillate and the concentrated salt solutions, you may want to collect them in marked containers and use them for the Go Further activity.

If the tubing is below the liquid, the condensed liquid may be drawn back into the tubing. If this occurs, help students to shake the liquid back out of the tubing into the cooled flask. If the liquid spills back into the heated flask, students will need to repeat the distillation.

Observations

DATA TABLE   Sample data are shown.

Time (minutes)	Temperature (°C)
0	22
2	26
4	40
6	60
8	80
10	100
12	100
14	100
16	100

Part B: Distillation of Salt Water by Evaporation

11. Set up the apparatus, as shown in Figure 2. Wrap the electrical or masking tape around both ends of the plastic tube so that the tube will fit tightly into the necks of the plastic bottles.

12. Place 100 mL of tap water in the clear bottle. Use a glass marking pencil to mark the height of the water. Pour the water down the drain.

13. Place 100 mL of the salt-water solution in the black bottle.

14. Insert one end of the plastic tubing into the neck of the black bottle, and the other end into the neck of the clear bottle.

15. Set both bottles on a window sill that has exposure to sunlight during at least half of the day. Set the black bottle on the wooden board so that it is at a higher position than the clear bottle. Arrange the bottles so that the black bottle receives sunlight as much as possible, while the clear bottle is kept out of the sun as much as possible.

16. Check the bottles daily until at least 75 percent of the liquid has been transferred to the clear bottle.

17. Pour the liquid from the black bottle clear container into a graduated cylinder and record the volume.

18. Observe the appearance of the two liquids. Then pour the liquids down the drain. Depending on the location and configuration of your classroom, students may have to work in larger groups while doing Part B or you may need to do Part B as a demonstration. Depending on the height of your window ledges and tables, you may be able to place the clear bottles on the floor. With such a setup, you will not need to elevate the black bottles. If your classroom has a northern exposure, you could use incandescent lights to heat the black bottles.

Black-painted plastic bottle — Tubing — Seal with duct tape — Clear plastic bottle — Board

Figure 2

Analysis and Conclusions

1. **Using Tables and Graphs** Draw a graph of your data from Part A. Plot time along the horizontal axis and temperature along the vertical axis. Label the point on your graph that corresponds to the time when you started to collect distilled liquid in the cooled flask.

Student graphs should show a rising curve with a plateau close to 100°C.

_____

2. **Observing** Did you observe any evidence that the liquids in the heated and cooled flasks had different compositions?

Students may say that the salt solution appeared cloudy as it became more concentrated or that

some salt crystals formed. They may also say that there was no observable difference.

_____

3. **Designing Experiments** Suggest at least one procedure that you could use to demonstrate that the liquids in the heated and cooled flasks have different compositions.

Students may suggest heating both liquids in open containers until all the water evaporated. There

would be a solid residue with the salt solution upon evaporation, but no residue with the distilled

water. Students may also suggest measuring and comparing the densities of the liquids. The salt

solution would have a greater density. If students suggest tasting the liquids, remind them that they

should not taste any material in the laboratory.

_____

4. **Applying Concepts** How do you know that distillation is a physical change rather than a chemical one?

Distillation is a physical change because no new substances are formed during the distillation.

A mixture of existing substances is separated.

_____

_____

_____

5. **Designing Experiments** What is the major difference between the experiments in Part A and Part B? What effect does this difference have on the experiments?

The major difference between the experiments is the heat source—a gas burner (or hot plate) in

Part A and sunlight in Part B. This difference affects the rate at which the distillation occurs.

_____

_____

_____

6. **Comparing and Contrasting** List the advantages of each method used in this investigation for distilling water.

Part A advantages: change occurs faster, not dependent on availability of sunlight;

Part B advantages: requires simpler equipment, conserves non-renewable energy sources,

can be more easily imitated in a non-laboratory environment

7. **Classifying** During vaporization, a liquid changes to a gas or a vapor. Explain how the temperature at which vaporization takes place determines whether the process is described as evaporation or boiling. (*Hint:* These terms occur in the titles for Parts A and B of this investigation.)

If vaporization occurs at a temperature below the boiling point of a liquid, the process is described

as evaporation. When vaporization occurs at the boiling point, the process is classified as boiling.

Go Further

Distilled water can be distinguished from salt water based on a difference in density. You can use a fresh, raw egg to demonstrate this difference. Predict what you will observe when you place the egg in the liquids. Have your teacher supervise your experiment. Wash your hands thoroughly with soap or detergent after you complete the experiment.

The egg should float easily in salt water if the concentration is at least 5 mL of table salt in 200 mL of water. A fresh egg should not float in distilled water. Students may also want to test tap water. In some regions tap water will contain enough dissolved salts so that the egg will rise slightly in the water. The size of the egg can also affect the results.

Investigating Space Between Particles in Matter

Refer students to pages 68 and 69 in their textbooks for a discussion of the arrangement of particles in solids and liquids.
SKILLS FOCUS: Measuring, Calculating, Drawing Conclusions
CLASS TIME: 30 minutes

Background Information

If you have ever seen water drain through beach sand, you know that there are spaces between the grains of sand. Because the grains of sand are relatively small and separate, you can pour sand almost as if it was a liquid. There are also spaces between the tiny particles that make up all matter.

In this investigation, you will first measure the volume of the space between grains of sand by filling a container with sand and water. Then, you will measure the volume of the space between the particles in a liquid by mixing two liquids together.

Problem

How much space is there between grains of sand or between particles in liquids?

Pre-Lab Discussion

Read the entire investigation. Then, work with a partner to answer the following questions.

1. **Using Analogies** Why is there space between marbles in a bowl? What factors might determine how much space there is between particles in a solid or liquid?

   Because the marbles are round, there will be spaces between them when they are

   packed in a container. Students may say that the size and shape of particles in a

   solid or liquid will affect how closely they can be packed together. (They may also

   mention the forces of attraction between particles.)

   _____

2. **Predicting** What do you expect to happen to the height of the material in the beaker when you begin to add water to the sand? Explain your answer.

   The height will not change because water can occupy the spaces between the grains of sand.

   _____
   _____
   _____
   _____
   _____

3. **Predicting** In the investigation, you will mix 100 mL of water with 100 mL of isopropyl alcohol. Predict whether the volume of this mixture will be less than, equal to, or more than 200 mL. Explain your answer.

Students may choose "less than" if they may assume that the alcohol and water molecules can be

more closely packed in the mixture than they are in either the alcohol or the water. Some may

choose "equal to" if they assume that the volume of the space between the particles does not

change when the liquids are mixed.

Materials (per group)

2 250-mL graduated cylinders   Adjust quantities of sand, water, and alcohol
100-mL graduated cylinder   used to match available graduated cylinders.
isopropyl alcohol   Provide 95% isopropyl alcohol.
sand
glass stirring rod

Safety 🔲 🔒 🧤 ☠ 🔥 🧪

Put on safety goggles and a lab apron. Be careful to avoid breakage when working with glassware. Always use caution when working with laboratory chemicals, as they may irritate the skin or stain skin or clothing. Never taste any chemicals unless instructed to do so. Keep alcohol away from any open flame. Wash your hands thoroughly after carrying out this investigation. Note all safety alert symbols next to the steps in the Procedure and review the meaning of each symbol by referring to the Safety Symbols on page xiii.

Review with students the safety information in the MSDS for isopropyl alcohol before performing this investigation.

Procedure

🧤 1. Fill a 250-mL graduated cylinder to its 200-mL mark with sand.

2. Fill the 100-mL graduated cylinder to the 100-mL mark with water. Slowly pour a little water into the graduated cylinder containing the sand. Continue pouring until the level of the water in the sand reaches the 200-mL line. Observe the volume of water remaining in the 100-mL graduated cylinder. Record this volume in Data Table 1.

3. Calculate the volume of water added to the sand by subtracting the volume of water remaining in the graduated cylinder from the total volume of water. Record your result in Data Table 1.

☠ 4. Pour 100 mL of isopropyl alcohol into the 250-mL graduated
🔥 cylinder. **CAUTION:** *Isopropyl alcohol is poisonous and flammable.*

5. Fill the 100-mL graduated cylinder to the 100-mL mark with water. Slowly pour the water into the graduated cylinder containing the isopropyl alcohol. Use the glass stirring rod to mix the two liquids. Observe the volume of the mixture. Record this volume in Data Table 2.

6. Subtract the volume of the alcohol-water mixture from the total volume of alcohol and water. Record this difference in Data Table 2. Wash your hands thoroughly after completing the investigation.

Observations   Sample data are shown.

DATA TABLE 1

Material	Volume (mL)
Total water	100
Remaining water	52
Water added = total water − remaining water	48

DATA TABLE 2

Material	Volume (mL)
Alcohol	100
Water	100
Mixture	190
Volume change = mixture − (alcohol + water)	10

Analysis and Conclusions

1. **Analyzing Data** What was the total volume of the space between the grains of sand?

   The space between the grains of sand was equal to the water added to the sand, which was 48 mL.

2. **Drawing Conclusions** Based on this investigation, how do you know that there is space between the particles in alcohol or water?

   There must be space between the particles because the total volume of the mixture is less than

   the sum of the measured volumes of alcohol and water.

3. **Formulating Hypotheses** Why did the total volume of water and alcohol decrease when the liquids were mixed together?

   Students may say that the shapes and sizes of the particles (molecules) of alcohol

   and water allowed them to be more closely packed when the liquids were mixed.

   (Some students may say that forces of attractions between alcohol and water draw

   the particles closer together in the mixture.)

Go Further

If the distances between the particles of a material change, will the volume of the material change? Design an experiment to determine the percentage change in volume that occurs when materials such as water, paraffin, or shortening change from solid to liquid or from liquid to solid. When your teacher has approved your experiment, perform it under your teacher's supervision, using all necessary safety procedures. Report your observations and conclusions.

Water has the unusual property of expanding upon freezing. Encourage students to compare this behavior to that of other more typical materials such as paraffin. Examine student plans for safety and review with students the MSDS safety information for any materials that they will use before approving student experiments. Supervise all student laboratory work.

Constructing Models of Atoms

Background Information

Refer students to pages 108–118 in their textbooks for a discussion of atomic structure. **SKILLS FOCUS:** Using Models **CLASS TIME:** 45 minutes

With an electron microscope, scientists can observe the arrangement of atoms on the surface of a material. But they cannot observe the arrangement of subatomic particles within an atom. Scientists use models to describe the structure of atoms.

Atomic models are revised as scientists learn more about atoms. Thomson revised Dalton's model of atoms as solid spheres when he discovered that atoms contained subatomic particles. To explain why most alpha particles could pass through a thin metal foil without being deflected, Rutherford proposed an atomic model with a dense, positively charged nucleus. The nucleus contains protons and neutrons. In the Bohr model of the atom, electrons move in fixed orbits around the nucleus, like planets around a sun. The currently accepted model of the atom assumes that the movement of electrons is less predictable. In the current model, an electron cloud is used to describe the likely locations for electrons in atoms.

Isotopes are atoms of a given element that contain different numbers of neutrons. Isotopes have the same atomic number, but different mass numbers. In this investigation, you will construct a model of an isotope. Then, you will evaluate your model and identify ways in which it can be improved.

Problem

How might the structure of an atom be modeled?

Pre-Lab Discussion

Read the entire investigation. Then, work with a partner to answer the following questions.

1. **Classifying** How do isotopes of the same element differ?

   The isotopes of an element have different numbers of neutrons.

2. **Using Tables and Graphs** How can you use the information in Figure 1 to determine the number of protons, neutrons, and electrons in an isotope?

   The number of electrons and protons is equal to the atomic number. The number of neutrons

   can be calculated by subtracting the atomic number from the mass number, which is included

   in the name of the isotope.

3. **Using Models** What will you use the following items to represent: red pushpins, green pushpins, beads, pipe cleaners?

Red pushpins represent protons, green pushpins represent neutrons, beads represent electrons, and

pipe cleaners represent energy levels.

_____

_____

4. **Using Models** How will you model different isotopes of the same element?

Isotopes are modeled by varying the number of green pushpins, which represent neutrons

that are attached to the plastic-foam ball.

_____

_____

5. **Drawing Conclusions** Which model of the atom does the model you will construct most resemble? Explain your answer.

The model resembles the Bohr model of an atom because the electrons have paths that resemble

the orbits of planets.

_____

_____

Materials *(per group)*

2 plastic-foam balls
pipe cleaners
red pushpins
green pushpins
beads   Provide beads that are smaller than the pushpins but large enough to thread onto the pipe cleaners.
2 coat hangers
fishing line   Provide about 2 m for each model that students construct.
scissors

Safety ⬛⬛

Put on safety goggles. Be careful when handling sharp instruments. Note all safety alert symbols next to the steps in the Procedure and review the meaning of each symbol by referring to the Safety Symbols on page xiii.

Procedure

1. Construct a model of one of the isotopes assigned by your teacher. Use the information in Figure 1 to predict the number of protons, neutrons, and electrons in the isotope. In the data table, record this information and the name of the isotope.

Figure 1

Element	Atomic Number	Stable Isotopes
Hydrogen	1	hydrogen-1, hydrogen 2
Helium	2	helium-3, helium-4
Lithium	3	lithium-6, lithium-7
Boron	5	boron-10, boron-11
Carbon	6	carbon-12, carbon-13
Nitrogen	7	nitrogen-14, nitrogen-15
Oxygen	8	oxygen-16, oxygen-17, oxygen-18
Neon	10	neon-20, neon-21, neon-22
Magnesium	12	magnesium-24, magnesium-25, magnesium-26
Silicon	14	silicon-28, silicon-29, silicon-30
Sulfur	16	sulfur-32, sulfur-33, sulfur-34, sulfur-36
Chlorine	17	chlorine-35, chlorine-37
Argon	18	argon-36, argon-38, argon-40

Assign two isotopes of a single element to each group. Groups with more than two students can be assigned elements with more than two stable isotopes.

2. In your model, red pushpins will represent protons, green pushpins will represent neutrons, and beads will represent electrons. Collect the appropriate number of each item for your model.

3. The plastic-foam ball will represent the nucleus. Insert the appropriate number of red and green pushpins into the ball to represent the correct number of protons and neutrons.

4. Recall that the first energy level can hold 2 electrons, the second energy level can hold 8 electrons, and the third energy level can hold 18 electrons. Calculate the number of energy levels occupied by electrons when atoms of your isotope are in the ground state. Record this number in the data table.

5. Use pipe cleaners to construct the appropriate number of energy levels for your isotope, as shown in Figure 2. Twist the ends of several pipe cleaners together to make the energy levels long enough to circle the nucleus, but do not close up the pipe-cleaner circles.

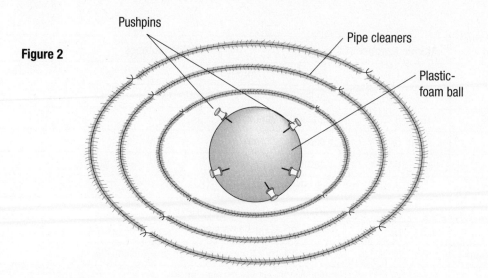

Figure 2

6. Place the appropriate number of beads on each pipe-cleaner circle to represent the electrons in each energy level. In the data table, record the number of electrons in each energy level.

7. Place the energy levels around the nucleus. If there is more than one occupied energy level, place the levels in the correct order.

8. Use fishing line to attach the nucleus and energy levels to a coat hanger, as shown in Figure 3. Your model is now complete.

9. Repeat Steps 1–8 to model the second isotope of your element.

The easiest way to attach the fishing line to the ball is to wrap and tie the fishing line around one or more of the pushpins.

Figure 3

Name _____ Class _____ Date _____

Observations

DATA TABLE Sample data are shown.

Isotope	Chlorine-35	Chlorine-37
Atomic number	17	17
Mass number	35	37
Number of protons	17	17
Number of neutrons	18	20
Number of electrons	17	17
Number of energy levels occupied by electrons	3	3
Number of electrons in first energy level	2	2
Number of electrons in second energy level	8	8
Number of electrons in third energy level	7	7

Analysis and Conclusions

1. **Using Models** Why were pushpins with the same mass used to represent protons and neutrons in your model?

   Protons and neutrons have nearly the same mass. _____

   _____

   _____

2. **Using Models** Why were the objects used to represent electrons smaller than the objects used to represent protons and neutrons?

   An electron has a much smaller mass than a proton or a neutron (about 1/2000 as massive).

   _____

   _____

   _____

3. **Comparing and Contrasting** How were the two models that you constructed similar? How were they different?

   The models had the same number of red pushpins and beads because isotopes have the same

   number of protons and electrons. The models had a different number of green pushpins because

   isotopes have different numbers of neutrons. _____

   _____

4. **Applying Concepts** Explain why a model of an atom must always contain the same number of protons and electrons.

Because atoms are neutral (zero net charge), they always have the same number of positively

charged protons and negatively charged electrons.

_____

_____

5. **Evaluating** What are some inaccuracies in the way your models represent the nucleus?

The models represent the nucleus as too large compared to the overall volume of an atom.

The models represent the protons and neutrons as attached to the nucleus. In fact, the collection

of protons and neutrons is the nucleus.

_____

_____

6. **Evaluating and Revising** In what two ways does your model fail to accurately depict the electrons in an atom?

Electrons in atoms are in constant motion. Electrons do not travel in fixed paths around

the nucleus.

_____

_____

_____

Go Further

Describe a physical model that could more closely represent the currently accepted model of an atom. Focus on how the model could best represent the behavior of electrons.

Models will vary, but should reflect the fact that electrons are in constant motion and that the locations of the electrons are unpredictable. One approach would be to use a fan to blow the objects representing electrons around within a container. Students might suggest using the appropriate number of small flying insects within a closed container to represent the motion of electrons. Students may propose a general approach, using a computer program to randomly assign "electrons" to given locations around a nucleus. Those locations would be constantly changing.

Chapter 4   Atomic Structure

Modeling the Location of an Electron in an Atom

Refer students to pages 108–118 in their textbooks for a discussion of atomic structure. **SKILLS FOCUS:** Inferring, Using Models **CLASS TIME:** 25 minutes

Background Information

In the atomic models of the early twentieth century, electrons were said to move around the nucleus along specific paths, much as the planets move around the sun. However, experimental evidence has indicated that the precise position of an electron in an atom cannot be known or predicted. Scientists can speak only of the probability of finding electrons at various locations, not of their exact positions.

Probability is a measure of how often a certain event will occur out of a total number of events. For example, there are two ways a coin can land—with its head facing up or its tail facing up. Each side has a 50 percent (or one out of two) probability of landing face up for any toss.

An **electron cloud** provides a visual model for the probable behavior of an electron in an atom. The electron cloud shows the likelihood that an electron will be found in a given part of the atom around the nucleus. If the electron is not likely to be found at a particular position, the cloud appears less dense. If the electron is more likely to be found at a particular position, the cloud has a denser appearance, as shown in Figure 1.

In this investigation, you will use probability to describe the location of an electron in an atom.

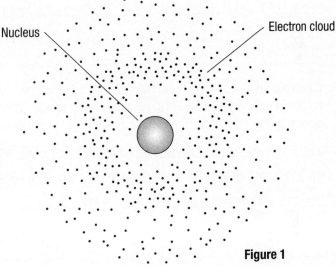

Figure 1

Problem

How can the location of an electron in an atom be described?

Pre-Lab Discussion

Read the entire investigation. Then, work with a partner to answer the following questions.

1. **Applying Concepts** Scientists use probability to predict the behavior of electrons in an atom. What is probability?

   Probability is the likelihood of an event occurring. Probability is equal to the number of times a

   particular event occurs divided by the total number of events.

2. **Applying Concepts** According to the way you will mark your die at the beginning of this investigation, what is the probability of the electron being found in the zone closest to the "nucleus" (0–4 cm)? In the second closest zone (4–6 cm)? In the third closest zone (6–8 cm)?

1/6; 4/6 = 2/3; 1/6

3. **Predicting** Describe the results you expect to observe.

Most colored-in squares will be between 4 cm and 6 cm from the center, while fewer

colored-in squares will be between 0 cm and 4 cm, and between 6 cm and 8 cm.

4. **Inferring** What can you infer about the probable locations of an electron in an atom from the above prediction?

The electron is not likely to be found at the closest possible distances to the nucleus, nor is it likely

to be very far away. The most probable location of the electron is within a band on either side of

a given radius from the nucleus.

5. **Comparing and Contrasting** Do you expect your results to be identical to those of other students, or similar to those of other students, or completely different from those of other students? Explain your answer.

Students should expect similar, but not identical results because not all students will fill in exactly

the same squares, nor will they obtain exactly the same results when they roll the die. On the average,

however, their results should not differ greatly.

Materials (per group)

game die
masking tape
graph paper Provide graph paper with about 2 squares per centimeter.
pencil
red pencil
metric ruler

Procedure

1. Cover all six sides of the die with masking tape. Mark one of the sides with one dot, four of the sides with two dots each, and the remaining side with three dots.

2. Select a square near the center of the graph paper and use a red pencil to color it red. This red square will represent the nucleus of a hydrogen atom with one electron.

3. Toss the die. Use a regular pencil to color in a square according to the following rules:

   If the number 1 appears face up on the die, color in any square that is between 0 cm and 4 cm from the "nucleus."

   If the number 2 appears face up on the die, color in any square that is between 4 cm and 6 cm from the "nucleus."

   If the number 3 appears face up on the die, color in any square that is between 6 cm and 8 cm from the "nucleus."

4. Repeat Step 3, tossing the die and marking the graph for a total of 50 tosses. Record your results in the data table.

Observations Sample data are shown.

DATA TABLE

Distance from "Nucleus"	Number of Colored-in Squares
0–4 cm	6–10
4–6 cm	30–38
6–8 cm	6–10

Analysis and Conclusions

1. **Observing** In which zone are most of the colored-in squares on your diagram?

   The second zone, which is between 4 cm and 6 cm from the "nucleus" _____

   _____

2. **Using Models** What does each colored-in square on your diagram represent?

   Each square represents a chance of finding the electron in a particular location around the nucleus. ___

   _____

3. **Inferring** Based on your data, where would you be most likely to find an electron? Explain your answer.

   The electron would be most likely found in the region with the most colored-in squares,

   which is between 4 cm and 6 cm from the "nucleus." _____

   _____

4. Comparing and Contrasting Compare your diagram to a classmate's. Are they identical? In what ways are they alike or different?

The average concentration of colored-in squares at the various distances is similar.

The actual positions of the colored-in squares are different in each diagram.

5. Drawing Conclusions Can the exact position of an electron in an atom be determined? What can you know about an electron's location?

The exact position of an electron cannot be determined. The probability that an electron is located

at a certain distance from the nucleus can be known.

6. Predicting Suppose you had tossed the die 100 times. How do you think your results would have compared with the results you obtained by tossing the die 50 times?

The probabilities should remain about the same, although the number of darkened squares in each

area would approximately double.

Go Further

Redesign the procedure in this investigation to model the behavior of the two electrons in a helium atom. Can the electrons be in the same location at the same time? Can they be in the same location at different times? Describe the modified procedure and the results you might expect.

Students might suggest using a second die to represent the second electron and tossing both dies each time. They could use different colored pencils to represent the probable locations of each electron. To adjust for the possibility of the electrons occupying the same location at different times, students might fill in only half a square at a time. They could complete the square for the other electron on a later toss. The overall distribution would not change. More filled squares would be in the zone between 4–6 cm than in the zones between 0–4 cm or 6–8 cm.

Chapter 5   The Periodic Table   **Investigation 5A**

Using Clues to Identify Elements

Refer students to pages 130–145 in their textbooks for a discussion of the periodic table, classes of elements, and representative groups. **SKILLS FOCUS:** Analyzing Data, Classifying, Drawing Conclusions **CLASS TIME:** 45 minutes

Background Information

Chemical elements can be classified according to their properties as metals, nonmetals, and metalloids. **Metals** are good conductors of heat and electricity. Many metals are malleable and ductile. **Nonmetals** are poor conductors of heat and electricity, and solid nonmetals tend to be brittle. **Metalloids** have properties between those of metals and nonmetals.

Elements in the same group on the periodic table have the same number of **valence electrons,** which are electrons in the highest occupied energy level of an atom. The number of an A group matches the number of valence electrons in atoms of each element in the group. For example, the Group 4A elements each have four valence electrons per atom. The exception to this pattern is the element helium, which is in Group 8A but has only two valence electrons.

Because elements in a group have the same number of valence electrons, they tend to have similar properties. The most reactive metals are the **alkali metals** in Group 1A on the far left side of the periodic table. The Group 2A elements are the **alkaline earth metals,** which are somewhat less reactive than the alkali metals. Groups of elements become less metallic in their properties from left to right across the periodic table. The most reactive nonmetals are the **halogens** in Group 7A. Group 8A contains the **noble gases,** which are colorless and odorless, and rarely react with other elements.

In this investigation, you will use a list of clues to identify 34 elements and place them in their correct locations in the periodic table.

Problem

Where do the elements described in the clues fit in the periodic table?

Pre-Lab Discussion

Read the entire investigation. Then, work with a partner to answer the following questions.

1. **Analyzing Data** How will the index cards be useful when you are reading the clues to the elements?

   Each clue can be summarized on an index card. Index cards that contain clues about the same

   element can be easily compared. An index cardcan be set aside when all the elements referred

   to in the clue are identified.

   _____

   _____

   _____

   _____

2. **Inferring** Do you have to know a specific, identifying property for each element in order to place all 34 elements in the partial periodic table? Explain your answer.

No, many of the elements will be identified by a process of elimination. For example, if all the

elements in a group have been identified and only one empty box remains in that group, then the

remaining element belongs in that box.

_____

_____

3. **Classifying** Are elements with similar properties in the same row or the same column of the periodic table?

Elements with similar properties are in the same column or group.

_____

_____

_____

4. **Analyzing Data** Explain how information about an element's physical state at room temperature will help you fill in the partial periodic table.

As shown in the periodic table in the textbook, elements that are gases at room temperature

are nonmetals, which are located on the right of the periodic table (except for hydrogen).

_____

_____

5. **Classifying** How would information about number of valence electrons be useful for placing elements in the periodic table?

When the number of valence electrons is known, the representative group to which the element

belongs is known.

_____

6. **Analyzing Data** Why is it important to review the clues after you have read all of the clues once?

The elements cannot all be identified and located after a single reading of the individual clues.

Information from multiple clues must be combined. Once some of the boxes are filled, some

clues will become more useful.

_____

_____

_____

Materials *(per group)*

25 index cards

copy of the periodic table from the textbook for reference

Procedure

1. Work in pairs. Examine the partial periodic table that follows the list of clues. Note that it contains spaces for the 34 elements in Periods 1 through 5 and Groups 1A through 8A. The locations of the metalloids are shaded.

2. For this investigation, these 34 elements have been randomly assigned a number from 1 to 34. (*Hint:* This number has no relation to the atomic number or mass of the element.) By using the list of clues, you will identify where each element belongs in the partial periodic table.

3. Read the clues in order. You will probably find it useful to summarize the information in each clue by using index cards, to which you can refer later as needed. Fill in the partial periodic table by placing each element's assigned number in the appropriate box. Use a pencil so that you can correct any mistakes.

4. Sometimes a single clue will enable you to identify an element and place its number in the correct box. In most cases, however, you will need to combine information from different clues in order to identify the element.

5. Reread the clues as many times as necessary. When you are certain that you have correctly identified all the elements referred to in a clue, set that index card aside.

List of Clues

1. Elements 2, 5, 18, 29, and 33 are colorless, odorless, unreactive gases. Of these gases, element 29 has the largest atomic mass.

2. Elements 13, 19, 23, and 34 have six valence electrons, and element 13 is a metalloid.

3. Elements 9, 14, 16, and 21 are highly reactive metals in the same group. Of these metals, element 16 is the least reactive.

4. Elements 1, 8, 11, 13, 14, 17, 24, and 29 are in the same period.

5. Elements 11, 26, 27, and 28 have three valence electrons.

6. Elements 1, 4, 6, and 30 are found in the same group. Element 6 is in chlorophyll molecules.

7. Elements 10, 22, 24, and 32 are in the same group. Element 22 is a liquid at room temperature.

8. Elements 2, 10, 15, and 34 are nonmetals in the same period.

9. Elements 7, 15, 17, and 25 are in the same group. Of these, only element 7 is a gas at room temperature.

10. Elements 12, 20, and 26 are metalloids. Elements 20 and 12 are in the same group.

11. Element 30 is important to maintain strong bones and teeth.

12. An atom of element 21 has one more proton than an atom of element 2.

13. Elements 3 is a nonmetal with one valence electron.

14. Element 27 is the most abundant metal in Earth's crust.

15. Element 31 is a solid at room temperature. Most of the compounds in your body contain this element.

16. Element 18 has two electrons.

17. Element 33 has a smaller atomic mass than element 5.

18. Element 32 is the most reactive nonmetal.

19. Element 20 and element 19 are combined in a compound found in glass.

20. Glass that contains element 26 does not shatter easily.

21. Element 19 is the most abundant element in Earth's crust.

Observations

Partial Periodic Table

Answers are shown.

1A		2A		3A	4A	5A	6A	7A	8A
1 3									18
2 16		4		26	31	7	19	32	33
3 9		6		27	20	15	34	10	2
4 21		30		28	12	25	23	22	5
5 14		1		11	8	17	13	24	29

Analysis and Conclusions

1. **Drawing Conclusions** Identify each element in the list of clues by matching its assigned number to the correct name of the element.

1 strontium, 2 argon, 3 hydrogen, 4 beryllium, 5 krypton, 6 magnesium, 7 nitrogen, 8 tin, 9 sodium,

10 chlorine, 11 indium, 12 germanium, 13 tellurium, 14 rubidium, 15 phosphorus, 16 lithium,

17 antimony, 18 helium, 19 oxygen, 20 silicon, 21 potassium, 22 bromine, 23 selenium, 24 iodine,

25 arsenic, 26 boron, 27 aluminum, 28 gallium, 29 xenon, 30 calcium, 31 carbon, 32 fluorine,

33 neon, 34 sulfur

_____

_____

_____

_____

2. **Analyzing Data** Were you able to place some elements in the partial periodic table with just a single clue? Use examples to explain.

Yes, examples include tellurium (metalloid with six valence electrons), magnesium (metal found

in chlorophyll), bromine (liquid at room temperature), aluminum (most abundant metal in Earth's

crust), carbon (contained in most compounds in the human body), and fluorine (most reactive

nonmetal).

_____

_____

_____

_____

_____

3. **Analyzing Data** Provide at least two examples of when you needed to use more than one clue to identify an element.

Helium (element 18) is a colorless, odorless, unreactive gas (clue 1) with two electrons (clue 16).

Indium (element 11) has three valence electrons (clue 5) and is in the same period as tellurium,

element 13 (clues 2 and 4).

_____

_____

_____

_____

_____

_____

_____

4. **Applying Concepts** Why were you able to use clues about atomic mass to place elements, even though the periodic table is organized by atomic number?

The atomic mass of elements within a group increases from top to bottom in the group.

_____

_____

_____

_____

5. **Comparing and Contrasting** Which elements are not included in the partial periodic table? Compare the number of elements in the partial periodic table to the number of known elements.

The partial periodic table does not include transition metals or elements in Periods 6 and 7.

Of the 113 known elements, only 34 are in the partial periodic table.

_____

_____

_____

_____

_____

_____

_____

Go Further

Now that you have identified the elements from the list of clues, write at least five additional clues based on information from Chapter 5.

Student answers will vary. Examples of acceptable responses: Element 24 (iodine) is required by the thyroid gland. Elements 7 and 15 (nitrogen and phosphorus) are important components of fertilizers.

Chapter 5   The Periodic Table   🔍 **Investigation 5B**

Comparing Chemical Properties Within a Group

Refer students to pages 131–138 in their textbooks for a discussion of the periodic table, page 139 for a discussion of valence electrons, and page 141 for a description of the alkaline earth elements. **SKILLS FOCUS:** Observing, Comparing **CLASS TIME:** 45 minutes

Background Information

The properties of elements repeat in a regular pattern across the periods in the periodic table. From left to right across each period, elements tend to be less metallic and more nonmetallic. Elements in the same group in the table have similar properties because they have the same number of valence electrons. A valence electron is an electron that is in the highest occupied energy level of an atom. These electrons play a key role in chemical reactions. The properties of elements within a group are not identical because the valence electrons are in different energy levels.

The elements in Group 2A in the periodic table are known as alkaline earth metals. Many properties of alkaline earth metals change in a predictable way from top to bottom within the group. One of those properties is reactivity, or the tendency to combine chemically with other substances. The reactivity of an element can be demonstrated by how the element reacts or how its compounds react with other substances.

The formation of a precipitate in a solution is one clue that a chemical change has occurred. A precipitate is a solid that forms and separates from a liquid mixture. In this investigation, you will mix solutions of similar alkaline earth compounds with a set of test solutions and observe whether or not precipitates form. You will use the results to predict how the reactivity of the alkaline earth metals changes from top to bottom within Group 2A.

Problem

How does reactivity vary among the alkaline earth metals?

Pre-Lab Discussion

Read the entire investigation. Then, work with a partner to answer the following questions.

1. **Controlling Variables** Why is it important not to mix the test solution in one well with the solution in another well on your spot plate?

   If the test solutions were mixed, it would not be possible to tell which combinations of solutions

   produced precipitates.

2. **Designing Experiments** Why is the order of the rows in the well plate the same as the order of elements in the periodic table?

   With the compounds tested in order of the placement within Group 2A, it is easier to see the

   pattern of the results.

3. **Controlling Variables** What are the manipulated, responding, and controlled variables in this investigation?

Manipulated: the alkaline earth metal in the nitrate compound; responding: formation of a

precipitate (reactivity); controlled: the solutions used to test reactivity

4. **Predicting** Write a prediction of how the reactivity of the alkaline earth metals will change from the top of Group 2A to the bottom.

Reactivity will increase from the top of group 2A to the bottom.

Materials *(per group)*

spot plate

sheet of notebook paper

dropper bottles containing solutions
  of the following compounds:

    magnesium nitrate

    barium nitrate

    calcium nitrate

    potassium carbonate

    potassium chromate

    potassium sulfate

    strontium nitrate

To prepare the aqueous solutions:

0.2 M $Mg(NO_3)_2$	29.7 g in 1 L
0.1 M $Ca(NO_3)_2$	16.4 g in 1 L
0.1 M $Sr(NO_3)_2$	21.2 g in 1 L
0.1 M $Ba(NO_3)_2$	26.1 g in 1 L
0.2 M K_2CO_3	27.6 g in 1 L
0.2 M K_2SO_4	34.9 g in 1 L
0.2 M K_2CrO_4	38.8 g in 1 L

Safety

Put on safety goggles and a lab apron. Be careful to avoid breakage when working with glassware. Some chemicals used in this investigation are toxic. Always use special caution when working with laboratory chemicals, as they may irritate the skin or stain skin or clothing. Never touch or taste any chemical unless instructed to do so. Follow your teacher's instructions for disposing of used chemicals. Wash your hands thoroughly after carrying out this investigation. Note all safety alert symbols next to the steps in the Procedure and review the meaning of each symbol by referring to the Safety Symbols on page xiii.

Review with students the safety information in the MSDS for each chemical before performing the investigation. Supervise students closely to be sure that they follow all recommended safety procedures and do not get the solutions on the skin or in their eyes or mouths.

Procedure

1. Place the spot plate in the center of a sheet of notebook paper, as shown in Figure 1. There should be four wells per column and three wells per row.

2. Along the side of the notebook paper next to each of the four rows of wells, write the names of the four alkaline earth metals that are present in each nitrate compound you are using. Write the names in the order shown in Figure 1. This is the order of these four elements in Group 2A.

3. Label the paper above each of the three columns of wells, as shown in Figure 1.

4. Place 3 drops of potassium carbonate in each of the four wells under the label Potassium Carbonate. Place 3 drops of potassium sulfate in each of the four wells under the label Potassium Sulfate. Place 3 drops of potassium chromate in each of the four wells under the label Potassium Chromate. Make sure that each solution is placed in the wells of only column one. **CAUTION:** *Some chemicals used in this investigation are toxic. Be careful not to get the solutions on your skin.*

5. Place 3 drops of magnesium nitrate in each of the three wells in the row labeled Magnesium. Observe whether or not a precipitate forms in each well and record the results in the data table.

6. Place 3 drops of calcium nitrate in each of the three wells in the row labeled Calcium. Observe whether or not a precipitate forms in each well and record the results in the data table.

Figure 1

7. Place 3 drops of strontium nitrate in each of the three wells in the row labeled Strontium. Observe whether or not a precipitate forms in each well and record the results in the data table.

8. Place 3 drops of barium nitrate in each of the three wells in the row labeled Barium. Observe whether or not a precipitate forms in each well and record the results in the data table.

9. Follow your teacher's instructions for disposing of the chemicals on the spot plate. Wash the spot plate and your hands thoroughly with soap or detergent and warm water. Have students drain their spot plates into a designated chemical waste container.

Observations   Sample data are shown.

DATA TABLE

Alkaline Earth Metal	Carbonate	Sulfate	Chromate
Magnesium	White precipitate	No precipitate	No precipitate
Calcium	White precipitate	Small amount of white precipitate	No precipitate
Strontium	White precipitate	White precipitate	No precipitate
Barium	White precipitate	White precipitate	Yellow precipitate

Analysis and Conclusions

1. **Observing** What evidence did you observe of a chemical change occurring in any of the wells?

   A white or yellow precipitate formed.

2. **Analyzing Data** Which alkaline earth metal formed the smallest number of precipitates?

   Magnesium

3. **Analyzing Data** Which alkaline earth metal formed the most precipitates?

   Barium

4. **Drawing Conclusions** Based on your data, list the alkaline earth metals in order of their reactivity, from most reactive to least reactive. What is the relationship between reactivity and the location of each alkaline earth metal in the periodic table?

   Barium, strontium, calcium, magnesium; The more reactive alkaline earth elements are nearer the

   bottom of the group.

5. **Evaluating and Revising** Did your data support or contradict your prediction?

   The data supported the prediction that reactivity increases from top to bottom within the group.

6. **Predicting** Group 1A in the periodic table contains alkali metals. Based on your investigation of the Group 2A elements, which element in Group 1A, other than francium, would you predict to be most reactive? Least reactive?

   Cesium; lithium

7. **Predicting** Can the results for reactivity in this investigation be applied to the elements in Group 7A? Explain your prediction.

   No, because Group 7A elements are nonmetals and reactivity for nonmetals increases from bottom

   to top within the group.

Go Further

If you had a solution containing a mixture of magnesium nitrate, strontium nitrate, and barium nitrate, how could you separate the mixture? (*Hint:* Review the information in the data table.)

Add potassium chromate so that barium forms a precipitate. Pour off the liquid and add potassium sulfate to it so that strontium forms a precipitate. Pour off the remaining liquid in which the magnesium nitrate is dissolved.

Chapter 6   Chemical Bonds   Investigation 6A

Playing the Ionic Compounds
Card Game

Refer students to pages 170–175 in their textbooks for a
discussion of naming compounds and writing formulas.
SKILLS FOCUS: Calculating, Observing, Applying Concepts,

Background Information

Relating Cause and Effect **CLASS TIME:** 45 minutes

Ionic compounds are composed of charged particles called **ions.**
Positively charged ions are called **cations,** and negatively charged
ions are called **anions.** Although ionic compounds are composed of
ions, they are electrically neutral. The sum of the positive charges of
the cations and the negative charges of the anions is zero. The formula
of an ionic compound can be determined from the ratio of cations and
anions needed to produce a total charge equal to zero. The symbol for
the cation always appears first in the formula.

The names of ionic compounds are based on the names of their
ions. For most cations, the name of the cation is the same name as the
element name. However, many transition metals form more than one
ion. For these ions, a Roman numeral is used to show the charge. For
example, Fe^{2+} is iron(II) and Fe^{3+} is iron(III). Anions are named by
combining part of the name of the element and the ending *–ide.* For
example, the name for O^{2-} is oxide. A covalently bonded group of
atoms that has a positive or negative charge is called a **polyatomic
ion.** These ions have names that reflect their composition.

In this investigation, you will practice naming ionic compounds
and writing their formulas by playing a card game.

Problem

How are the names and formulas of ionic compounds determined?

Pre-Lab Discussion

*Read the entire investigation. Then, work with a partner to answer the
following questions.*

1. **Inferring** What is the object of the game?

   The object of the game is to make as many matches as possible. A match consists of a

   set of cation and anion cards that match the formula for the compound represented by a

   player's cation and anion name cards. Players receive one point for each ion in the formula.

2. **Classifying** How many cation symbol cards, cation name cards,
   anion symbol cards, and anion name cards are required for this
   card game?

   Forty cation symbol cards, 10 cation name cards, 40 anion symbol cards, and 10 anion

   name cards are required.

3. **Inferring** How many cards of each type does each player receive at the beginning of a round?

Each player receives three cation symbol cards, three anion symbol cards, one cation

name card, and one anion name card.

4. **Inferring** What happens after a player makes a correct match?

The player draws new ion symbol cards and ion name cards to replace the ones shown in the

match. The used name cards are set aside and are out of play. The used ion symbol cards

are placed in the appropriate discard piles.

5. **Making Judgments** When does the game end?

The game ends when either the cation or anion name cards are used up.

Materials *(per group)*
100 unlined index cards

Procedure
1. Work in groups of four. Use the index cards to prepare four decks of playing cards. Examples of cards are shown in Figure 1.

   a. **Cation symbol cards.** Prepare four cation symbol cards for each of the following cations. Write the symbol for each cation on the front of an index card. On the back of each card, write "Cation Symbol."

   Na^+ K^+ Mg^{2+} Ca^{2+} Al^{3+} Fe^{2+} Fe^{3+} Cu^+ Cu^{2+} Zn^{2+}

   b. **Cation name cards.** Prepare one cation name card for each of the following cations. Write the name of each cation on the front of an index card. On the back of each card, write "Cation Name."

   sodium potassium magnesium calcium aluminum
   iron(II) iron(III) copper(I) copper(II) zinc

   c. **Anion symbol cards.** Prepare four anion symbol cards for each of the following anions. Write the symbol for each anion on the front of an index card. On the back of each card, write "Anion Symbol."

   F^- Cl^- O^{2-} S^{2-} PO_4^{3-} CO_3^{2-} NO_3^- N^{3-} Br^- OH^-

   d. **Anion name cards.** Prepare one anion name card for each of the following anions. Write the name for each anion on the front of an index card. On the back of each card, write "Anion Name."

   fluoride chloride oxide sulfide phosphate
   carbonate nitrate nitride bromide hydroxide

Figure 1

2. After you finish preparing the cards, shuffle each deck of cards separately and place the decks facedown on the table.

3. To determine who goes first, have each player draw a cation symbol card. The player who draws the ion with the highest charge goes first. If players draw the same charge, they should draw another card. Replace the cards and shuffle the cation symbol deck. Play continues clockwise.

4. To start the game, each player draws three cation symbol cards, three anion symbol cards, one cation name card, and one anion name card. Then, turn over one card from each deck of symbol cards to start a discard pile, as shown in Figure 2.

Figure 2

5. The object of the game is to gather the correct number and type of symbol cards to match the formula of the compound represented by the selected cation and anion name cards. As soon as you think you have a match, declare it and show your cards. If you are correct, you will receive one point for each ion in the compound. For example, you would receive three points for the ions in $MgCl_2$.

6. When you show your cards, any other player can challenge your match by providing the correct formula. If your formula is incorrect (the charges do not add up to zero) or if your formula does not match your name cards, the challenger gets the points.

7. During a player's turn, the player may do one of the following:

   a. Draw a card from either the cation symbol deck or discard pile, or from the anion symbol deck or discard pile, and discard a cation or anion symbol card to the appropriate discard pile; or

   b. Draw a new cation name card, anion name card, or both, and place the old name cards at the bottom of the appropriate decks.

   If you can make a match after drawing a card, you must declare it before discarding any cards. Once cards are discarded, the turn is over, and play continues.

8. If there is no challenge after you declare a match, record the formula, the name, and the number of points in the data table. If there is a challenge, the group must determine who is correct and who gets the points. If you challenge another player and receive the points, record "Challenge" in the data table instead of the name of the compound.

9. After you declare a match and the group determines who gets the points, draw new ion symbol cards and ion name cards to replace the ones you showed to make a match. Put the used ion symbol cards in the appropriate discard pile. Set the used name cards aside and out of play. At that point, your turn is over, and play continues.

10. If either the cation symbol cards or the anion symbol cards are all used, mix the appropriate discard pile, turn it over, and continue play. When either the cation name cards or the anion name cards are all used, the game is over. The winner is the player with the most points.

Observations

DATA TABLE Sample data are shown.

Match	Compound Name	Compound Formula	Points
1	Calcium nitrate	$Ca(NO_3)_2$	3
2	Iron(III) carbonate	$Fe_2(CO_3)_3$	5
3	Sodium chloride	NaCl	2
4	Aluminum bromide	$AlBr_3$	4
5	Challenge	$Zn(OH)_2$	3
6	Copper(I) oxide	Cu_2O	3
7			
8			
9			
10			
		Total	20

Name _____ Class _____ Date _____

Analysis and Conclusions

1. **Calculating** Describe how to determine the correct ratio of ions in a compound.

   Use the ratio of cations to anions that produces a net charge of zero.

   _____

   _____

2. **Inferring** Explain why it is not possible to write a formula for a compound of sodium and calcium.

   Because both elements form only cations, the sum of the charges on their ions can never equal

   zero. When an ionic compound forms, one element must lose electrons and one element must

   gain electrons during the transfer of electrons.

   _____

   _____

   _____

   _____

3. **Applying Concepts** Each of the chemical names below contains an error. Describe the nature of the error in each name.

   a. Potassium sulfur

   The correct name for an anion of sulfur is sulfide.

   _____

   _____

   b. Oxide potassium

   The ions are in the wrong order. The name of the cation comes before the name of the anion in

   the name of an ionic compound. The correct name is potassium oxide.

   _____

   _____

   c. Copper oxide

   Copper can form two different cations—copper(I) and copper(II). The name should indicate which

   ion is present.

   _____

   _____

4. **Relating Cause and Effect** How many anions are required to balance one aluminum ion? Explain your answer.

Three anions are required because an aluminum ion has a charge of 3^+.

_____

_____

5. **Drawing Conclusions** How are the name and formula of an ionic compound determined?

In the name of an ionic compound, the name of the cation is followed by the name of the anion.

The formula of an ionic compound can be determined from the ratio of cations and anions needed

to produce a total charge equal to zero. The symbol for the cation always comes first in the formula.

_____

_____

_____

_____

Go Further

In this investigation, you used the charges on ions to determine the formulas of compounds. How could you change this game so you could play it with covalent compounds? Design a card game that you could use to practice writing formulas and naming covalent compounds containing two elements.

Students may need to review pages 174 and 175 in their textbooks.

Comparing Ionic and Molecular Compounds

Refer students to pages 158–169 in their textbooks for a discussion of ionic and covalent bonds. **SKILLS FOCUS:** Observing, Comparing and Contrasting, Predicting, Inferring, Drawing Conclusions, Evaluating and Revising **CLASS TIME:** 45 minutes

Background Information

Ions in an ionic compound and molecules in a molecular compound are held together by forces of attraction called **chemical bonds.** An **ionic bond** is the force that holds positively charged cations and negatively charged anions together in a crystal lattice. Each cation is attracted to all the neighboring anions in the lattice. Each anion is attracted to all the neighboring cations in the lattice.

In molecules, atoms are held together by covalent bonds. In a **covalent bond,** two atoms share a pair of valence electrons. The atoms are held together by the attractions between the protons in each nucleus and the shared electrons. If one atom in a covalent bond has a greater attraction for electrons than the other atom does, the electrons are not shared equally between the atoms. The atom with the greater attraction has a partial negative charge, while the other atom has a partial positive charge. This type of covalent bond is called a **polar covalent bond.** When the electrons are shared equally between the atoms, the bond is called a **nonpolar covalent bond.** Whether a molecule is polar or nonpolar depends on the type of covalent bonds and the shape of the molecule.

In this investigation, you will use ease of melting to compare the strength of the ionic bonds in sodium chloride to the strength of intermolecular attractions in paraffin. Paraffin is a mixture of hydrocarbons, which are molecular compounds that contain only hydrogen and carbon. Then, you will compare the ability of the molecules in sugar and the molecules in paraffin to dissolve in water.

Problem

How do different forces of attraction affect the behavior of ionic compounds and molecular compounds?

Pre-Lab Discussion

Read the entire investigation. Then, work with a partner to answer the following questions.

1. Inferring How would you expect the strength of the forces that hold a solid together to affect the melting point of the solid?

The stronger the forces, the higher the melting point would be.

_____

_____

2. **Predicting** A solid can dissolve in water if the particles in the solid are attracted to water molecules. Would you expect an ionic compound to dissolve easily in water? A compound with polar molecules? A compound with nonpolar molecules? Explain your answers. (*Hint:* Water molecules are strongly polar.)

The ends of polar molecules such as water have partial positive and negative charges. Therefore,

water molecules are attracted to ions and other polar molecules. Water molecules are not

attracted to nonpolar molecules. Therefore, ionic compounds and polar molecules dissolve

in water much more easily than nonpolar molecules do.

3. **Controlling Variables** Identify the manipulated and responding variables in this investigation.

The manipulated variable is the type of compound, and the responding variables are the ease of

melting and the ease of dissolving in water.

4. **Formulating Hypotheses** Record your hypothesis of whether the bonds that hold ions together in a crystal are stronger than the intermolecular attractions that hold molecules together in a solid.

The bonds that hold ions together are stronger.

5. **Evaluating** What results in this investigation would support your hypothesis?

The hypothesis that the bonds that hold ions together in a crystal are stronger than the

intermolecular attractions that hold molecules together in a solid would be supported if the

paraffin melts more easily than the sodium chloride does.

Materials (per group)

sodium chloride	clay triangle	sugar
paraffin	Bunsen burner	test-tube rack
3 spatulas	tongs	clock or watch
2 crucibles	2 test tubes with stoppers	Provide laboratory grade sodium chloride, not table salt, which may contain other substances.
ring stand with iron ring	glass-marking pencil	

Safety 🥽 🧤 🔪 ⚗ 🔥

Put on safety goggles and a lab apron. Be careful to avoid breakage when working with glassware. Tie back loose hair and clothing when working with flames. Do not reach over an open flame. Use extreme care when working with heated equipment or materials to avoid burns. Note all safety alert symbols next to the steps in the Procedure and review the meaning of each symbol by referring to the Safety Symbols on page xiii.

Procedure

1. Use a spatula to place a pea-sized quantity of sodium chloride in a crucible. Use a second spatula to place a pea-sized quantity of paraffin in a second crucible.

2. Use the ring stand, iron ring, and clay triangle to support the crucible of sodium chloride above a burner.

3. Light the burner and observe the contents of the crucible for 1 minute. Keep the flame away from the contents of the crucible. Record your observations in the data table. **CAUTION:** *Be careful when working with flames. Tie back loose hair and clothing.*

4. Use tongs to carefully remove the crucible from the flame. Gently place the crucible in a safe place on the lab table where you will not accidentally touch it as it cools. **CAUTION:** *Use extreme care when working with heated equipment or materials to avoid burns. Do not touch objects after they have been heated. Allow them to cool completely first.*

Iron ring

Crucible

Clay triangle

Ring stand

Burner

Burner tubing

Figure 1

5. Repeat Steps 2 through 4 with the crucible of paraffin. Turn off the gas supply to the burner when you are done.

6. Label two test tubes *1* and *2* with the glass-marking pencil. Fill the test tubes halfway with water.

7. Use a new spatula to place a pea-sized quantity of sugar in test tube 1. Use the spatula that you used for paraffin in Step 1 to place a pea-sized quantity of paraffin in test tube 2.

8. Stopper the test tubes. Holding the stoppers firmly in place, shake each test tube to speed up the dissolving of the salt and paraffin.

9. Observe the contents of the test tubes and record your observations.

Observations

DATA TABLE Sample data are shown.

Solid Material	Melting	Dissolving in Water
Sodium chloride	Did not melt	_____
Paraffin	Melted	Does not dissolve
Sugar	_____	Does not dissolve

Analysis and Conclusions

1. **Inferring** Based on your data on melting, which forces are stronger—the ionic bonds in sodium chloride or the attractions between molecules in paraffin? Explain your answer.

The ionic bonds in sodium chloride are stronger than the intermolecular attractions in paraffin

because the paraffin melted, but the sodium chloride did not melt.

2. **Inferring** Based on your data on dissolving in water, which material is more likely to contain polar molecules—sugar or paraffin? Explain your answer.

Sugar is more likely to contain polar molecules because it dissolved in water, and the paraffin

did not dissolve in water

3. **Evaluating and Revising** Did your data support or contradict your hypothesis?

The data support the hypothesis that ionic bonds are stronger than molecular attractions.

4. **Predicting** Which type of compound—ionic or molecular—would you expect to have a higher boiling point? Explain your answer.

An ionic compound would have a higher boiling point because more energy is needed to separate

the particles of the ionic compound.

Go Further

Suppose you had a sample of sodium chloride and paraffin mixed together. How could you separate the sodium chloride from the paraffin?

One simple method would be to mix the sample with water and separate the solution of sodium chloride from the undissolved paraffin. Then, evaporate the water to retrieve the sodium chloride. Students may suggest additional methods.

Using Single-Replacement Reactions to Compare Reactivities

Refer students to page 202 in their textbooks for a discussion of single-replacement reactions. **SKILLS FOCUS:** Observing, Inferring, Applying Concepts, Evaluating and Revising, Drawing Conclusions **CLASS TIME:** 30 minutes

Background Information

In nature, elements can occur either free (uncombined with other elements) or chemically combined in a compound. The tendency of an element to combine with other substances is called the reactivity of that element. The more reactive an element is, the more likely it is to combine with other substances. In a **single-replacement reaction,** one element takes the place of another element in a compound. In general, more reactive elements replace less reactive elements. As a result of the reaction, the less reactive element is freed from the compound. Consider the following reaction.

$$Zn + CuSO_4 \rightarrow Cu + ZnSO_4$$

The more reactive zinc replaces copper and combines with the sulfate ion. The less reactive copper is released from the compound and becomes a free element.

When a metal is placed in hydrochloric acid (HCl), a single-replacement reaction can occur. If the metal is more reactive than the hydrogen in the acid, the metal will replace the hydrogen, and bubbles of hydrogen gas (H_2) will be produced. The more reactive a metal is, the more vigorously it will react with hydrochloric acid.

The alkali metals and alkaline earth metals have only one or two electrons in their highest energy level. By losing those electrons, these elements can easily acquire a stable electron configuration with a completely filled highest energy level. As a result, the alkali metals and alkaline earth metals tend to be highly reactive.

In this investigation, you will determine whether various metals undergo single-replacement reactions when placed in hydrochloric acid. Based on your observations of these reactions, you will then rank the metals by reactivity.

Problem

Which metals are most reactive?

Pre-Lab Discussion

Read the entire investigation. Then, work with a partner to answer the following questions.

1. **Predicting** If any of the metals react with hydrochloric acid, what kind of compound will be formed?

   Reaction of a metal with HCl will form a metal chloride (such as magnesium chloride or aluminum

   chloride) and hydrogen gas.

   _____

   _____

2. **Inferring** How will your observations help you determine which metals are the most reactive? Explain your answer.

The more reactive metals will react quickly with the HCl, rapidly releasing hydrogen gas. The metals

that are the most reactive will produce the most bubbles and show the most evidence of chemical

change, such as a change in color or dissolving in the acid.

_____

_____

_____

3. **Controlling Variables** Identify the manipulated, responding, and controlled variables in this investigation.

   a. Manipulated variable

     Type of metal

_____

   b. Responding variable

     Visible signs of a chemical reaction, such as bubbling, change of color or temperature, or

     dissolving of the metal

_____

   c. Controlled variables

     Volume and concentration of HCl

_____

4. **Formulating Hypotheses** State a hypothesis about which metals are the most reactive.

The alkali metals and alkaline earth metals are the most reactive.

_____

_____

_____

5. **Predicting** Based on your hypothesis, predict which metal will react most vigorously with hydrochloric acid. Explain the reason for your prediction.

Magnesium, an alkaline earth metal, will react most vigorously with HCl. The other metals used

are neither alkali metals nor alkaline earth metals.

_____

_____

_____

_____

Name _____ Class _____ Date _____

Materials (per group)

glass-marking pencil

5 test tubes

test-tube rack

10-mL graduated cylinder   Add 170 mL of 6 M HCl to enough water to form 1 L of solution. Wear safety

1 *M* hydrochloric acid   goggles, a lab apron, and neoprene gloves while doing this. Always add acid
to water, never water to acid.

zinc (Zn) Provide mossy zinc.

copper (Cu) Cut up uninsulated copper wire or pieces of copper sheeting into 1-cm lengths.

aluminum (Al) Provide aluminum shot or turnings.

iron (Fe) Provide small iron nails or pellets.   Polish each metal sample with steel
wool to remove surface oxide that can

magnesium (Mg) Provide magnesium ribbon cut into 1 cm lengths.   interfere with the reaction with HCl.

Safety 🜂 🛡 🜍 🜕 🜖 ☠ 🜚 🜛

Put on safety goggles and a lab apron. Be careful to avoid breakage
when working with glassware. Wear plastic disposable gloves
when handling chemicals, as they may irritate the skin or stain
skin or clothing. Never touch or taste any chemical unless instructed
to do so. Follow your teacher's instructions for disposing of the
used hydrochloric acid. Wash your hands with warm water and
soap or detergent before leaving the laboratory. Note all safety
alert symbols next to the steps in the Procedure and review the
meaning of each symbol by referring to the Safety Symbols on
page xiii.   Review the MSDS for hydrochloric acid with students before performing this investigation.

Procedure

1. Use the glass-marking pencil to label each test tube with the
   symbol for each metal listed in Materials. Place the test tubes in
   a test-tube rack.

2. One at a time, place the appropriate metal in each test tube.
   Carefully pour 5 mL of hydrochloric acid into each of the
   five test tubes, using the graduated cylinder. **CAUTION:**
   Put on gloves when working with hydrochloric acid. Handle
   hydrochloric acid with care. It is corrosive. If it spills on your
   skin, rinse it off with plenty of cold water and notify your teacher
   immediately.

3. Observe what happens to the metal in each test tube and
   feel each test tube as the reaction proceeds. Record your
   observations in the data table.

4. When you have completed the investigation, follow your
   teacher's instructions for disposing of the used acid. Rinse the
   pieces of metal several times with water and put them into a
   container provided by your teacher. Do not put any metal in the
   sink.

   Provide a container in which students can deposit the used, rinsed metals. Used acid may be rinsed down
   the drain with 10 volumes of cold water. If your school is served by a septic system, dispose of the used
   acid as chemical waste.

Observations   Sample data are shown.

DATA TABLE

Metal	Observations
Magnesium (Mg)	Rapid bubbling; magnesium disappears; test tube warm
Aluminum (Al)	Rapid but less active bubbling than magnesium; test tube warm
Iron (Fe)	Very slow bubbling
Copper (Cu)	No reaction
Zinc (Zn)	Slow bubbling

Analysis and Conclusions

1. **Analyzing Data** Which of the metals that you tested in this investigation are more reactive than hydrogen? Explain your answer.

   Magnesium, aluminum, iron, and zinc. These metals all showed evidence of reaction with HCl.

   _____

   _____

   _____

2. **Analyzing Data** Which of the metals that you tested in this investigation are less reactive than hydrogen? Explain your answer.

   Copper; copper did not react visibly with HCl.

   _____

   _____

   _____

3. **Drawing Conclusions** The rate at which hydrogen gas is produced as a result of these single-replacement reactions is an indication of the relative reactivity of the metals. List the metals in order of their reactivity from the most reactive to the least reactive.

Magnesium, aluminum, zinc, iron, copper _____

_____

_____

_____

4. **Inferring** Were these reactions endothermic or exothermic? Explain your answer.

Exothermic. The test tubes in which the reactions occurred most vigorously felt warm to the touch.

_____

_____

_____

_____

5. **Evaluating and Revising** Did the results of the lab support or contradict your hypothesis?

The results should support the hypothesis that alkaline earth metals are among the more reactive

metals. _____

_____

_____

_____

6. **Calculating** Write a balanced chemical equation for the single-replacement reaction, if any, that occurred between the acid and each metal. Refer to Figure 1 for the charges of the ions involved.

Element	Charge of Ion
H	1+
Cl	1−
Mg	2+
Al	3+
Fe	3+
Cu	2+
Zn	2+

Figure 1

   a. Magnesium

   $Mg + 2HCl \rightarrow H_2 + MgCl_2$ _____

   b. Aluminum

   $2Al + 6HCl \rightarrow 3H_2 + 2AlCl_3$ _____

   c. Iron

   $2Fe + 6HCl \rightarrow 3H_2 + 2FeCl_3$ _____

   d. Copper

   No reaction _____

   e. Zinc

   $Zn + 2HCl \rightarrow H_2 + ZnCl_2$ _____

Name _____ Class _____ Date _____

7. Inferring What could you do to determine whether the gas produced as a result of these reactions is hydrogen?

Collect the gas in an inverted or partly closed test tube. Then, insert a flaming splint into the test tube.

A pop is heard as the hydrogen burns.

8. Applying Concepts Nonmetals can also be involved in single-replacement reactions. If chlorine is more reactive than bromine, write a balanced chemical equation for the reaction between chlorine gas (Cl_2) and potassium bromide (KBr).

$Cl_2 + 2KBr \rightarrow Br_2 + 2KCl$

Go Further

Balance each of the following chemical equations. Then, classify each reaction as a synthesis, decomposition, or single-replacement reaction.

1. $Cu + AgNO_3 \rightarrow Ag + Cu(NO_3)_2$

$Cu + 2AgNO_3 \rightarrow 2Ag + Cu(NO_3)_2$

single-replacement

2. $H_2 + O_2 \rightarrow H_2O$

$2H_2 + O_2 \rightarrow 2H_2O$

synthesis

3. $Al + ZnCl_2 \rightarrow Zn + AlCl_3$

$2Al + 3ZnCl_2 \rightarrow 3Zn + 2AlCl_3$

single-replacement

4. $Al(OH)_3 \rightarrow Al_2O_3 + H_2O$

$2Al(OH)_3 \rightarrow Al_2O_3 + 3H_2O$

decomposition

Chapter 7   Chemical Reactions

Recognizing a Synthesis Reaction

Refer students to page 200 and pages 208 and 209, respectively, in their textbooks for a discussion of synthesis reactions and energy changes during chemical reactions.

Background Information

SKILLS FOCUS: Observing, Calculating, Inferring, Classifying, Analyzing

In a **synthesis reaction,** two or more substances combine to form a single substance. The substances that combine can be elements, compounds, or both. The general equation for a synthesis reaction is

Data CLASS TIME: 40 minutes

$$A + B \rightarrow AB$$

The symbols A and B represent two elements or compounds that combine to form the compound AB. For example, when a metal combines with oxygen from the air, a synthesis reaction occurs. A compound called a metal oxide is produced. The reaction can be described by the following word equation:

$$\text{Metal} + \text{Oxygen} \rightarrow \text{Metal oxide}$$

In this investigation, you will heat copper metal in air. Then, you will examine the product to determine whether a synthesis reaction has occurred.

Problem

How can you know when a synthesis reaction has occurred?

Pre-Lab Discussion

Read the entire investigation. Then, work with a partner to answer the following questions.

1. **Calculating** If the balance indicated that the evaporating dish has a mass of 44.8 g and you want to have exactly 5.0 g of copper, what should the balance read with the copper in the evaporating dish?

   The total mass of the copper and the evaporating dish should be 44.8 g + 5.0 g = 49.8 g.

   _____

2. **Inferring** Why is it necessary to spread the copper powder out in a thin layer in Step 5? (*Hint:* What substance do you expect to react with the copper?)

   The copper powder must be spread out so that as much of its surface area as possible will be

   exposed to the air.

3. **Predicting** What evidence of a chemical change might you observe in this investigation?

   A change in color and mass may be observed. Students may also predict that a flame, smoke, or odor

   will be produced.

4. **Predicting** What observation would be evidence of a synthesis reaction? Explain your answer.

   An increase in mass would be evidence of a synthesis reaction. It would indicate that something in

   the air has combined with the copper.

Materials *(per group)*

ring stand	evaporating dish	copper powder
iron ring	triple-beam balance	clock or watch
wire gauze	scoop	tongs
Bunsen burner		

Safety

Review the MSDS safety information for copper powder
with students before performing this investigation.

Put on safety goggles, plastic gloves, and a lab apron. Be careful when
using matches. Use caution when handling breakable equipment. Tie
back loose hair and clothing when working with flames. Do not reach
over an open flame. Use extreme care when working with heated
equipment or materials to avoid burns. Note all safety alert symbols
next to the steps in the Procedure and review the meaning of each
symbol by referring to the Safety Symbols on page xiii.

Procedure

1. Set up the ring stand, iron ring, and wire
   gauze as shown in Figure 1.

2. Place the Bunsen burner on the base of
   the ring stand. Do not light the burner
   yet. Adjust the position of the iron ring
   so that its center is directly over the
   burner and about 5 cm above
   the top of the burner.

3. Place the evaporating dish on
   the balance and find its mass to the
   nearest 0.1 g. Record this mass in the
   data table.

4. To measure 5.0 g of copper powder,
   add 5.0 g to the mass of the
   evaporating dish and move the
   riders on the balance to this
   number.

5. Using the scoop, slowly add copper
   powder to the evaporating dish until
   the pointer of the balance is centered. In the data table, record
   the mass of the copper powder and evaporating dish.

6. Place the evaporating dish containing the copper powder on the
   wire gauze. Use the scoop to spread out the copper powder in a
   thin layer in the bottom of the dish.

7. Light the Bunsen burner and heat the evaporating dish for 5 to
   10 minutes until you observe a change in the color of the copper
   powder. **CAUTION:** *Tie back loose hair and clothing before working
   with flames. Do not reach over an open flame.*

8. Turn off the Bunsen burner and allow the evaporating dish to
   cool for 10 minutes. Use tongs to place the evaporating dish
   on the balance and find its mass. **CAUTION:** *The evaporating*

Figure 1

Evaporating dish

Iron ring

Wire gauze

Ring stand

Bunsen burner

Base of ring stand

dish and its contents may still be hot. Handle the evaporating dish only with tongs. In the data table, record the mass of the evaporating dish and its contents.

Have students complete the calculations in the data table or work on another short assignment while waiting for the evaporating dish to cool.

9. Use the scoop to examine the product of the reaction. Observe its color or colors. Record your observations below the data table.

Observations   Sample data are shown.

DATA TABLE

Measurement	Mass (g)
Mass of evaporating dish	
Mass of evaporating dish and copper powder	
Mass of copper powder	5.0
Mass of evaporating dish and product after heating	
Mass of product	5.4–6.2

Observations of Product

Part or all of the copper powder has changed into a mixture of black and dark red granules.

_____

Analysis and Conclusions

1. **Observing** What did you observe as a result of heating the copper powder that might indicate that a chemical reaction took place?

   The contents of the evaporating dish changed in color, mass, and texture.

2. **Inferring** Explain why there was a change in mass as a result of heating the copper powder in the evaporating dish.

   Oxygen from the air combined with the copper powder and added to its mass.

3. **Classifying** What type of chemical reaction occurred?

   Synthesis (The reaction can also be classified as oxidation-reduction.)

4. **Inferring** Was this reaction endothermic or exothermic? Explain your answer.

   The reaction was endothermic. Energy had to be absorbed for the reaction to occur.

5. **Calculating** Calculate the percent change in mass by using the following formula.

   $$\text{Percent change in mass} = \frac{\text{Change in mass}}{\text{Mass of copper}} \times 100\%$$

   The mass is likely to change by 8–24 percent.

6. **Drawing Conclusions** There are actually two different oxides of copper produced as a result of this reaction. They are copper(I) oxide and copper(II) oxide. If all the copper changed to copper(I)

oxide, the mass would change by 12 percent. If all the copper changed to copper(II) oxide, the mass would change by 25 percent. Based on the percent change in mass, what must have been produced as a result of the reaction?

Probably a mixture of copper(I) and copper(II) oxide

7. **Calculating** Write a balanced chemical equation for the synthesis reactions that took place.

$2Cu + O_2 \rightarrow 2CuO$

$4Cu + O_2 \rightarrow 2Cu_2O$

8. **Evaluating** Compare the percent change in mass that you calculated with those calculated by your classmates. What variables could account for differences between your results and those of your classmates?

Answers may include the temperature of the burner flame, the length of time the copper was

heated, the accuracy of mass measurements, or how well the copper powder was distributed in

the evaporating dish.

9. **Controlling Variables** How could these variables be controlled so that the results obtained are more precise?

Make sure that all burner flames are the same. Heat all samples for exactly the same length of time.

Measure masses. Distribute the copper powder evenly.

10. **Observing** Copper(II) oxide is black and copper(I) oxide is red. Do your observations support your answer to Question 7? Explain your answer.

Yes, there will be both black and red particles in the evaporating dish.

Go Further

Caulking compound is used to make a watertight seal around bathtubs, sinks, and pipes. A synthesis reaction occurs when caulking compound is placed on a surface and exposed to the air. This reaction leads to hardening of the soft caulking compound. To investigate the role of water in this reaction, place a small amount of caulking compound on two small pieces of wood or cardboard. Place one of the pieces in a beaker and cover it with water. Leave the other piece exposed to the air. After 5 minutes, use a glass stirring rod to probe each sample of caulking compound and compare the firmness of the two samples. Record your observations. Repeat this observation every 5 minutes for 30 minutes or until one of the samples becomes firm and rubbery. Report your conclusions about the role of water in this synthesis reaction.

Water is a reactant in the chemical reaction that leads to hardening of the caulking compound. Students should find that submerging the caulking compound in water accelerates this process.

Chapter 8   Solutions, Acids, and Bases   Investigation 8A

Comparing Antacids

Refer students to pages 240–249 in their textbooks for a discussion of acid-base chemistry. **SKILLS FOCUS:** Observing, Measuring, Inferring, Analyzing Data, Designing Experiments, Drawing Conclusions, Evaluating and Revising **CLASS TIME:** 45 minutes

Background Information

Acids are substances that produce hydronium ions (H_3O^+) when dissolved in water. **Bases** are substances that produce hydroxide ions (OH^-) when dissolved in water. The reaction between an acid and a base is called **neutralization.** Antacids are basic substances that are taken to neutralize excess stomach acid. Different brands of antacids may differ in a number of ways, including their chemical composition, the quantity of acid neutralized per dose, and the speed with which neutralization occurs.

An **indicator** is a substance that changes color in the presence of acids and bases. Indicators are used to show whether a solution is acidic or basic and to show when a neutralization reaction is complete.

In this investigation, you will use an indicator to compare the quantity of acid that several antacids neutralize. The amount of indicator that you will use is very small and will not affect the reaction that you are studying.

Problem

Which brand of antacid neutralizes the most acid per dose?

Pre-Lab Discussion

Read the entire investigation. Then, work with a partner to answer the following questions.

1. **Predicting** In Part A of this investigation, which sodium hydroxide solution do you predict will neutralize more acid? Explain your answer.

   The 0.5 *M* NaOH solution will neutralize more acid because it is more concentrated.

   _____

   _____

   _____

2. **Designing Experiments** In Part A of this investigation, how will you determine which sodium hydroxide solution neutralized more acid?

   The sodium hydroxide solution that neutralized more acid will leave less acid remaining in the

   solution. As a result, less NaOH solution will be needed to neutralize the remaining acid.

   _____

   _____

   _____

   _____

3. **Formulating Hypotheses** State a hypothesis that you could test in Part B of this investigation.

Student hypotheses should be specific and subject to testing by an experiment that students

could perform. Examples of acceptable answers are the hypotheses that all the antacids are

equal in neutralizing power or that brand A has more neutralizing power than brands B and C have.

_____

_____

4. **Designing Experiments** Describe an experiment you could perform to test your hypothesis.

Students should describe a modification of the procedure in Part A of the investigation to compare

the neutralizing power of the antacids.

_____

_____

_____

5. **Controlling Variables** What are the manipulated, responding, and controlled variables in the experiment that you described in your answer to Question 4?

Answers will depend on student experimental designs, but may include type of antacid as a

manipulated variable, final pH or quantity of acid neutralized as a responding variable, and

quantity of indicator and concentration of base as controlled variables.

_____

_____

Suggested Materials (per group)

glass-marking pencil

2 250-mL beakers

10-mL graduated cylinder

50-mL graduated cylinder

0.1 M hydrochloric acid (HCl) solution

dropper bottle of bromthymol blue solution

3 glass stirring rods

0.1 M sodium hydroxide (NaOH) solution

0.5 M NaOH solution

buret of 0.1 M NaOH solution on ring stand

3 different brands of antacid tablets

3 spoons

2 dropper pipets

Ask your teacher for any additional materials that you will need to carry out Part B of this investigation.

Prepare all solutions with distilled or deionized water. Use neoprene gloves, safety goggles, and a lab apron when preparing the HCl and NaOH solutions. Working in a fume hood, prepare 0.1 M HCl by adding 44 mL of concentrated HCl to enough water to make 1 L of solution. To prepare 0.5 M NaOH, dissolve 20 g NaOH in enough water to make 1 L of solution. Dilute part of this solution with 4 volumes of water to prepare 0.1 M NaOH. Set up burets of 0.1 M NaOH solution in advance for students. You will need to refill the burets as students perform this investigation.

Name _____ Class _____ Date _____

Safety 🛡🏠🧤🖐🥼☠🔥

Put on safety goggles, plastic gloves, and a lab apron. Be careful to avoid breakage when working with glassware. Never touch or taste any chemical unless instructed to do so. Always use caution when working with laboratory chemicals, as they may irritate the skin or stain skin or clothing. Wash your hands thoroughly after carrying out this investigation. Note all safety alert symbols next to the steps in the Procedure and review the meaning of each symbol by referring to the Safety Symbols on page xiii.

Before performing this investigation, check the eyewash and shower in the laboratory to make sure that they are operational, and demonstrate their location and use to students. Share the safety information in the MSDS for each chemical with students and demonstrate safe, accurate use of the buret before students begin the investigation.

Design Your Experiment
Part A: Comparing the Neutralizing Power of Basic Solutions

🧤 1. Use a glass-marking pencil to label two 250-mL beakers 0.1 M NaOH and 0.5 M NaOH.

🖐 2. Use the 50-mL graduated cylinder to place 50 mL of 0.1 M HCl
🥼 solution into each beaker.

3. Add 1 drop of the bromthymol blue solution to the beaker labeled 0.1 M NaOH and stir with a glass stirring rod. Count each drop as you continue to add bromthymol blue solution 1 drop at a time, until the solution becomes yellow. Add the same number of drops of bromthymol blue solution to the beaker labeled 0.5 M NaOH and stir with the same glass stirring rod.

4. Use the 10-mL graduated cylinder to add 5 mL of 0.1 M NaOH solution into the beaker labeled 0.1 M NaOH. Stir the solution with a clean glass stirring rod.

☠ 5. In the sink, rinse the 10-mL graduated cylinder thoroughly with water. Then, use the graduated cylinder to add 5 mL of 0.5 M NaOH solution into the beaker labeled 0.5 M NaOH. Stir the solution with a clean glass stirring rod. **CAUTION:** *Handle the 0.5 M NaOH solution with care. It is poisonous and can burn skin and clothing.*

6. To compare the quantity of HCl remaining in each beaker, place the beaker labeled 0.5 M NaOH under the buret. Record the initial volume of the 0.1 M NaOH solution that is in the buret in Data Table 1. Show students how to read and operate the burets.

7. In the sink, rinse all three glass stirring rods thoroughly with water. Stir the contents of the beaker labeled 0.5 M NaOH with a clean glass stirring rod as you slowly add 0.1 M NaOH solution from the buret to the beaker. Stop adding NaOH solution to the beaker as soon as the color of the solution in the beaker changes to blue. Observe the volume of solution remaining in the buret. Record this volume in Data Table 1.

8. Subtract the volume of NaOH solution remaining in the buret from the initial volume of the NaOH solution to determine the volume of NaOH solution that you added to the beaker. Record this volume in Data Table 1.

9. Ask your teacher to refill your buret with 0.1 *M* NaOH solution. Repeat Steps 6 through 8 with the beaker labeled 0.1 *M* NaOH.

Part B: Using Indicators to Determine Antacid Strength

10. Design an experiment to compare the neutralizing power of three different brands of antacid tablets. Record the hypothesis that you will test.

Possible answer: One tablet of antacid brand A neutralizes more acid than one tablet of

brands B and C.

_____

_____

_____

11. Write a detailed plan of how you will carry out your experiment. You may choose to base your experiment on the method of comparing the neutralizing power of solutions that you used in Part A of this investigation. Construct Data Table 2 in which to record your observations in the space provided on page 82. If you need more space, attach additional sheets of paper.

Using Part A as a guide, students should design a controlled experiment to compare the

strengths of three different antacid tablets by measuring how much acid each tablet can

neutralize. In their experiments, students may choose to measure the neutralizing powder of

each antacid brand on a per-tablet or per-gram basis. Students should explain all the steps

involved, specify what data is to be collected, and provide a complete materials list.

_____

_____

_____

_____

_____

_____

_____

_____

_____

_____

_____

12. What are the manipulated, responding, and controlled variables in your experiment?

a. Manipulated variable

Typical experimental designs will include the brand of antacid as the manipulated variable.

b. Responding variable

Typical experimental designs will include pH or the volume of NaOH solution added to

neutralize the remaining acid as the responding variable.

c. Controlled variables

Controlled variables may include the volume or concentration of HCl and NaOH solutions,

temperature, and the indicator used.

13. What safety precautions will you need to take in your experiment?

Students need to wear safety goggles, lab aprons, and plastic gloves when working with

solutions of acids or bases.

14. List the possible results of your experiment and whether each possible result would support or contradict your hypothesis.

Results of the experiment may indicate that one brand of antacid neutralizes more acid

per tablet (or per gram) than the others or that two or all three brands neutralize equal quantities

of acid per tablet (or per gram).

15. Show your written experimental plan to your teacher. When your teacher approves your plan, carry out your experiment and record your observations in your data table.

Name _____ Class _____ Date _____

Observations Sample data are shown.

DATA TABLE 1

Beaker	Initial Volume of NaOH Solution in Buret (mL)	Final Volume of NaOH Solution in Buret (mL)	Volume of NaOH Solution Used (mL)
0.1 *M* NaOH	100	55	45
0.5 *M* NaOH	100	75	25

DATA TABLE 2

If you need more space, attach an additional sheet of paper.

Antacid Brand	Initial Volume of NaOH Solution in Buret (mL)	Final Volume of NaOH Solution in Buret (mL)	Volume of NaOH Solution Used (mL)
Tum-Eze	100	54	46
Speedy Relief	100	77	23
Alkasimple	100	62	38

Name _____ Class _____ Date _____

Analysis and Conclusions

1. Inferring What can you infer from the volume of NaOH solution that you added to each beaker in Steps 7 through 9?

The volume of NaOH solution added indicated the quantity of hydrochloric acid remaining in

each beaker.

_____

_____

_____

_____

2. Analyzing Data Based on the results of Part A of this investigation, which NaOH solution neutralized more acid in Steps 4 and 5 of Part A? Explain your answer.

The 0.5 M NaOH solution neutralized more acid. The data showed that less acid remained in the

0.5-M beaker than in the 0.1-M beaker.

_____

_____

_____

_____

3. Analyzing Data Which antacid tablet neutralized the most acid? Which tablet neutralized the least acid? Explain your answers.

Answers should reference the data from Part B. The sample data indicate that the Speedy Relief

brand neutralized the most acid per tablet.

_____

_____

_____

_____

4. Evaluating and Revising Did your data support or contradict your hypothesis? Explain your answer.

Answers will depend on student hypotheses. In their explanations, students should

reference their data from Part B.

_____

_____

_____

_____

_____

5. Observing How did the antacid tablets differ from the NaOH solutions you used in Part A of this investigation? How did these differences affect the way you tested the tablets?

The tablets were solid and had different volumes and masses, unlike the NaOH solutions that

were liquids and had no particular volumes or masses. Therefore, students had to crush or

dissolve the tablets before testing them. Students may have chosen to determine the masses of

the tablets. Students also had to decide whether to compare equal masses or equal doses

(number of tablets) of the antacids.

6. Drawing Conclusions What chemical properties other than the quantity of acid that it neutralized might make one brand of antacid tablet better than another?

Answers may include the rate of dissolving or neutralization, whether the reaction

produces bubbles of a gas, and whether the tablets contain substances that affect taste

or health.

Go Further

Safety officers at chemical factories must plan for the possibility that a large quantity of a dangerous acid might be spilled in a work area. Use resources in the library or on the Internet to research what methods and materials are used to safely clean up acid spills. Use your knowledge of neutralization reactions to explain how these emergency procedures work

Handbooks and Web sites that deal with industrial safety and hazardous materials cleanup can provide the necessary information. Basic solutions and highly absorbent materials are often used to neutralize or remove spilled acids.

Chapter 8   Solutions, Acids, and Bases   **Investigation 8B**

Comparing Solubilities and Rates of Dissolving

Refer students to pages 228 and 239 in their textbooks for a discussion of solutions, solubility, and factors that affect rates of solution. **SKILLS FOCUS:** Inferring, Predicting, Measuring, Using Tables and Graphs, Applying Concepts, Drawing Conclusions
CLASS TIME: Part A, 30 minutes; Part B, 45 minutes

Background Information

When one substance dissolves in another, the mixture is called a solution. The substance that dissolves is the **solute.** A substance that dissolves other substances is called a **solvent.** The rate at which a solid solute dissolves depends on several factors including temperature, stirring, and the surface area of the solute. **Solubility** is the maximum amount of a solute that can dissolve in a given amount of a solvent at a certain temperature. The solubility of different substances varies, but it is always the same for a given substance at a given temperature.

In this investigation, you will determine the effect of surface area on the rate at which table salt (sodium chloride, NaCl) dissolves in water. You will also investigate how temperature affects the solubility of ammonium chloride (NH_4Cl) in water.

Problem

How do surface area and temperature affect the rate of dissolving and solubility?

Pre-Lab Discussion

Read the entire investigation. Then, work with a partner to answer the following questions.

1. **Controlling Variables** In Part A, what is the manipulated variable that you will use to investigate the rate of dissolving?

   Particle size (or surface area) of the solute
   _____

2. **Predicting** In Part A, what do you predict will be the effect of the manipulated variable on the rate of dissolving?

   Smaller particles with more surface area will dissolve more quickly.
   _____

3. **Predicting** In Part B, what do you predict will be the effect of the manipulated variable on solubility?

   More solid will dissolve at higher temperatures.
   _____

Materials *(per group)*

rock salt (sodium chloride, NaCl)   clock or watch

table salt (sodium chloride, NaCl)   3 glass stirring rods

paper towel   thermometer

hand lens   ammonium chloride (NH_4Cl)

3 150-mL beakers   small spoon

triple-beam balance   hot plate

2 scoops   graph paper

100-mL graduated cylinder

Sodium chloride (NaCl) can be substituted for ammonium chloride, but the solubility increase with temperature is much less dramatic than for NH_4Cl. To save time and to simplify the massing procedure for students, you may wish to dispense 5-g to 10-g samples of sodium chloride for students to mass.

Name _____ Class _____ Date _____

Review with students the safety information in the MSDS for ammonium chloride before performing this investigation. Provide only non-mercury thermometers.

Safety

Put on safety goggles, plastic gloves, and a lab apron. Be careful to avoid breakage when working with glassware. Use extreme care when working with heated materials to avoid burns. Never touch or taste any chemical unless instructed to do so. Wash your hands thoroughly after carrying out this investigation. Note all safety alert symbols next to the steps in the Procedure and review the meaning of each symbol by referring to the Safety Symbols on page xiii.

Procedure

Part A: The Effect of Surface Area on Rate of Dissolving

1. Place a few grains of rock salt and a few grains of table salt on a paper towel. Observe the rock salt and table salt. Then, use a hand lens to compare the particles of rock salt and the particles of table salt. Record which salt has the smaller particles in Data Table 1.

2. Place a beaker on the balance. Measure and record the mass of the beaker.

3. Use the scoop to place a sample of rock salt in the beaker. Measure the mass of the beaker and salt. Add or remove rock salt from the beaker if necessary until the mass of the beaker and salt is 5 to 10 grams more than the mass of the beaker alone. Record the mass of the beaker and salt.

4. Repeat Steps 2 and 3 with a second beaker and a sample of table salt. Be sure that the mass of table salt in the beaker does not differ from the mass of the rock salt by more than 0.1 g.

5. Use a graduated cylinder to add 75 mL of room-temperature water to each beaker. Note the time. Observe the solutions for 2 minutes. After 2 minutes, look for any signs of dissolving. Record your observations.

6. Place a glass stirring rod in each beaker. Note the time. Working with a partner, stir the water gently in each beaker. Be sure to stir both samples at the same time and at the same slow rate. Note the time when each sample completely dissolves. Record the time it took for each salt sample to dissolve completely.

Part B: The Effect of Temperature on Solubility

7. To investigate solubility, put 50 mL of room-temperature water into a clean beaker. Use a thermometer to measure the temperature of the water. Record this temperature in Data Table 2. Remove the thermometer from the beaker.

8. Add one spoonful of ammonium chloride to the water in the beaker. Stir vigorously with a clean glass stirring rod until no more of the solid will dissolve. Make sure that you allow enough time for the solid to dissolve. **CAUTION:** *Be careful handling ammonium chloride and its solutions, which are poisonous.*

9. Repeat Step 8 until no more ammonium chloride will dissolve. Note the number of spoonfuls of ammonium chloride that you added. Be sure to allow enough time for each spoonful of ammonium chloride to dissolve before adding more. Record the number of spoonfuls that dissolved in Data Table 2.

10. Place the beaker of ammonium chloride solution on a hot plate. Place the thermometer in the beaker. Turn the hot plate to the medium-low setting and warm the solution to 40°C. **CAUTION:** *Be careful handling the hot plate and hot solutions. They can cause burns.*

11. Remove the thermometer from the beaker. Add more spoonfuls of ammonium chloride to the beaker. Stir the solution and use the thermometer to check the temperature of the solution after you add each spoonful. Note the total number of spoonfuls of ammonium chloride that you added. Be sure to allow enough time for each spoonful of ammonium chloride to dissolve before adding more. Use the heat setting of the hot plate to keep the temperature constant as you add ammonium chloride to the beaker.

12. Record the total number of spoonfuls that have dissolved.

13. Turn up the hot plate to warm the solution to 60°C. Then, repeat Steps 11 and 12 with the solution at this temperature.

14. Turn up the hot plate to warm the solution to 80°C. Then, repeat Steps 11 and 12 with the solution at this temperature.

15. When you have recorded all of your data, turn off the hot plate and allow the solution to cool. Follow your teacher's instructions for disposing of the used chemicals. Wash your hands thoroughly with warm water and soap or detergent before leaving the laboratory.

16. On a sheet of graph paper, make a graph of the solubility of ammonium chloride versus temperature. Plot temperature on the horizontal axis and solubility (in spoonfuls per 50 mL water) on the vertical axis.

Used solutions may be flushed down the drain with at least 10 volumes of water. If your school is served by a septic system, do not dispose of chemical waste in this way. Instead, allow the used solutions to evaporate and dispose of them as dry chemical waste.

Observations Sample data are shown.

DATA TABLE 1

Type of Sodium Chloride	Particle Size	Mass of Beaker (g)	Mass of Beaker and Salt (g)	Mass of Salt (g)	Appearance of Mixture After 2 Minutes Without Stirring	Time to Dissolve (seconds)
Rock salt	Larger			7.0 g	Most salt is undissolved.	Longer
Table salt	Smaller			7.0 g	Most salt is undissolved.	Shorter

DATA TABLE 2

Temperature (°C)	Number of Spoonfuls of Ammonium Chloride Dissolved
18–20	Data will depend on the size of the spoons supplied. The solubility of ammonium chloride in 50 mL of water is approximately 18 g at 20°C, 22 g at 40°C, 28 g at 60°C, and 32 g at 80°C.
40	
60	
80	

Analysis and Conclusions

1. Inferring How did stirring affect the rate at which the salt dissolved? Explain how you think stirring caused this effect.

The rate of dissolving was greater in stirred water because stirring moved the more concentrated

part of the solution away from the solid salt and moved the less concentrated part of the solution

closer to the solid salt, allowing more particles of salt to move into solution.

2. Inferring Why do you think the different types of salt dissolved at different rates?

Dissolving takes place at the surfaces of solids. The more finely divided a solid is, the greater its

surface area and rate of dissolving will be. Therefore, the smaller particles of table salt dissolved

more quickly than the larger particles of rock salt.

3. Predicting Predict what effect, if any, you think the size of salt grains would have on their solubility. Explain your answer.

The solubility is the same for all sizes of salt grains because the same substance is involved.

4. Using Graphs Based on your graph and your observations in Part B, what do you think the solubility of ammonium chloride (in spoonfuls per 50 mL water) would be at 10°C? At 70°C? At 100°C?

Graphs should show an upward curve, indicating an increase in solubility with increasing

temperature. Exact values will depend on spoon size. The actual solubility in grams NH_4Cl per

50 mL water is approximately 16 at 10°C, 30 at 70°C, and 38 at 100°C.

Go Further

Design an experiment to determine the effect of temperature on the rate of dissolving of a different solid in water. Write a detailed plan of your experiment. Your plan should state a hypothesis, identify variables, and describe the procedures and safety precautions that you will use. Show your plan to your teacher. When your teacher approves your plan, carry out your experiment and report your results and conclusions.
Examine student plans for sound experimental design and safety. Most solid
substances dissolve more quickly at higher temperatures.

Chapter 9   Carbon Chemistry

Testing for Nutrients in Foods

Background Information

Nutrients are those substances in food that are necessary for health. There are three main classes of organic nutrients. The first class, **carbohydrates,** consists of sugars and starches, which are polymers of the sugar glucose. The second class, lipids, includes fats and oils. The third class consists of **proteins,** which are polymers of amino acids. Because the compounds in each class of nutrients contain different functional groups, a different chemical test can be used to detect each type of nutrient.

> Refer students to pages 278, 280, and 283 in their textbooks for a discussion of carbohydrates, proteins, and digestion. **SKILLS FOCUS:** Observing, Analyzing Data, Comparing and Contrasting, Designing Experiments **CLASS TIME:** Part A, 35 Minutes; Part B, 45 minutes

For carbohydrates, there are two tests, one to detect sugars and one to detect starches. A mixture called Benedict's solution changes color when it is heated with many types of sugars, and a solution of iodine changes color in the presence of starch. A solution of copper sulfate, called biuret reagent, changes color when it reacts with proteins. A bright red dye called Sudan IV dissolves in lipids, but not in water. If a material has the ability to dissolve Sudan IV dye, this is a sign that the material contains lipids.

In this investigation, you will observe the reaction of each of these test materials with samples of glucose (a sugar), starch, vegetable oil, and powdered gelatin (protein). Then, you will design an experiment using each of the test materials to determine which classes of organic nutrients are present in several foods.

Problem

Which foods contain sugars, starches, lipids, and proteins?

Pre-Lab Discussion

Read the entire investigation. Then, work with a partner to answer the following questions.

1. **Controlling Variables** Why is a test tube of water included in the Procedure for Part A of this investigation? Explain your answer.

   The test tube is a control. Tests on the water will be negative, allowing easy comparison to positive

   tests for other materials.

   _____

2. **Predicting** In Part A of this investigation, which food substance(s) do you expect to react with each test material?

   a. Benedict's solution

   Glucose

   b. Iodine solution

   Cornstarch

c. Sudan IV dye

Vegetable oil

d. Biuret reagent

Gelatin

3. **Controlling Variables** Identify the manipulated, responding, and controlled variables in Part A of this investigation.

   a. Manipulated variables

   Food substances

   b. Responding variables

   Reactions between test materials and food substances

   c. Controlled variables

   Chemical test procedures

4. **Predicting** Which nutrients do you think are present in each food that you will test in Part B of this investigation?

   a. Orange juice

   Sugar

   b. Potato

   Starch (Some potatoes contain enough sugar to detect with Benedict's solution.)

   c. Whole milk

   Proteins, lipids, sugar

   d. Skim milk

   Proteins, sugar

   e. Margarine

   Lipids

   f. Egg yolk

   Lipids, proteins

   g. Egg white

   Proteins

5. Designing Experiments Describe a set of procedures you could use in Part B to test your predictions.

Students should describe a modification of the procedures in Part A to test each

food for the presence of sugar, starch, lipids, and proteins.

_____

_____

_____

_____

_____

_____

_____

_____

_____

_____

_____

_____

_____

_____

_____

_____

_____

Materials *(per group)*

500-mL beaker	tongs	Benedict's solution and biuret reagent can be purchased. They can also be prepared. To prepare Benedict's solution, dissolve 173 g sodium citrate $(Na_3C_6H_5O_7 \cdot 2H_2O)$ and 200 g sodium carbonate (Na_2CO_3) in 800 mL of distilled water. Do not use sodium bicarbonate. Separately, dissolve 17.3 g of copper sulfate $(CuSO_4)$ in 100 mL of distilled water. Mix the two solutions slowly and add distilled water to bring the volume to 1 liter.
hot plate	clock or watch	
paper towel	iodine solution	
glass-marking pencil	Sudan IV dye	
5 test tubes	5 stoppers for test tubes	
test-tube rack	biuret reagent	
4 spatulas	orange juice	
glucose	minced potato	
cornstarch	whole milk	
powdered gelatin	skim milk	
2 dropper pipets	margarine	To prepare biuret reagent, make a 0.1 M solution of sodium hydroxide by dissolving 4 g NaOH in 1 L of water. Add 2.2 g $CuSO_4 \cdot 5H_2O$. Prepare fresh biuret reagent no more than one day in advance and store it away from light.
vegetable oil	egg yolk	
3 10-mL graduated cylinders	egg white	
Benedict's solution		

Because of the quantity of materials required for this investigation, you may want students to work in groups of three or four.

Safety

Put on safety goggles and a lab apron. Wear plastic disposable gloves when handling chemicals, as they may irritate the skin or stain skin or clothing. Be careful to avoid breakage when working with glassware. Use extreme care when working with heated equipment or materials to avoid burns. Keep Sudan IV dye away from any open flame. Observe proper laboratory procedures when using electrical equipment. Never touch or taste any chemical unless instructed to do so. Wash your hands thoroughly after carrying out this investigation. Note all safety alert symbols next to the steps in the Procedure and review the meaning of each symbol by referring to the Safety Symbols on page xiii.

You may wish to boil the eggs in advance reduce the hazard of *Salmonella* contamin tion. If you do, remin students that they wi need to find a way to test the insoluble coo egg white and yolk.

Design Your Experiment
Part A: Observing Chemical Tests for Nutrients

1. Fill a 500-mL beaker about one-fourth of the way with water. Place the beaker on the hot plate. Turn the hot plate to a high setting and bring the water to a boil. **CAUTION:** *Be careful using the hot plate and handling boiling water and hot glassware.*

2. On a sheet of paper towel, write *glucose, cornstarch, gelatin,* and *vegetable oil* near different corners of the towel.

3. Use a glass-marking pencil to label five test tubes 1 through 5 and place them in the test-tube rack. Using a separate clean spatula for each substance and just enough of each substance to cover the end of the spatula, place glucose in test tube 1, cornstarch in test tube 2, and gelatin in test tube 3. Use a dropper pipet to place 4 drops of vegetable oil in test tube 4. Store the spatulas and pipet in the appropriate places on the paper towel when they are not in use.

4. Use a graduated cylinder to add 3 mL of water to each test tube, including test tube 5.

5. Fill each of the test tubes halfway with Benedict's solution.

6. Use tongs to place the test tubes into the beaker of boiling water. Leave the test tubes in the boiling water for 5 minutes.

7. After 5 minutes have passed, use tongs to return each test tube to the test-tube rack. Observe any changes in the appearance of the contents of each test tube. Record your observations in Data Table 1.

8. Thoroughly wash the five test tubes and discard the contents in the sink. Carefully dry the test tubes and place them back in the test-tube rack.

9. Repeat Steps 3 and 4.

10. Use a dropper pipet to add 1 or 2 drops of iodine solution to each test tube. Note whether the iodine remains brown or if it changes to another color. Record your observations in Data Table 1.

11. Again, wash and dry the test tubes, and repeat Steps 3 and 4.

12. Use a clean spatula to add a few grains of Sudan IV dye to each test tube. **CAUTION:** *Do not get any dye on your skin or clothing. Keep the dye away from any open flames.*

13. Place a stopper firmly into each test tube and shake the test tubes gently. Observe whether the dye has been absorbed by any material in the test tube. Record your observations in Data Table 1. **CAUTION:** *Make sure that the test tubes are securely closed to avoid spilling.*

14. Wash and dry the test tubes, and repeat Steps 3 and 4. Use a clean dropper pipet to add 3 drops of biuret reagent to each test tube. Observe any changes in the appearance of the contents of each test tube. Record your observations in Data Table 1. **CAUTION:** *Biuret reagent is poisonous and can burn and stain skin and clothing.*

Part B: Using Chemical Tests to Identify Nutrients

15. Design an experiment to test the predictions you made in Pre-Lab Discussion Question 4. Write a detailed plan of how you will carry out your experiment. Use your knowledge of chemical tests for organic nutrients from Part A of this investigation to help you plan your procedures. Construct Data Table 2 in which to record your observations in the space provided on page 94.

Experimental designs should be based on the tests used in Part A.

_____

_____

_____

_____

_____

16. What are the manipulated, responding, and controlled variables in your experiment?

a. Manipulated variables

Typical experimental designs will list the foods as manipulated variables.

b. Responding variables

Typical experimental designs will list the reactions between the test materials and

foods as the responding variable.

c. Controlled variables

Controlled variables may include the volume or mass of each food tested, the volume of

water added to each sample, and the procedure for performing each test.

17. What safety precautions will you need to take?

Check students' plans for appropriate safety precautions. Students should wear safety

goggles, lab aprons, and plastic gloves when working with the test chemicals. Monitor

students closely when they work with hazardous chemicals or hot equipment.

18. Show your written experimental plan to your teacher. When your teacher approves your plan, carry out your experiment and record your observations.

Observations Sample data are shown.

DATA TABLE 1

Test Tube	Food	Benedict's Solution	Iodine Solution	Sudan IV Dye	Biuret Reagent
1	Sugar	Red-yellow	No change	No change	No change
2	Cornstarch	No change	Blue-black	No change	No change
3	Gelatin	No change	No change	No change	Pink-violet
4	Vegetable oil	No change	No change	Red-orange	No change
5	Water	No change	No change	No change	No change

DATA TABLE 2

If you need more space, attach additional sheets of paper.

Food	Benedict's Solution	Iodine Solution	Sudan IV Dye	Biuret Reagent
Orange juice	Red-yellow	No change	No change	No change
Potato	Red-yellow	Blue-black	No change	No change
Whole milk	Red-yellow	No change	Red-orange	Pink-violet
Skim milk	Red-yellow	No change	No change	Pink-violet
Margarine	No change	No change	Red-orange	No change
Egg yolk	No change	No change	Red-orange	Pink-violet
Egg white	No change	No change	No change	Pink-violet
Water	No change	No change	No change	No change

Analysis and Conclusions

1. Observing Which food(s) reacted with Benedict's solution in Part B?

Orange juice, potato, whole milk, and skim milk reacted.

_____

_____

2. Observing Which food(s) reacted with iodine solution?

The potato reacted.

_____

_____

3. Analyzing Data What change did you observe in the Sudan IV dye test? Which foods caused this change?

A red-orange color from the dissolving dye spread through the whole milk, margarine, and egg yolk.

_____

_____

_____

4. Analyzing Data What color change did you observe for the biuret solution test? Which foods caused this change?

A pink-to-violet color appeared for the whole milk, skim milk, egg yolk, and egg white.

_____

_____

_____

5. Comparing and Contrasting Based on your data from Part B, what is the major difference between whole milk and skim milk?

Based on the results of the Sudan IV test, whole milk contains lipids but there is no noticeable

amount of lipids in skim milk.

_____

_____

6. Comparing and Contrasting Which nutrient did you find in the egg yolk that you did not find in the egg white?

The egg yolk contains lipids.

_____

_____

_____

7. Evaluating and Revising Which of your predictions did your data support?

Answers should be consistent with student predictions and data. _____

_____

_____

_____

_____

_____

_____

8. Drawing Conclusions On a diet consisting almost entirely of milk, human babies grow rapidly and maintain good health. Use your data to explain how this is possible.

Milk contains substances from all three groups of organic nutrients—carbohydrates (in the form

of sugar), lipids, and proteins. _____

_____

_____

_____

Go Further

Benedict's solution does not react with all sugars. Design an experiment to compare the reactions of Benedict's solution with various sugars. After your teacher approves your experimental plan, obtain samples of several sugars and perform your experiment. Then, use a biology or chemistry textbook to determine the molecular structures of the sugars you used in your experiment. Compare your data to these structures. Formulate a hypothesis about the relationship between the molecular structure of a sugar and its ability to react with Benedict's solution.

Benedict's solution reacts with sugars that have a carbonyl group (a double bond between a carbon atom and an oxygen atom). These sugars are called reducing sugars. They include all monosaccharides, such as glucose and fructose, and most disaccharides, such as lactose. The major exception is sucrose. (When glucose and fructose join to form sucrose, the bond forms between carbon atoms in the carbonyl group.)

Chapter 9   Carbon Chemistry

🔍 **Investigation 9B**

Cross-Linked Polymers

Refer students to pages
275–280 in their
textbooks for a
discussion of polymers.
SKILLS FOCUS:
Observing, Inferring,
Comparing and
Contrasting **CLASS**
TIME: 30 minutes over
2 days (Day 1, 15 minutes;
Day 2, 15 minutes)

Background Information

A **polymer** is a large molecule that forms when smaller molecules called monomers are linked together through covalent bonds. In some polymers, all of the monomer molecules are identical. Other polymers contain more than one type of monomer. Under certain conditions, two polymer molecules can be joined at different locations along the molecule by covalent bonds called cross-links. These links can also form between two sections of a single polymer molecule. The existence of cross-links can make the polymer more elastic (able to return to its original shape after being pushed or pulled) and stronger (harder to tear apart).

Figure 1

Some cross-linked polymers form a type of colloid called a gel when they are dispersed in a liquid such as water. Gels have a loose, irregular structure, which prevents the liquid from flowing. In a water-based gel, the amount of water also affects the physical properties of the gel. Adding water to a gel makes it more like a liquid in its properties. Reducing the amount of water makes the gel more like a solid.

In this investigation, you will observe the properties of cross-linked protein polymers in gelatin.

Problem

How does cross-linking affect the physical properties of polymers?

Pre-Lab Discussion

Read the entire investigation. Then, work with a partner to answer the following questions.

1. **Formulating Hypotheses** State a hypothesis about how increasing the amount of gelatin added to a given volume of water will affect the amount of cross-linking in the resulting polymer.

   As more gelatin is added to a given volume of water, more cross-linking occurs, and the strength

   and flexibility of the polymer increases.

2. **Observing** How can you test the gelatin to determine the extent of cross-linking that has occurred?

   The gelatin with more cross-links cannot be as easily torn apart when it is twisted and stretched.

   It will return to its original shape more quickly.

3. **Controlling Variables** Identify the manipulated, responding, and controlled variables.

   a. Manipulated variable

     The amount of gelatin in a given volume of water _____

   b. Responding variable

     The elasticity and strength of the resulting polymer _____

   c. Controlled variables

     Water temperature and time _____

4. **Inferring** Wood glue, like gelatin, consists of proteins extracted from the bones and tissues of animals, which are mixed with water. As the water evaporates, the glue hardens. Explain what causes the glue to harden.

    Answers may vary, but should indicate that more cross-links form as the water evaporates,

    making the glue more solid and stronger.

Materials *(per group)*

250-mL beaker
measuring spoons (in SI units of volume)
hot plate
3 paper cups
20 mL (4 teaspoons) sugar-free gelatin mix
3 wooden splints

> If SI measuring spoons are not available, use spoons that measure in units of tablespoons and teaspoons, using the conversion factor of 15 mL to 1 tablespoon and 4.9 mL to 1 teaspoon.

Safety

Put on safety goggles and a lab apron. Be careful to avoid breakage when working with glassware. Never touch or taste any chemical unless instructed to do so. Use extreme care when working with heated equipment or materials to avoid burns. Observe proper laboratory procedures when using electrical equipment. Note all safety alert symbols next to the steps in the Procedure and review the meaning of each symbol by referring to the Safety Symbols on page xiii.

Procedure

Day 1

 1. Label the three paper cups with your name.

 2. Place 100 mL of water in the beaker. Place the beaker on a hot plate and turn the hot plate to a high setting. **CAUTION:** *The hot plate and beaker will get very hot. Be careful not to burn yourself.*

   3. When the water boils, reduce the setting to low. Using the measuring spoons, carefully remove 30 mL (2 tablespoons) of hot water and place it in one of the paper cups. **CAUTION:** *Use heat-resistant gloves when removing hot water from the beaker.*

4. Add 2.4 mL (0.5 teaspoon) of gelatin to the paper cup. Stir the gelatin with one of the wooden splints until the gelatin is mixed completely in the water. **CAUTION:** *Do not taste the gelatin.*

5. Repeat Steps 2 and 3, placing 4.9 mL (1.0 teaspoon) of gelatin in the second cup and 9.8 mL (2.0 teaspoons) of gelatin in the third cup. Turn off the hot plate and set the paper cups aside to cool.

6. Observe the gelatin. Record your observations in the data table. Leave the gelatin exposed to air in an area where it will remain undisturbed overnight.

Day 2

7. Tear the paper cup away from the 2.4-mL gelatin sample.

8. Observe the gelatin disk. To investigate its elasticity and strength, try to twist it, squash it, and pull it apart. Try to change the polymer's shape slowly, and then rapidly. Record your observations in the data table.

9. Repeat Steps 7 and 8 with the other two gelatin samples. The polymer gels may be disposed of in a dry waste container.

Observations Sample data are shown.

DATA TABLE

Gelatin Volume (in 30 mL water)	Sample Properties: Day 1	Sample Properties: Day 2
2.4 mL (0.5 teaspoon)	Liquid slightly thicker than water	Resembles gelatin dessert; good elasticity: returns to shape quickly after twisting and squashing; poor strength: easily pulls apart
4.9 mL (1.0 teaspoon)	Thick liquid	More rubbery than first sample; very elastic: returns to shape quickly after twisting and squashing; limited strength: pulls apart easily, but not as easily as first sample
9.8 mL (2.0 teaspoons)	Very thick liquid	Most rubbery solid; highly elastic: returns to shape after twisting and squashing; good strength: does not pull apart very easily

Analysis and Conclusions

1. **Observing** How did the polymer gels change when you left them out overnight?

   The liquids became more solid and elastic.

2. **Inferring** Which gelatin sample do you think contained more cross-links? Explain your answer.

   The sample with the most gelatin added to the water had the most cross-links because

   it was strongest and most elastic.

3. **Evaluating and Revising** Did the results of this investigation support or contradict your hypothesis? Explain your answer.

   The results support the hypothesis that when more gelatin is added to a quantity of water, more

   cross-links form. An increase in the number of cross-links increases the strength and elasticity

   of the polymer.

Go Further

Flour made from grains such as wheat contains proteins called gliadin and glutelin. When dough (water mixed with the flour) is kneaded, these protein molecules are stretched, and cross-linked bonds form between them. Use resources in the library or on the Internet to find out how this cross-linking in bread dough takes place. Then, use the information you find to design an experiment to test how too little or too much kneading affects the dough. Show your teacher a written plan for your experiment. When your teacher approves your plan, carry out your experiment and report the results.

Stretching and cross-linking of gliadin and glutelin molecules during kneading forms a gel called gluten. The cross-links in gluten increase the elasticity of the dough so that bubbles of carbon dioxide gas (from yeast, baking soda, or baking powder) can be contained by the dough. Expansion of these gas bubbles during baking gives bread its light, porous texture. While kneading is essential to form gluten, too much kneading can cause the cross-links to break, which produces a dough that is strong but inelastic.

   Review student experimental plans for safety, practicality, and design. Well-designed experimental plans should identify the materials and variables involved and should include a detailed description of the procedure. The procedure should test a prediction that follows from a clearly stated hypothesis.

Chapter 10   Nuclear Chemistry   **Investigation 10A**

Modeling Radioactive Decay

Refer students to pages 292–301 in their textbooks for a general discussion of radioactivity and half-life.

Background Information

SKILLS FOCUS: Using Models, Measuring, Using Tables and Graphs, Comparing and Contrasting, Analyzing Data, Calculating

Radioactive material decays by emitting **alpha particles, beta particles,** or **gamma rays.** During the process of nuclear decay, a radioisotope spontaneously changes into a different element. The time it takes for one-half of a sample of a radioisotope to decay into another element is called **half-life.** The half-lives of various radioisotopes vary from less than a second to billions of years.

CLASS TIME: 45 minutes

A capacitor is a device that can store a large quantity of electric charge and then slowly release that charge. The process of releasing charge is called discharging. The ability of a capacitor to store charge can be measured in units called microfarads. Like a radioisotope, a discharging capacitor has a half-life. Unlike radioactive materials, capacitors do not give off nuclear radiation. As a result, a discharging capacitor can be used as a safe model of radioactive decay.

In this investigation, you will determine the half-lives of two capacitors. Then, you will use your observations to explain the difference between the decay of two radioactive elements.

Problem

How can a model help describe the decay of radioactive isotopes?

Pre-Lab Discussion

Read the entire investigation. Then, work with a partner to answer the following questions.

1. **Using Analogies** What property of a capacitor makes it useful for modeling the decay of a radioactive isotope?

   Like the decay of a radioactive isotope, the discharge of a capacitor has a half-life.

   _____

   _____

   _____

   _____

2. **Designing Experiments** How will you observe the discharge of the capacitors?

   The discharge of the capacitors will be observed by measuring the difference in voltage between

   the two sides of the capacitor.

   _____

   _____

   _____

3. Predicting The rating of each capacitor (4600 or 6000 microfarads) indicates its ability to store charge. Which capacitor do you expect to have the longer half-life?

The capacitor with the higher rating (6000 microfarads) will have the longer half-life.

_____

_____

4. Designing Experiments You will use the power source to charge the capacitors. Why do you think you will need to disconnect the power source from each capacitor before you discharge the capacitor?

The power source keeps the capacitor charged as long as the power source and capacitor

are connected.

_____

5. Controlling Variables Identify the manipulated, responding, and controlled variables in this investigation.

    a. Manipulated variable

      Rating of capacitor

    _____

    b. Responding variable

      Voltage across the capacitor

    _____

    c. Controlled variables

      Power source, voltmeter

    _____

Materials *(per group)*

4 alligator clips

5 insulated wires

2 capacitors (4600 and 6000 microfarads)

DC voltmeter

DC power source

switch

clock or watch with second hand

graph paper

metric ruler

The voltage range of the voltmeter should be equal to or slightly greater than the power source. For example, if you use a 0–10V voltmeter, use a 9-V power source.
Be sure that the positive terminal of the capacitor is connected to the positive terminal of the power source, or the capacitor might be damaged.
Use wire-cutting pliers to cut 15-cm lengths of wire and to remove 2 cm of insulation from each end of the wires.
Actual numbers of alligator clips and wires used may vary, depending on the type of switch and on the external leads of the capacitors and voltmeter used. Provide fresh batteries or an electronic DC power source. Other capacitors rated between 2000 and 6000 microfarads may be substituted if necessary.

Name _____ Class _____ Date _____

Safety 🥽 🧤

Put on safety goggles. Observe proper laboratory procedures when using electrical equipment. Keep all electrical equipment away from water. Do not apply more voltage to the capacitors than their safe operating voltage. Note all safety alert symbols next to the steps in the Procedure and review the meaning of each symbol by referring to the Safety Symbols on page xiii. Inform students of the rated voltage of the capacitors. Remind students not to exceed this voltage. Excessive voltage can cause the capacitors to burn or explode.

Procedure

🥽 1. Work in groups of three. Use alligator clips and insulated wires
🧤   to connect the 4600-microfarad capacitor, voltmeter, power source, and switch as shown in Figure 1. To avoid damaging the capacitor, make sure that the positive terminal of the capacitor is connected to the positive terminal of the power source and that the negative terminal of the capacitor is connected to the negative terminal of the power source. **CAUTION:** *Be very careful when using electricity. Do not close the switch yet. Before continuing with Step 2, have your teacher check your setup.*

Check student setups before allowing students to continue with Step 2. Make sure that all components are connected correctly.

2. Carefully examine the scale on the voltmeter. Because you will have to read the voltage very quickly, determine what each division on the voltmeter scale represents.

3. Close the switch and read the voltage. Do not start timing yet. Record this voltage in the data table next to 0 seconds.

Figure 1

4. One member of your group will be the timer. This person will watch the clock and alert the others in the group to each 10-second interval. A second group member, the reader, will watch and read the voltmeter and call out the voltage when the timer announces each 10-second interval. A third group member will be the recorder. This person will record the voltages in the data table.

5. Start timing the 10-second intervals as you open the switch. After 10 seconds, the timer should call out "10 seconds," while the reader tells what the voltage is. **Note:** *The reader should try to anticipate each 10-second interval. Otherwise, it may take more than 10 seconds to decide what the reading is.*

6. Continue to record the voltage for 230 seconds. If the voltage becomes too small to measure before that time, you may stop at that point. If necessary, you may continue the data table on another sheet of paper.

7. Replace the 4600-microfarad capacitor with the 6000-microfarad capacitor.

8. Repeat Steps 1 through 6 with the 6000-microfarad capacitor.

Observations Sample data are shown.

DATA TABLE

Time (seconds)	Voltage (volts) 4600-Microfarad Capacitor	Voltage (volts) 6000-Microfarad Capacitor	Time (seconds)	Voltage (volts) 4600-Microfarad Capacitor	Voltage (volts) 6000-Microfarad Capacitor
0	9.8	9.9	120	2.8	4.2
10	8.5	9.2	130	2.5	3.9
20	7.5	8.8	140	2.3	3.6
30	6.9	8.2	150	2.0	3.4
40	6.1	7.7	160	1.8	3.2
50	5.6	7.1	170	1.6	3.0
60	5.0	6.7	180	1.4	2.8
70	4.7	6.2	190	1.3	2.7
80	4.2	5.7	200	1.2	2.5
90	3.8	5.4	210	1.1	2.4
100	3.4	4.9	220	1.0	2.3
110	3.1	4.5	230	0.9	2.2

Analysis and Conclusions

1. **Using Graphs** On a sheet of graph paper, construct a graph of your data. Plot time on the horizontal axis and voltage on the vertical axis. Draw a smooth curve that comes as close as possible to each of your data points for the 4600-microfarad capacitor. Draw a second smooth curve for the data points for the 6000-microfarad capacitor. Label each curve with the rating of the capacitor it represents.

Student graphs should show two exponential decay curves. The 4600-microfarad capacitor will discharge faster than the 6000-microfarad capacitor.

Name _____ Class _____ Date _____

2. **Analyzing Data** Use your graph to find the half-life of the 4600-microfarad capacitor. To do this, calculate half of the voltage across this capacitor at 0 seconds. For example, if the voltage at 0 seconds was 10 volts, half of the voltage is 5 volts. Then, locate this voltage on the vertical axis. Use the metric ruler to draw a horizontal line from this voltage to the curve for the 4600-microfarad capacitor. Mark the point where this line intersects the curve. Then, draw a vertical line from this point down to the horizontal axis. The half-life is the time at which the vertical line intersects the horizontal axis. Record the half-life of the 4600-microfarad capacitor below.

Half-life of 4600-microfarad capacitor: _____ 60 _____ seconds

3. **Analyzing Data** Use the procedure you used to answer Question 2 to determine the half-life of the 6000-microfarad capacitor.

Half-life of 6000 microfarad capacitor: _____ 100 _____ seconds

4. **Evaluating** Did your data support or contradict your prediction?

The data support the prediction that the 6000-microfarad capacitor has the longer half-life.

_____

_____

5. **Analyzing Data** How long did the 4600-microfarad capacitor take to reach one-fourth of its original voltage?

120 seconds (2 half-lives)

6. **Calculating** If the voltage across the 4600-microfarad capacitor was 9.0 volts at 0 seconds, how many half-lives would be needed for the voltage to fall to 0.1 volts? How many seconds would that take?

A typical result is 7 half-lives or 420 seconds.

_____

_____

7. **Calculating** If the voltage across the 6000-microfarad capacitor was 9.0 volts at 0 seconds, how many half-lives would be needed for the voltage to fall to 0.1 volts? How many seconds would that take?

A typical result is 7 half-lives or 700 seconds.

_____

_____

8. **Comparing and Contrasting** Which capacitor would take longer to fall to a voltage that is too low for the voltmeter to measure? Explain your answer.

The 6000-microfarad capacitor would take longer because it has a longer half-life.

_____

_____

9. **Using Models** Carbon-14 has a half-life of 5730 years. Uranium-238 has a half-life of 4.47×10^9 years. A radioisotope can be used to date an object only if enough of the radioisotope remains in the object to measure. Use your observations of the two capacitors to explain why carbon-14 can be used to date objects as old as 50,000 years, but uranium-238 can be used to date the objects that ar millions of years old.

The 6000-microfarad capacitor has a longer half-life than the 4600-microfarad capacitor has. As a

result, the 6000-microfarad capacitor retains a measurable voltage longer than the 4600-microfarad

capacitor. Similarly, because uranium-238 has a much longer half-life than carbon-14, traces

of uranium-238 in an object can still be detected long after the amount of carbon-14 remaining in

the object has become too small to measure.

Go Further

Use resources in the library or on the Internet to research how a technique called fission-track dating can be used to estimate the age of an object.

Fission tracks in rocks and other materials are created when uranium-238 undergoes spontaneous fission. During fission, the uranium-238 nucleus splits into two fragments. These fragments are driven apart by the energy of the nuclear reaction, resulting in a trail of damage in the host material. In fission-track dating, samples of mica or glass (natural or synthetic) are treated with a solution, such as an acid, to make the tracks more visible. The tracks are then viewed under a microscope and counted. The age of the sample can be estimated from the number of tracks per square centimeter of sample and the concentration of uranium in the sample.

🔍 **Investigation 10B**

Detecting Nuclear Radiation

Refer students to pages 292–297 in their textbooks for a general discussion of radioactivity. **SKILLS FOCUS:** Observing, Comparing and Contrasting, Making Judgments, Evaluating and Revising **CLASS TIME:** 45 minutes

Background Information

A cloud chamber is a device that can be used to observe **radioactivity.** In the chamber, vapor of a substance such as alcohol is cooled to a low temperature. A particle of high energy passing through the chamber ionizes the molecules that the particle strikes in its path. Alcohol vapor condenses around the ions, producing a thin white trail. Each white trail reveals the path of a radioactive particle.

There are many sources of nuclear radiation. Cosmic rays, or high-energy particles from space, are one common source of nuclear radiation. Many rocks and building materials also produce small amounts of nuclear radiation. You can use a cloud chamber to determine whether background sources or radioactive samples produce measurable levels of radiation in your environment.

In this investigation, you will build a cloud chamber and use it to determine whether you are usually exposed to nuclear radiation.

Problem

Are you exposed to nuclear radiation in your daily life?

Pre-Lab Discussion

Read the entire investigation. Then, work with a partner to answer the following questions.

1. **Formulating Hypotheses** State a hypothesis about whether you are usually exposed to nuclear radiation.

   People are generally exposed to low levels of background radiation.

   _____

2. **Controlling Variables** Identify the manipulated, responding, and controlled variables in this investigation.

   a. Manipulated variable

   Source of nuclear radiation

   b. Responding variable

   Number of white trails observed (or number of radioactive particles detected)

   c. Controlled variables

   Temperature, time, cloud chamber used

3. **Predicting** Based on your hypothesis, predict what you will observe in Step 7.

   A small number of white trails will be observed.

   _____

4. Predicting Predict how your observations will differ in Steps 7 and 10. Explain the reasons for your prediction.

More white trails will be observed in Step 10 because the alpha source produces more

nuclear radiation than the surrounding sources of background radiation.

5. Inferring Why is dry ice used in this lab?

Dry ice lowers the temperature, making the alcohol vapor more likely to condense.

Materials *(per group)*

black felt	dropper pipet	clock or watch
scissors	isopropyl alcohol	sealed alpha-radiation source
large glass jar with screw-on lid	dry ice	powerful flashlight
thick blotting paper	plastic tray	small wooden block
fast-drying glue		Wear heavy, insulated gloves when handling dry ice.

Safety 🔲🔲🔲🔲🔲🔲🔲🔲

Put on safety goggles and a lab apron. Be careful to avoid breakage when working with glassware. Wear plastic disposable gloves when handling chemicals, as they may irritate the skin or stain skin or clothing. Never touch or taste any chemical unless instructed to do so. Keep alcohol away from any open flame. Be careful when handling sharp instruments. Be careful using dry ice. Never allow dry ice to touch your skin. Be careful with the alpha-radiation source. Alpha particles cannot pass through skin, but the source of the particles can be dangerous if swallowed or inhaled. Wash your hands thoroughly after carrying out this investigation. Note all safety alert symbols next to the steps in the Procedure and review the meaning of each symbol by referring to the Safety Symbols on page xiii.

Procedure

1. To construct a cloud chamber, use scissors to cut a circle of black felt slightly smaller than the inside diameter of the glass jar. **CAUTION:** *Be careful when using scissors.*

2. Place the felt circle in the bottom of the jar, as shown in Figure 1.

3. Cut a circle of thick blotting paper slightly smaller than the inside of the lid of the jar. Use fast-drying glue to stick the blotting paper to the bottom of the lid.

4. Use the dropper pipet to apply isopropyl alcohol to the blotting paper until it is saturated, but not so wet that alcohol drips from it. Let any excess alcohol drain into the sink. **CAUTION:** *Be careful handling isopropyl alcohol. It is poisonous.*

5. Screw the lid onto the jar.

Review the MSDS safety information for isopropyl alcohol, dry ice, and the alpha-radiation source with students before they perform this investigation. Sealed alpha-radiation sources appropriate for school laboratories are available from scientific supply companies. Keep the sources in a locked, labeled cabinet when students are not using them. Note how many are used and make sure that all are returned. Supervise students especially closely in this investigation. Before class, open the sources for use as directed by the manufacturer, but then tape a small square of aluminum foil over each of them. Use a needle to pierce a small, narrow hole through the foil for the radiation. Be careful not to allow the needle to touch the dangerous material inside the container.

6. Place the jar onto a large piece of dry ice that your teacher has placed into the tray. **CAUTION:** *Do not touch the dry ice. It can damage your skin.*

7. Working in a room that is partially darkened, direct the beam of the flashlight through the side of the jar. Observe the cloud chamber for the next 5 minutes. Count the number of white trails you observe. Record your observations in the data table. Partially darken the laboratory.

8. Unscrew the lid of the jar, leaving the jar in place on the dry ice. Put the wooden block on the felt at the bottom of the jar. If the blotting paper in the lid has begun to dry out, use the dropper pipet to place a few more drops of alcohol onto it. Obtain an alpha-radiation source from your teacher. Place the radiation source on top of the block. **CAUTION:** *Do not touch the radioactive material inside the alpha source.*

9. Screw on the lid of the jar again.

10. Direct the flashlight beam into the jar and watch what happens for the next 5 minutes. If possible, count the number of white trails you observe. Record your observations in the data table.

11. Return the radiation source to your teacher. Wash your hands thoroughly with warm water and soap or detergent before leaving the laboratory.

Figure 1

Observations   Sample data are shown.

DATA TABLE

Source of Nuclear Radiation	Number of White Trails
Background	5–30
Background plus alpha source	More than 100

Analysis and Conclusions

1. **Evaluating and Revising** From your observations, what can you conclude about your predictions?

   The observations should support the prediction that the background radiation present will

   produce fewer white trails than the alpha source will.

   _____

   _____

2. **Comparing and Contrasting** Compare the amount of nuclear radiation usually reaching you with the amount you would receive when near a radioactive sample.

   Much more radiation would be received near a radiation sample.

   _____

   _____

   _____

3. **Evaluating and Revising** From your observations, what can you conclude about your hypothesis?

   The observations should support the hypothesis that people are usually exposed to small

   amounts of nuclear radiation.

   _____

   _____

4. **Making Judgments** Based on your observations, how would you advise someone who wanted to protect people's health by completely eliminating exposure to nuclear radiation?

   Completely eliminating exposure to nuclear radiation is not a realistic goal. It is also not necessary

   for protecting people's health. Small quantities of nuclear radiation are present at all times.

   _____

   _____

Go Further

Suppose that you had a source of both alpha and beta radiation in a cloud chamber. What could you do to make the paths of the two kinds of particles different so that you could tell them apart? Explain your answer. (*Hint:* Recall that alpha and beta particles are oppositely charged.)

Placing a strong magnet or a device that produces an electric field near the cloud chamber would produce a magnetic field or an electric field. The opposite charges of the alpha and beta particles would cause their paths to curve in opposite directions.

Measuring Distance and Displacement

Refer students to pages 328–331 in their textbooks for a general discussion of vectors, distance, and displacement. **SKILLS FOCUS:** Measuring, Calculating **TIME REQUIRED:** 45 minutes

Background Information

Vectors have many uses. For example, you can use vectors to describe the distance an object travels and the displacement that results from an object's movement. Before you can make use of vectors, you must first select a frame of reference.

To use vectors to describe an object's position or movement on a flat surface, you must first define a frame of reference that includes the origin—a specific point that does not move. Two imaginary lines, or axes, that pass through the origin at right angles are then chosen, as shown in Figure 1. These two lines are the x-axis and the y-axis. Using the axes, you can describe the position of an object in terms of its x- and y-coordinates, for example, the point $(4, 8)$ on a graph. Note that the coordinates of the origin are $(0, 0)$.

Figure 1 shows that you can also define a vector to describe an object's position by drawing an arrow from the origin to the object's position. The object's coordinates $(7, 2)$ determine the length and direction of the vector. Figure 2 shows that any vector in the frame of reference can be broken down into x- and y-components. Therefore, any vector is also the **resultant vector** of its own x- and y-components. Resultant vectors are also used to represent the result of vector addition.

Figure 1

Figure 2

You can use a similar method to define a vector describing an object's displacement. To do this, draw a vector from the object's starting point to its ending point. Figure 3 shows the x- and y-coordinates of an object's starting and ending points. Note that the x- and y-components of the displacement vector are simply the difference between the x- and y-coordinates of the starting and ending points.

In this investigation, you will compare two methods of determining the length of a displacement vector.

Components of displacement vector:
$$x = x_{ending\ point} - x_{starting\ point} = 9 - 1 = 8$$
$$y = y_{ending\ point} - y_{starting\ point} = 10 - 4 = 6$$

Figure 3

Problem

How can vectors be used to determine displacement?

Pre-Lab Discussion

Read the entire investigation. Then, work with a partner to answer the following questions.

1. How will you determine the x- and y-coordinates of each position?

   By measuring the distance along each axis from the origin to the position

2. How will you determine the x- and y-components of the displacement vector?

   By subtracting the x- and y-coordinates of the starting point from the corresponding coordinates

   of the ending point

3. How will you calculate the length of the displacement vector?

   By taking the square root of the sum of the squares of the x- and y-components of the

   displacement vector

4. How will you measure the length of the displacement vector?

   By using string and a meter stick to measure the straight-line distance from the starting point

   to the ending point

Chapter 11   Motion

🔍 **Investigation 11B**

Investigating Free Fall

Refer students to pages 332–348 in their textbooks for a general discussion of velocity and acceleration. **SKILLS FOCUS:** Observing, Measuring **CLASS TIME:** 45 minutes

Background Information

Free fall is the movement of an object toward Earth because of gravity. An object that is in free fall experiences acceleration. **Acceleration** is the rate at which velocity changes. Acceleration occurs when there is a change in speed, change in direction, or both. During free fall, speed increases at a constant rate. But what happens when an object also moves horizontally as it falls? The curved path that results is known as projectile motion—a topic you will cover in more detail in Chapter 12. Do you think an object's horizontal motion will affect its fall?

In this investigation, you will compare the fall of two identical objects from the same height. The first object will fall straight down. The second object will be given an initial horizontal velocity at the start of its fall. You will determine how the horizontal motion of the second object affects the time it takes to fall.

Problem

What effect does horizontal motion have on the time an object takes to fall?

Pre-Lab Discussion

Read the entire investigation. Then, work with a partner to answer the following questions.

1. **Controlling Variables** Identify the manipulated, responding, and controlled variables in this investigation.

   a. Manipulated variable

   Horizontal motion
   _____

   _____

   b. Responding variable

   Time for the spheres to reach the floor
   _____

   _____

   c. Controlled variables

   Mass and volume of spheres, distance the spheres fall
   _____

   _____

2. **Formulating Hypotheses** State a hypothesis about the effect of horizontal motion on the time an object takes to fall.

   Horizontal motion does not affect the time an object takes to fall.
   _____

   _____

3. **Predicting** Make a prediction about the result of this investigation. Will one object fall more quickly than the other, or will both objects hit the floor at the same time?

The objects will fall at the same rate and hit the floor at the same time.

_____

_____

4. **Controlling Variables** Why are you told to let one object fall through a hole in the box, instead of rolling the object off the edge of the table?

Rolling the object off the edge of the table would give the object a horizontal velocity.

_____

_____

5. **Calculating** How will you determine the average time for the five trials?

Sum the five trial times and then divide the total by 5.

_____

_____

6. **Measuring** Why do you think you will need a stopwatch that can measure tenths of a second?

The spheres will take less than 1 second to fall to the floor.

_____

_____

_____

Materials (per group)

2 small spherical objects Provide steel ball bearings, plastic marbles, or golf balls.

stopwatch (that can measure tenths of a second)

meter stick

masking tape

Safety 🗷🗷

Put on safety goggles. Keep your hands and feet out of the path of falling objects. Note all safety alert symbols next to the steps in the Procedure and review the meaning of each symbol by referring to the Safety Symbols on page xiii.

Procedure
Part A: Timing Free Fall

1. Work with a classmate. Hold the object over the floor so that its bottom is in line with the top of the table, as shown in Figure 1. Have your classmate check that the object is being held at the correct height.

Figure 1

2. Position your classmate so that he or she can have a clear view of the object and the floor below. Have your classmate be prepared to start the stopwatch.

3. Count down from five and release the object when you reach zero. Have your classmate begin the stopwatch as soon as he or she sees you release the object. Your classmate will use the stopwatch to measure the time it takes the object to hit the floor. Record this time in the data table.

4. Repeat Step 3 four more times. To calculate the average time that the sphere takes to reach the floor, add all five times together, then divide the total by 5. Record this value in the data table.

5. Using the meter stick, measure and place a piece of masking tape on the floor 1 meter from the point directly under the edge of the tabletop, as shown in Figure 2.

Figure 2

6. Place the object to be dropped near the edge of the tabletop. Push the object off the table with just enough force so that it lands on or close to the tape. **CAUTION:** *To avoid hurting anyone, be careful not to push the object too hard.* Practice pushing the object off the table until you can make it land on or close to the tape nearly every time.

7. Repeat Step 6 one more time and have your classmate use the stopwatch to measure the time the object takes to fall to the floor. Record this time in the data table.

8. Repeat Step 7 four more times. To calculate the average time that the object takes to fall to the floor, add all five times together and then divide the total by 5. Record this value in the data table.

Part B: Comparing Free Fall

9. Hold one of the objects above the floor and in line with the top of the table, as in Step 1. Have your classmate roll a second object toward the edge of the table. When you see the rolling object fall off the edge of the table, release the object you are holding. Watch and listen to observe whether one object hits the floor before the other.

10. Repeat Step 9 four more times. Record your observations in the space provided for results of Part B below the data table.

Observations Sample data are shown.

DATA TABLE

Trial	Vertical Fall	Fall With Horizontal Motion
	Time (seconds)	Time (seconds)
1	0.4	0.5
2	0.3	0.3
3	0.5	0.3
4	0.4	0.4
5	0.4	0.5
TOTAL	2.0	2.0
Average	0.4	0.4

Results of Part B

Both objects hit the floor at approximately the same time.

_____

_____

_____

Analysis and Conclusions

1. **Calculating** What was the average time required for the object dropped straight down to hit the floor?

0.4 second (The value will depend on the height of the table.)

2. **Calculating** What was the average time the object with the initial horizontal velocity took to hit the floor?

0.4 second (The value will depend on the height of the table.)

3. **Observing** In Part B, did one sphere hit the floor before the other or did both spheres land at the same time?

Both spheres hit the floor at approximately the same time.

4. **Evaluating and Revising** Did your data support or contradict your hypothesis? Explain your answer.

Both spheres fell at the same rate. These data support the hypothesis that objects fall at the same

rate, regardless of their horizontal velocity.

Go Further

The greater an object's mass, the stronger is the force of gravity on the object. Does this mean that more massive objects fall more quickly than less massive objects? Design an experiment to answer this question. Write a detailed plan for your experiment. Describe the procedures you will use and identify all the variables involved. Show your plan to your teacher. If your teacher approves, carry out your experiment.

When air resistance is minimal, the force of gravity causes all falling objects to accelerate at the same rate regardless of their masses.

Using a Pendulum to Measure the Acceleration Due to Force of Gravity

Background Information

Refer students to pages 361 and 362 in their textbooks for a discussion of gravitational force. **SKILLS FOCUS:** Measuring, Calculating, Designing Experiments **CLASS TIME:** Part A, 20 minutes; Part B, 40 minutes

A freely falling object accelerates at a rate that depends on the force of gravity. Near the surface of Earth, acceleration due to gravity (g) is equal to approximately 9.8 m/s^2. There are several ways to measure acceleration due to gravity. In this investigation, you will use a method that makes use of a pendulum. A pendulum consists of a weight, also known as a bob, that swings back and forth from a rope or string. Because the fixed end of the string is tied in place, it exerts a centripetal force that pulls the falling weight into a circular path. The time required for a pendulum to complete a back-and-forth swing is called the period of the pendulum. In Part A of this investigation, you will determine whether the period of a pendulum depends on the angle from which the bob is released.

Because the friction forces acting on the pendulum are neglible, it can be assumed that the pendulum is acted on by a single force—the force of gravity. A simple equation relating the acceleration due to gravity, the length of the pendulum, and the period of the pendulum can be written. In Part B of this investigation, you will design and carry out an experiment in which you will use a pendulum and this equation to determine the value of g.

Problem

How can you use a pendulum to determine the acceleration due to gravity?

Pre-Lab Discussion

Read the entire investigation. Then, work with a partner to answer the following questions.

1. **Designing Experiments** In Part A of this investigation, how will you determine the period of the pendulum?

   By measuring the time required for the pendulum to complete 20 back-and-forth swings and then

   dividing that time by 20

   _____

   _____

2. **Predicting** In Part A of this investigation, how will the angle from which the pendulum is released affect the period of the pendulum?

   The angle from which the pendulum is released will have no effect on the period of the pendulum.

   _____

   _____

3. **Formulating Hypotheses** State a hypothesis that you could test in Part B of this investigation.

Student hypotheses should be specific and subject to test by an experiment that students can

perform. Possible answers include the hypotheses that the value of g is 9.8 m/s² and that

the length of the pendulum will have no effect on the calculated value of g.

4. **Designing Experiments** Describe an experiment that you could perform to test your hypothesis.

Students should describe a procedure that allows them to determine the period of a pendulum.

They can then use the period and the length of the pendulum to calculate g. They may want to

change the length of the pendulum and repeat the procedure to verify that the calculated value

of g is constant.

5. **Controlling Variables** Identify the manipulated, responding, and controlled variables in the experiment described in Question 4.

Answers will depend on student experiments, but may include the length of the pendulum as a

manipulated variable, the period of the pendulum and calculated value of g as responding

variables, and the position from which the pendulum is released as a controlled variable.

6. **Evaluating** What experimental result would support your hypothesis? What result would contradict your hypothesis?

Answers will depend on student hypotheses and experiments, but should follow logically from the

experiment described in the answer to Question 4. The answers should clearly support or contradict

the hypothesis described in the answer to Question 3. For example, suppose that the hypothesis

is that the length of the pendulum will have no effect on the calculated value of g. This hypothesis

will be supported if the same value for g is calculated for different pendulum lengths. The hypothesis

will be contradicted if different values for g are calculated for different pendulum lengths.

Materials (per group)

ring stand	meter stick
2 books	100-g mass
clamp	protractor
metal rod, approximately 30 cm long	stopwatch
2-m fishing line You can substitute fine, flexible wire for the fishing line.	graph paper

Ask your teacher to provide you with any additional materials that you will need to carry out Part B of this investigation.

Safety 🔖⚠

Wear safety goggles when performing this investigation. Note all safety alert symbols next to the steps in the Procedure and review the meaning of each symbol by referring to the Safety Symbols on page xiii.

Procedure

Part A: Determining If the Angle of Release Affects the Period of a Pendulum

🔖 1. Place the ring stand near the edge of a table, as shown in Figure 1. Place two textbooks on the base of the ring stand to prevent it from falling over. Use the clamp to attach the metal rod to the ring stand so that it extends beyond the edge of the table.

2. Tie one end of the fishing line to the portion of the metal rod that extends over the table. Tie the 100-g mass to the other end of the fishing line so that the center of the mass is 1.0 m below the metal rod, as shown in Figure 1.

Figure 1

3. Using the protractor to measure the angle, position the mass at an angle of 10 degrees. **Note:** *When the mass hangs straight down, the angle is 0 degrees.* Hold the mass in this position so that the fishing line is straight and extended. Have a group member start the stopwatch at the instant that you release the mass. Measure the time that the pendulum takes to make 20 complete back-and-forth swings. Record this time in Data Table 1. Also make note of the speed with which the pendulum swings back and forth.

4. Repeat Step 3 two more times, first releasing the mass at a 20-degree angle and then a 30-degree angle. For each trial, record in Data Table 1 the time the pendulum takes to complete 20 back-and-forth swings.

5. Calculate the period of the pendulum by dividing the time the pendulum takes to make 20 complete swings from each of the three positions by 20. Record these values in the appropriate places in Data Table 1.

6. Make a graph of your data. Plot the angle (10, 20, and 30 degrees) on the horizontal axis (x-axis) and the period of the pendulum on the vertical axis (y-axis). Draw a straight line through the data points.

Name _____ Class _____ Date _____

Part B: Design Your Own Investigation

⚠ 7. Plan an experiment that will make use of a pendulum to determine the acceleration due to gravity (g). The acceleration due to gravity of the pendulum bob can be calculated by dividing the length of the pendulum (L) by the period of the pendulum (T) squared.

$$g = \frac{39.5L}{T^2}$$

Record the hypothesis that you will test.

Possible hypotheses: The value of g is 9.8 m/s²; the length of the pendulum will have no effect

on the calculated value of g.

_____

8. Identify the manipulated, responding, and controlled variables in your experiment.

   a. Manipulated variable

   _____

   b. Responding variable

   _____

   c. Controlled variables

   _____

9. Write out a detailed step-by-step procedure that you will use. Your procedure should produce data that will test your hypothesis. As you plan your experiment, think about what equipment you will need, what measurements you will make, and how you will record and display your data (tables, graphs). Include any safety precautions that you need to take. Construct Data Table 2 in which to record your observations in the space provided on page 127.

   Possible Procedure: Use the pendulum setup from Part A.

   1. Using the protractor to measure the angle, position the mass at an angle of 20 degrees. Have a
      group member start the stopwatch at the instant you release the mass. Measure the time the
      pendulum takes to complete 20 back-and forth-swings. Record this time in Data Table 2.

   2. Use scissors to cut the mass from the fishing line. Retie the mass so that its center is 0.8 m below
      the metal rod.

   3. Repeat Step 1 for a pendulum length of 0.8 m.

   4. Repeat Step 2 and reduce the pendulum length to 0.5 m. Then, repeat Step 1.

   5. Calculate the period for each pendulum length by dividing the time required to complete 20 back-
      and-forth swings of the pendulum by 20. Use the equation shown in Part B, Step 7 to calculate the
      acceleration due to gravity for each pendulum length. Record these values in Data Table 2.

   6. Make a graph of your data. Plot the pendulum length on the horizontal axis and the calculated value
      of g on the vertical axis. Draw a straight line as close as possible to all three data points.

Name _____ Class _____ Date _____

Safety Precautions

Students need to wear safety goggles when working with pendulums. Students should be

careful when using scissors.

_____

_____

_____

10. Submit your written experimental plan to your teacher. When your teacher has approved your plan, carry out your experiment and record your observations in Data Table 2. Check student plans for practicality and safety before approving them.

Observations Sample data are shown.

DATA TABLE 1

Starting Position (degrees)	Time for 20 Swings (seconds)	Period (seconds)
10	50.1	2.5
20	48.7	2.4
30	52.4	2.6

DATA TABLE 2

If you need more space, attach additional sheets of paper.

Length of pendulum (m)	1.0	0.8	0.5
Time for 20 swings (seconds)	38	36	30
Period (seconds)	1.9	1.8	1.5
Calculated value of g (m/s^2)	10.9	9.8	8.8
Reference value of g (m/s^2)	9.8	9.8	9.8
Experimental error (%)	11	0	10

Analysis and Conclusions

1. **Observing** In Part A of this investigation, how did the angle from which you released the pendulum affect the maximum speed of the pendulum's motion?

   The pendulum's maximum speed was greater when the angle of release was larger.

   _____

   _____

2. **Analyzing Data** What did your results in Part A indicate about the relationship between the period of the pendulum and the position from which you released the pendulum?

   The angle from which the pendulum was released had no effect on the period of the pendulum.

   _____

   _____

3. **Evaluating and Revising** Did your results in Part B support or contradict your hypothesis? Explain your answer.

   Students should describe their data and explain its consequences for their hypotheses. The

   sample data show that reducing the length of a pendulum shortens the period of the pendulum.

   The sample data agree roughly with the prediction that the measured values of g will be near

   the accepted value of 9.8 m/s².

   _____

   _____

4. **Evaluating and Revising** Use the equation below to determine the experimental error for each of the calculated values for g. Record these error values in Data Table 2.

   $$\text{Experimental error} = \left(\frac{\text{Experimental value} - \text{Accepted value}}{\text{Accepted value}} \right) \times 100\%$$

   Why might your calculated values of g differ from the accepted value?

   The length of string and time may not have been measured accurately. Friction between the fishing

   line and the metal rod may have interfered with the experiment.

   _____

   _____

Go Further

Predict how the mass of a pendulum affects the period of the pendulum and the calculated value of g. Design an experiment to test your predictions. Show your teacher a detailed description of your experimental plan. When your teacher approves, carry out your experiment and report your results.

Because mass does not appear in the equation in Step 7, it has no effect on the period of a pendulum or on the calculated value of g.

🔍 **Investigation 12B**

Testing Galileo's Hypothesis

Refer students to pages 361, 362, and 365–369 in their textbooks for a discussion of the force of gravity and how it accelerates falling objects.

Background Information

SKILLS FOCUS: Measuring, Calculating **CLASS TIME:** 45 minutes

In 1638, Galileo Galilei published a book that described the motion of freely falling objects. In this book, Galileo hypothesized that freely falling objects accelerate at a constant rate. However, Galileo could not test his hypothesis directly because the precise and accurate instruments needed to measure time and distance did not exist. To solve this problem, he designed an experiment to test his hypothesis indirectly by carefully measuring the time and distance of balls rolling down ramps. When a ball rolls down a ramp with a small incline, it accelerates more slowly than it does during free fall.

In this investigation, you will determine whether a steel ball accelerates at a constant rate as it rolls down ramps of varying lengths. Then, you will determine how the steepness of a ramp affects the acceleration of the ball.

Problem

How do the length and steepness of a ramp affect the rate of acceleration of an object rolling down the ramp?

Pre-Lab Discussion

Read the entire investigation. Then, work with a partner to answer the following questions.

1. **Formulating Hypotheses** State a hypothesis about whether the gravitational force on an object changes as it rolls down a ramp.

   The force of gravity remains constant as the object rolls down the ramp.

2. **Predicting** Based on your hypothesis, predict how the ball will accelerate as it rolls down the ramp. Explain your answer.

   The force of gravity on the ball is constant, and Newton's second law of motion states that a

   constant force produces a constant acceleration. As a result, the acceleration of the ball should

   be constant.

3. **Controlling Variables** Identify the manipulated, responding, and controlled variables in this experiment.

   a. Manipulated variables Distance, steepness of ramp

   b. Responding variable Time for the ball to reach the bottom of the ramp

   c. Controlled variable Mass of ball

4. **Predicting** How do you expect the steepness of the ramp to affect the acceleration of the ball?

   A steeper ramp will increase the acceleration of the ball.

Materials *(per group)*

1.5-m board

2 books

meter stick

steel ball, approximately 4 cm in diameter

stopwatch

calculator

Sand and inspect the boards to make sure that they are smooth and free of splinters. You may want to glue or nail a strip of molding onto the board to guide the steel ball's path.

Safety 🖐 🥽

Wear safety goggles. Handle the board carefully to avoid splinters. Note all safety alert symbols next to the steps in the Procedure and review the meaning of each symbol by referring to the Safety Symbols on page xiii.

Procedure

Part A: Determining Acceleration

🖐 🥽 1. Work with a partner. Put one of the books on the floor. Place one end of the board on the book to form a ramp. Then, place the meter stick on the board with its zero end at the bottom of the ramp, as shown in Figure 1. Mark a line at distances of 0.5 m and 1.0 m from the end of the board. Move the meter stick so that its zero is aligned at the 1.0 m mark you just made on the board and mark a line at a distance of 1.5 m from the end of the board. Refer to Data Table 1, which you will use to compile data obtained in Steps 2 and 8 of Part A.

Book

Board

Meter stick

Figure 1

2. Position the steel ball at the mark located 1.5 m from the bottom of the ramp. Have your partner start the stopwatch at the instant you release the ball. Have your partner stop the stopwatch when the ball reaches the bottom of the ramp. **CAUTION:** *Stop the ball when it reaches the bottom of the ramp.* Record the time of Trial 1 for a distance of 1.5 m in the data table.

3. Repeat Step 2 four more times. Record the times of Trials 2 to 5 for a distance of 1.5 m.

4. Position the steel ball at the mark located 1.0 m from the bottom of the ramp. Release the ball and time the ball as it rolls down the ramp, as in Step 2. Record the time of Trial 1 for a distance of 1.0 m.

5. Repeat Step 4 four more times. Record the times of Trials 2 to 5 for a distance of 1.0 m.

6. Position the steel ball at the mark located 0.5 m from the bottom of the ramp. Release the ball and time its roll down the ramp as before. Record the time of Trial 1 for a distance of 0.5 m.

7. Repeat Step 6 four more times. Record the times of Trials 2 to 5 for a distance of 0.5 m.

8. Calculate and record the average time for each distance. To do this, add the five times together and divide the total by 5.

Part B: Determining If the Steepness of the Ramp Affects the Ball's Acceleration

9. Place another book under the elevated end of the board to make the ramp steeper.

10. Repeat Steps 2 through 8. Record your measurements and calculations in Data Table 2.

11. It can be shown that for an object starting from rest and accelerating at a constant rate, the acceleration is equal to $2D/T^2$, where D is the distance and T is the time of travel. Use the values of D and T in Data Tables 1 and 2 to calculate the acceleration of the ball for each distance and ramp height. Record the results in Data Table 3.

Observations

Sample data are shown. Actual results will depend on the thickness of the books and the amount of friction between the ball and the ramp.

DATA TABLE 1

	Ramp Supported by One Book		
Trial	Distance = 1.5 m Time (s)	Distance = 1.0 m Time (s)	Distance = 0.5 m Time (s)
1	3.5	3.1	2.0
2	3.6	3.1	2.1
3	3.6	3.0	2.2
4	3.5	3.2	2.0
5	3.6	3.2	2.2
TOTAL	17.8	15.6	10.5
Average	3.6	3.1	2.1

DATA TABLE 2

	Ramp Supported by Two Books		
Trial	Distance = 1.5 m Time (s)	Distance = 1.0 m Time (s)	Distance = 0.5 m Time (s)
1	2.5	2.0	1.6
2	2.7	2.1	1.5
3	2.8	2.2	1.6
4	2.7	2.1	1.5
5	2.7	2.0	1.6
TOTAL	13.4	10.4	7.8
Average	2.7	2.1	1.6

DATA TABLE 3

Height of Ramp	Distance = 1.5 m	Distance = 1.0 m	Distance = 0.5 m
	Acceleration (m/s²) = 2D/T²		
1 book	0.23	0.21	0.23
2 books	0.41	0.45	0.39

Analysis and Conclusions

1. **Analyzing Data** Compare the accelerations that you calculated for the three distances in Part A. Did your data agree with your prediction? Explain your answer.

   There may be some variation in the calculated acceleration, but acceleration did not change as

   a result of changing the distance the ball rolled. The sample data supported the prediction that

   the ball will accelerate at a constant rate.

2. **Evaluating and Revising** Did your data support your hypothesis? Explain your answer.

   Although there was some experimental error, the sample data supported the hypothesis that

   the gravitational force and acceleration are constant as a ball rolls down a ramp.

3. **Analyzing Data** How did the steepness of the ramp affect the rate of acceleration?

   The steeper the ramp was, the greater was the rate of acceleration.

4. **Inferring** Why would it be much more difficult to perform this experiment with a very steep ramp or with a freely falling object?

   The ball would roll down the ramp or fall so quickly that it would be difficult to time accurately.

5. **Evaluating and Revising** How could this experiment be improved to produce more accurate data?

   A more precise and accurate method of timing would produce more accurate data.

Go Further

How would changing the mass of the steel ball rolling down the ramp affect the results of this experiment? Design an experiment to answer this question. Write a detailed plan for your experiment. Your plan should state the hypothesis to be tested, identify variables, and describe the procedures and safety precautions you will take. Show your plan to your teacher. When your teacher approves your plan, carry out your experiment and report your results.

Well-designed experimental plans should include detailed procedures that will test a clearly stated hypothesis. An example of an acceptable hypothesis is that increasing the mass of the ball will (or will not) increase its rate of acceleration. In the absence of friction, changing the mass of the ball should not affect the rate of acceleration. Frictional forces may cause a small change in the rate of acceleration.

Investigating Sinking and Floating

Background Information

Refer students to pages 400–404 in their textbooks for a discussion of buoyancy. **SKILLS FOCUS:** Predicting, Evaluating and Revising **TIME REQUIRED:** 45 minutes

When an object is placed in a fluid, the force of gravity causes part or all of the object to sink below the upper surface of the fluid. At the same time, the fluid exerts an upward push, or **buoyant force,** on the object. The part of the object below the surface displaces the fluid. The size of the buoyant force is equal to the weight of the fluid that the object displaces. Fluids exert a buoyant force on all objects, regardless of whether the objects sink or float.

Consider an object submerged in a fluid. If the object has the same density as the fluid, then the weight of the object will be equal to the weight of an equal volume of fluid. In that case, the buoyant force will be equal to the weight of the object. As a result, the object will remain at any depth where it is placed. If the object is less dense than the fluid, the buoyant force on the object will be greater than the weight of the object. In this case, the object will rise to the surface and float. If the object is more dense than the fluid, the buoyant force on the object will be less than the weight of the object, and the object will sink.

This principle explains why a grain of sand sinks in water, whereas a basketball that has a much greater weight can float. Sand is denser than water. Therefore, the weight of the sand grain is greater than the buoyant force it receives from the water. The buoyant force acting on the basketball is greater than the weight of the basketball. As a result, the basketball floats.

In this investigation, you will predict which objects will float in water. Then, you will perform experiments to test your predictions.

Problem

What happens to the ability of an object to float as its mass and volume change?

Pre-Lab Discussion

Read the entire investigation. Then, work with a partner to answer the following questions.

1. **Controlling Variables** Identify the manipulated, responding, and controlled variables in this investigation.

   a. Manipulated variables

   Mass (number of BBs), volume of the floating container (canister or bottle)

   _____

   b. Responding variables

   Level of water, level of the canister in the water

   _____

    c. Controlled variables

      Floating container (canister), fluid (water), diameter of container for fluid (beaker)

2. Predicting Predict how adding BBs to the canister will affect the following variables.

    a. The level of the canister in the water

      The canister will float at a lower level (more deeply) in the water.

    b. The level of the water in the beaker

      The level of the water will rise.

3. Predicting The bottle you will use in Steps 10 through 13 is larger than the canister. Which container do you predict will float at a lower level (more deeply) in the water? Explain your answer.

    The canister will float at a lower level (more deeply) than the bottle because the masses of the two

    containers will be equal, but the bottle has a greater volume. Therefore, the average density of the

    bottle is less dense and will float higher in the water.

4. Applying Concepts What factors determine whether an object sinks or floats in water?

    The density of an object determines whether it sinks or floats. It will float if its density is less than

    that of water. It will sink if its density is greater than that of water. Students may also express this

    concept in terms of weight and buoyant force.

Materials *(per group)*

film canister	BBs Provide approximately 100 BBs per lab group in a
masking tape	paper towels nonglass container.
metric ruler	triple-beam balance
250-mL beaker	plastic bottle Use a bottle with a larger diameter than the film canister, but small enough to fit in the beaker.

The canister and plastic bottle must have straight sides; tapered containers will not work well in this investigation. A plastic medicine bottle or similar container can be used if a film canister is not available.

Safety ⬚ ⬚ ⬚

Put on safety goggles. Be careful to avoid breakage when working with glassware. Wipe up any spilled water immediately to avoid slips and falls. Note all safety alert symbols next to the steps in the Procedure and review the meaning of each symbol by referring to the Safety Symbols on page xiii.

Procedure

Markings at 0.5 cm intervals

Canisier

Tape

Figure 1

⬚ 1. Attach a strip of masking tape to the side
⬚   of the film canister, extending from the
⬚   bottom to the top of the canister. Starting
     from the bottom of the canister, use the
     metric ruler and a pencil to accurately
     mark 0.5-cm intervals on the side of the
     canister, as shown in Figure 1.

2. Repeat Step 1, using the plastic bottle.

3. Fill the beaker approximately three-
   fourths full with water. Place 20 BBs
   in the canister. Place the canister in the
   beaker with its open end pointed upward.
   Add or remove BBs from the canister, one
   at a time, until approximately half of the canister floats below
   the surface of the water. **Note:** *To remove BBs, take the canister
   out of the beaker. To add BBs, leave the canister in the beaker while
   carefully placing the BBs in the canister.* Count the BBs as you add
   or remove them from the canister. In the first row of Data Table
   1, record the number of BBs in the canister. Remember to
   include the first 20 BBs that you added.

4. Use the metric ruler to measure the level of the water in the beaker
   from the tabletop to the surface of the water. Record this measurement
   in Data Table 1. Also determine the level of the canister in the water
   and record this measurement in Data Table 1.

5. Predict how the level of the canister in the water and the level
   of the water in the beaker will change if you remove 10 BBs
   from the canister. Record your prediction as Prediction 1 in
   Data Table 1.

6. Now test your prediction. Take the canister out of the beaker, first
   tapping it gently against the inside of the beaker to minimize any
   water loss from the beaker. Remove 10 BBs from the canister and
   carefully place the canister back in the beaker. In Data Table 1,
   record the number of BBs in the canister, the level of the canister
   in the water, and the level of the water in the beaker.

7. Replace the 10 BBs that you removed from the canister. Predict
   how the level of the canister and the level of the water will
   change if you add 10 more BBs to the canister. Record your
   prediction as Prediction 2 in Data Table 1.

8. Test your prediction by carefully adding 10 BBs to the canister. In Data Table 1, record the number of BBs in the canister, the level of the canister in the water, and the level of the water in the beaker.

9. Carefully remove the canister of BBs from the beaker, while minimizing any water loss from the beaker. Use paper towels to dry the outside of the canister. Use the triple-beam balance to determine the mass of the canister and BBs. Record this mass in Data Table 2. Without changing the positions of the riders on the balance, remove the canister and set it aside.

10. Place the plastic bottle on the balance. Add BBs to the bottle until its mass is equal to the mass of the canister and the BBs it contains. Record this mass in Data Table 2.

11. Predict which container will float more deeply in the water by placing a check mark in the appropriate row below Prediction 3 in Data Table 2. Also predict which container will cause the greater rise of the water level in the beaker by placing a check mark in the appropriate row below Prediction 4 in Data Table 2.

12. Test your predictions by placing the canister into the beaker. In Data Table 2, record the number of BBs in the canister, the level of the canister, and the level of the water. Carefully remove the canister.

13. Repeat Step 12, using the plastic bottle.

Observations   Sample data are shown.

DATA TABLE 1

Action	Number of BBs	Level of Canister in Water (cm)	Level of Water in Beaker (cm)
Float canister halfway below surface of water	50	3.0	6.7
Remove 10 BBs	40	2.5	6.6
Add 10 BBs	60	3.5	6.8

Prediction 1 _____

Prediction 2 _____

DATA TABLE 2

Container	Mass of Container and BBs (g)	Prediction 3 (Identify the container that will float more deeply in water.)	Level of Container in Water (cm)	Prediction 4 (Identify which container will cause the greater rise of the water level in the beaker.)	Level of Water in Beaker (cm)
Canister			3.0		6.7
Bottle			1.5		6.7

Analysis and Conclusions

1. **Analyzing Data** How did the number of BBs in the canister affect the level at which the canister floated in the water?

   The greater the number of BBs (and mass), the deeper the canister floated in water.

2. **Evaluating and Revising** Did your observations support your predictions of how the number of BBs in the canister would affect the level of the canister in the water and the level of the water in the beaker? Explain your answer.

   The observations supported the predictions that adding BBs to the canister would cause the

   canister to float more deeply in the water and cause the water level to rise. This result

   occurred because adding BBs to the canister increased its weight and effective density.

   As a result, the canister sank farther into the water.

3. **Comparing and Contrasting** Compare the volume of the canister containing the BBs to the volume of water that the canister displaced. Which was greater?

   The total volume of the canister was greater than the volume of water it displaced.

4. **Predicting** Assume that the canister is made of a material that is less dense than water. What would happen if you filled the canister with water and then placed it in the beaker of water? Explain your answer.

   The canister would float because it is less dense than the water.

5. **Drawing Conclusions** Explain why the canister and the bottle floated at different levels in the water.

The bottle has a larger cross-sectional area than the canister. Therefore, when displaced in

water, the bottle does not have to sink as deeply in order to displace the volume of water needed

to generate the buoyant force required to keep the bottle afloat.

_____

6. **Comparing and Contrasting** Compare the water level when the canister was floating in the beaker to the water level when the plastic bottle was floating in the beaker in Steps 12 and 13. Explain your result.

The water level was approximately the same in each case. The mass of the canister with its BBs

was equal to the mass of the plastic bottle with its BBs. Because both displaced the same volume

of water when floating, the water level in the beaker was also the same.

_____

7. **Applying Concepts** Suppose a boat is in a swimming pool. You are sitting in the boat and holding a rock. You drop the rock into the pool. The rock sinks to the bottom without splashing any water out of the pool. Using what you learned in this investigation, explain whether the water level in the pool will be higher, lower, or the same after you drop the rock into the pool.

The water level will be lower. When the rock is in the boat, it displaces a volume of water that

has a weight equal to its own weight. Because the rock is denser than water, it cannot displace

sufficient water on its own to float. When the rock is sitting at the bottom of the pool, it displaces

only its own volume. Therefore, the rock displaces more water when it is in the boat than when it is

in the water. As a result, the pool's water level is lower when the rock is in the water.

_____

Go Further

Use your knowledge of forces and buoyancy to predict the result of the experiment described below. Then, with your teacher's approval and supervision, carry out the experiment to test your prediction.

A beaker of water is sitting on a balance. The balance indicates the mass of the beaker of water. Taking great care not to touch the sides of the beaker, you dip your finger into the water. Does the reading on the balance change? If it does, will it increase or decrease?

Supervise students closely as they perform the experiment. Students should wear safety goggles and lab aprons, and use caution to avoid breaking the glass beaker. The reading on the scale will increase. When a finger is inserted into the water, it experiences an upward buoyant force equal to the weight of the water it displaces. Newton's third law of motion requires that the finger exert a downward reaction force on the water. The water and the beaker transmit this force to the balance. The reading on the balance reflects this downward force as though it were additional weight.

Chapter 13   Forces in Fluids

Investigating Siphons

Refer students to page 390–397 in their textbooks for a discussion of pressure in fluids. **SKILLS FOCUS:** Observing, Predicting, Drawing Conclusions **TIME REQUIRED:** 45 minutes

Background Information

A siphon is a tube filled with liquid that connects two containers. Liquid can flow through the siphon from one container to the other. The direction of this flow depends on forces that act on the liquid. One of these forces is gravity. If one of the containers is higher than the other, the force of gravity will cause liquid to flow down through the siphon from the higher container into the lower one.

Fluid pressure due to fluid depth also affects the flow through a siphon. **Pressure** is the amount of force per unit area. All liquids exert pressure against their containers. The deeper a liquid is, the greater the pressure it can exert. The pressure exerted on the bottom of a beaker is due to the weight of the fluid above it. Therefore, fluid pressure due to fluid depth is also related to the force of gravity. If the two containers have different levels of liquid, the liquid will flow through the siphon from the container with greater fluid depth (and pressure) to the container with less fluid depth (and pressure).

In this investigation, you will predict how water will flow through a siphon. Then, you will perform an experiment to test your prediction.

Problem

How does water flow through a siphon?

Pre-Lab Discussion

Read the entire investigation. Then, work with a partner to answer the following questions.

1. **Formulating Hypotheses** State a hypothesis about how water flows through a siphon.

   Water flows through a siphon from a container at a higher elevation to a container at a

   lower elevation. Water also flows from a container at higher pressure to one at lower pressure.

   As a result, if two containers are on the same level surface, water will flow from the container

   where the water is deeper and exerts greater pressure to the one where the water is shallower.

2. **Predicting** Based on your hypothesis, predict how the water will flow through a siphon that connects each of the following pairs of identical beakers.

   a. Both beakers contain equal volumes of water, but one beaker is at a higher elevation than the other.

   Water will flow from the higher beaker to the lower one.

   _____

b. Both beakers are at the same height, but one beaker contains more water than the other.

Water will flow from the beaker that contains more water to the one that contains less.

_____

c. Both beakers are at the same height and contain equal volumes of water.

Water will not flow between the beakers.

_____

3. **Controlling Variables** Identify the manipulated, responding, and controlled variables in this investigation.

a. Manipulated variables

Elevation of each beaker, volume of water in each beaker

_____

b. Responding variables

Movement of water through the siphon connecting the beakers

_____

c. Controlled variables

Size of beakers, dimensions of tubing

_____

Materials (per group)

2 600-mL beakers Use graduated beakers. utility clamp
ring stand 40 cm flexible tubing Use tubing with an inside
iron ring clock or watch diameter of 0.5 to 1.0 cm.
wire gauze

Safety 🧪🥼🧤

Put on safety goggles and a lab apron. Be careful to avoid breakage when working with glassware. Wipe up any spilled water immediately to avoid slips and falls. Note all safety alert symbols next to the steps in the Procedure and review the meaning of each symbol by referring to the Safety Symbols on page xiii.

Procedure

🧤 1. Add approximately 275 mL of water to each beaker.

2. Position an iron ring and a wire gauze low on the ring stand, as shown in Figure 1. Use a utility clamp to secure one of the beakers on the wire gauze, as shown. Place the second beaker next to the ring stand.

3. In the data table, record your prediction of what will happen to the water in the beakers when a siphon is used to connect the beakers. Predict whether you expect water to flow through the siphon. If you predict that water will flow through the siphon, which direction do you expect the water to flow?

Utility clamp

Ring stand

600-mL beaker

Iron ring

Wire gauze

Figure 1

4. Place the flexible tubing in the sink. Hold one end of the tubing under the faucet and allow water to run through the tubing. When water begins to flow out the lower end of the tubing, use your finger to block the lower end. When the entire length of the tubing has filled with water, use another finger to cover the upper end. Be sure that no air remains in the tubing. Do not allow the water to flow out of the tubing.

5. Keeping the ends of the tubing covered, place one end of the tubing in the bottom of each beaker. Remove your finger from the ends of the tube only after both ends of the tube are submerged. Observe the beakers for 1 minute. Note any changes in the water level in the beakers. Record your observations in the data table.

6. Remove the elevated beaker from the ring stand. Add or remove water from each beaker so that one beaker contains 400 mL of water and the other contains 100 mL of water. Place both beakers on the tabletop. Repeat Steps 3 through 5.

7. Add or remove water from each beaker so that each beaker contains 300 mL of water. Place both beakers on the tabletop. Repeat Steps 3 through 5.

Name _____ Class _____ Date _____

Observations Sample data are shown.

DATA TABLE

Positions of Beakers	Volume of Water in Beakers (mL)	Predictions	Observations
One beaker at a higher elevation than the other	275 mL in each		Water flowed from the elevated beaker to the lower beaker.
Both beakers on table	400 mL and 100 mL in the other		Water flowed from the beaker with 400 mL water to the beaker with 100 mL water.
Both beakers on table	300 mL in each		No movement of water

Analysis and Conclusions

1. **Evaluating** Did your observations support your hypothesis?

   The observations should support the hypothesis that water flows through a siphon from an

   elevated container to a lower one and from a container at higher pressure to one at lower

   pressure.

2. **Inferring** What force was responsible for the result you observed in Step 5?

   Gravity was responsible for the result observed in Step 5.

3. **Inferring** What was responsible for the result you observed in Step 6?

   The difference in pressure between the two beakers was responsible for the result observed

   in Step 6.

4. **Predicting** Explain what you would have to do in order to move the water from the lower beaker to the upper beaker in the setup you used in Step 5.

   Only gravity and pressure cause water to flow through a siphon. As a result, it would be necessary

   to increase the pressure in the lower beaker or reduce the pressure in the upper beaker. This could

   be done by connecting one of the beakers to an air pump.

5. **Predicting** Suppose two beakers sitting side by side are filled to the same depth, but one beaker is wider than the other. What would you expect to observe when the beakers are connected by a siphon? Explain your answer.

   The water will not flow between the beakers. Water flows through a siphon when the

   two containers are filled to different depths, not when they contain different volumes.

Go Further

How do you think the diameter of the tubing you used in this investigation affected the rate at which water flowed between the beakers? Design an experiment to answer this question. Write a detailed plan for your experiment. Your plan should state the hypothesis to be tested, identify the manipulated, responding, and controlled variables, and describe the procedures and safety precautions you will use. You will need to find a way to measure the rate at which water flows through a siphon. Show your plan to your teacher. When your teacher approves your plan, carry out your experiment, and report your results and conclusions.

Check student plans for safety, practicality, and sound experimental design. Well-designed experimental plans should include detailed procedures that will test a clearly stated hypothesis. An example of an acceptable hypothesis is that increasing the diameter of the tubing will increase the rate at which water flows between the containers. Students may wish to use a stopwatch to record the time it takes a certain volume of water to move from one container to another. Replacing the beakers with graduated cylinders will allow students to measure the volumes more accurately.

Chapter 14   Work, Power, and Machines   Investigation 14A

Comparing the Mechanical Advantage of Levers

Refer students to pages 417–429 in their textbooks for a discussion of actual mechanical advantage and levers.

SKILLS FOCUS: Measuring, Calculating, Designing Experiments **CLASS TIME:** 45 minutes

Background Information

A **lever** consists of a rigid bar that is free to rotate around a fixed point. The fixed point on the bar rotates around the **fulcrum.** Like all machines, a lever changes the size of a force that is applied to it, the direction of a force applied to it, or both. The force exerted on a lever is the **input force.** The distance between the fulcrum and the point where the input force acts is the **input arm.** The force that the lever exerts on the load is the **output force.** The distance between the fulcrum and the output force is the **output arm.** Note that the output force may be larger or smaller than the input force, depending on the type of lever.

There are three types of levers, called first-class, second-class, and third-class levers. The three classes differ in the relative positions of the fulcrum and the input and output forces. A first-class lever, such as a seesaw, has its fulcrum between the input and output forces. In a second-class lever, such as a wheelbarrow, the output force, is between the input force and the fulcrum. A third-class lever, such as a broom, has its input force between the fulcrum and the output force.

The **mechanical advantage** of any machine is the number of times that the machine multiplies the input force. The **actual mechanical advantage** (AMA) of a lever is equal to the output force divided by the input force.

$$AMA = \frac{\text{Output force}}{\text{Input force}}$$

In this investigation, you will determine and compare the actual mechanical advantage of first-class and second-class levers. Then, you will design and carry out an investigation to determine the mechanical advantage of a third-class lever.

Problem

How do the mechanical advantages of first-class, second-class, and third-class levers differ?

Pre-Lab Discussion

Read the entire investigation. Then, work with a partner to answer the following questions.

1. **Designing Experiments** Why are you told in Step 1 to record the weight of the 500-g mass as the output force for every first-class and second-class lever that you will use in this investigation?

   The 500-g mass is the load that each lever will lift. Therefore, the output force of each lever is the

   force needed to lift the mass. This force is equal in size to the weight of the mass.

2. **Calculating** How will you calculate the actual mechanical advantage (AMA) of the levers in this investigation?

The actual mechanical advantage of each lever will be calculated by dividing the output force by

the input force.

3. **Predicting** What factors do you predict will affect the actual mechanical advantage of the levers in this investigation?

The relative lengths of the input and output arms and the efficiency of the levers will determine the

actual mechanical advantage of the levers.

4. **Controlling Variables** Identify the manipulated, responding, and controlled variables in this investigation.

a. Manipulated variables

Class of lever (positions of forces and fulcrum), lengths of lever arms

b. Responding variables

Input force, mechanical advantage

c. Controlled variable

Load (output force)

5. **Predicting** Which class of levers do you expect to have the greatest actual mechanical advantage? Explain your answer.

The greatest actual mechanical advantages will be found in second-class levers because the

input arms of these levers are always longer than their output arms. As a result, the actual mechanical

advantage of any second-class lever is greater than 1. A first-class lever can have an actual

mechanical advantage that is greater or less than 1 because its arms can be of any length. All

third-class levers have an actual mechanical advantage that is less than 1 because their output

arms are always longer than their input arms.

6. **Formulating Hypotheses** State a hypothesis that you could test in Part C of this investigation.

An example of an acceptable hypothesis is that the actual mechanical advantage of all

third-class levers is less than 1.

Materials (per group)

500-g mass with hook

spring scale Use spring scales with a capacity of 10–20 N.

wedge-shaped block of wood, about 10 cm high

meter stick

string

scissors

loop of wire Prepare short loops from 10 to 15-cm lengths of wire.

Safety 🔖

Put on safety goggles. To prevent injury from falling objects, do not wear sandals or open-toed shoes. Wear only closed-toed shoes in the laboratory. Note all safety alert symbols next to the steps in the Procedure and review the meaning of each symbol by referring to the Safety Symbols on page xiii.

Procedure

Part A: Determining the AMA of First-Class Levers

🔖 1. Work with a classmate. Hang the 500-g mass from the spring scale. Read the weight of the mass on the spring scale. Record this weight as the output force in each row of Data Table 1.

2. To make a first-class lever, place the wedge-shaped block of wood on the table to serve as a fulcrum. Place the 50-cm mark of the meter stick on the fulcrum so that the 100-cm end of the meter stick extends beyond the edge of the table, as shown in Figure 1. Use string to tie the 500-g mass to the meter stick at the 10-cm mark. This mass serves as the load that the lever will lift.

Block of wood   Meter stick

Wire loop

500-g mass

Spring scale

Figure 1

3. Place the wire loop around the meter stick at the 90-cm mark, 40 cm away from the fulcrum. Hang the spring scale from the wire loop.

4. In the first row of Data Table 1, record the distance from the fulcrum to the spring scale as the input arm. Record the distance from the fulcrum to the mass as the output arm.

5. Pull the spring scale down slowly and steadily to lift the mass. When the meter stick is horizontal, read the input force on the spring scale. Record this value in Data Table 1.

6. Leaving the mass and the spring scale at the same positions, move the fulcrum to the 30-cm mark. Record the lengths of the new input and output arms in Data Table 1.

7. Repeat Step 5.

8. Repeat Steps 6 and 7, but this time, move the fulcrum to the 20-cm mark.

9. Calculate the mechanical advantage of the first-class lever in all the positions you tested. Record these values in Data Table 1.

Part B: Determining the AMA of Second-Class Levers

10. To make a second-class lever, place the 10-cm mark of the meter stick on the fulcrum as shown in Figure 2. Tie the mass to the meter stick at the 50-cm mark.

Figure 2

11. Place the wire loop around the meter stick at the 90-cm mark, 80 cm away from the fulcrum. Attach the spring scale to the wire loop.

12. In Data Table 1, record the distance from the fulcrum to the spring scale as the input arm. Record the distance from the fulcrum to the mass as the output arm.

13. Have your partner hold the meter stick down on the fulcrum so that the meter stick does not slide or rise up off of the fulcrum. Pull the spring scale up slowly and steadily to lift the mass. When the meter stick is horizontal, read the input force on the spring scale. Record this value in Data Table 1.

14. Leaving the fulcrum and the spring scale at the same positions, move the mass to the 30-cm mark. Record the lengths of the new input and output arms in Data Table 1.

15. Repeat Step 13.

16. Repeat Steps 14 and 15, but this time, move the mass to the 20-cm mark.

17. Calculate the actual mechanical advantage of the second-class lever in all the positions you tested. Record these values in Data Table 1.

Part C: Design Your Own Investigation

⚠**18.** Design an investigation to determine the actual mechanical advantage of a third-class lever. Record the hypothesis that you will test.

Hypothesis

An example of an acceptable hypothesis is that the actual mechanical advantage of a third-class

lever is less than 1, but increases as the input arm is made longer.

19. In the lines below, write a detailed plan of how you will carry out your investigation. You may choose to base your investigation on the method of determining the actual mechanical advantage of a lever that you used in Parts A and B. Construct Data Table 2 in which to record your observations in the space provided on page 150.

1. To make a third-class lever, place the mass on the table and tie the mass to the meter stick at the 10-cm mark.

2. Place the wire loop around the meter stick at the 50-cm mark. Attach the spring scale to the wire loop.

3. Place the 90-cm mark of the meter stick on the fulcrum, 40 cm away from the spring scale and 80 cm away from the mass.

4. In Data Table 2, record the distance from the fulcrum to the spring scale as the input arm. Record the distance from the fulcrum to the mass as the output arm.

5. Have your partner hold the meter stick down on the fulcrum so that the meter stick does not slide or rise up off of the fulcrum. Pull the spring scale up slowly and steadily to lift the mass. Read the input force on the spring scale. Record this value in Data Table 2.

6. Leaving the fulcrum and the mass at the same positions, move the spring scale to the 30-cm mark. Record the lengths of the new input and output arms in Data Table 2.

7. Repeat Step 5.

8. Repeat Steps 6 and 7, but this time, move the spring scale to the 20-cm mark.

9. Calculate the actual mechanical advantage of the third-class lever in all the positions you tested. Record these values in Data Table 2.

20. What are the manipulated, responding, and controlled variables in your investigation?

a. Manipulated variable

The lengths of one or both lever arms

b. Responding variable

The input force

c. Controlled variables

The output force, the length of one lever arm

21. What safety precautions will you need to take in your investigation?

Students need to wear safety goggles and to take care when handling the 500-g mass.

Name _____ Class _____ Date _____

22. List the possible results of your investigation. State whether each possible result would support or contradict your hypothesis.

An example of an acceptable response is that the actual mechanical advantage of a third-class lever is less than 1, and the actual mechanical advantage may increase or decrease as the input arm is made longer. If the actual mechanical advantage is always less than 1, but increases as the input arm is made longer, then the sample hypothesis cited in Step 18 will be supported. Any other result would contradict this hypothesis.

23. Show your plan to your teacher. When your teacher approves your plan, carry out your investigation and record your observations in your data table.

Observations Sample data are shown.

DATA TABLE 1: Parts A and B

Fulcrum Position (cm)	Output Arm (cm)	Input Arm (cm)	Output Force (N)	Input Force (N)	Actual Mechanical Advantage
First-Class Lever					
50	40	40	5	5	1
30	20	60	5	2	2.5
20	10	70	5	1	5
Second-Class Lever					
10	40	80	5	3	1.7
10	20	80	5	2	2.5
10	10	80	5	1	5

DATA TABLE 2: Part C
If you need more space, attach additional sheets of paper.

Fulcrum Position (cm)	Output Arm (cm)	Input Arm (cm)	Output Force (N)	Input Force (N)	Actual Mechanical Advantage
Third-Class Lever					
90	80	40	5	10	0.5
90	80	60	5	7	0.7
90	80	70	5	6	0.8

Analysis and Conclusions

1. **Analyzing Data** How did moving the fulcrum of the first-class lever closer to the output force affect the actual mechanical advantage?

   The actual mechanical advantage became greater.

   _____

2. **Comparing and Contrasting** Did changing the lengths of the input and output arms affect the actual mechanical advantage of all three classes of levers in the same way? Explain your answer.

   Yes, increasing the input arm or decreasing the output arm increases the actual mechanical

   advantage of any lever.

3. **Evaluating and Revising** In Part C of this investigation, did your data support or contradict your hypothesis? Explain your answer.

   Answers will depend on student data, but should be justified by reference to the hypothesis

   and the data. The actual mechanical advantage of a third-class lever is less than 1, but increases as

   the input arm is made longer.

4. **Drawing Conclusions** Based on the mechanical advantages that you calculated for each class of lever, how do third-class levers differ from the other two types? How could a third-class lever be useful?

   The actual mechanical advantage of a third-class lever is always less than 1. As a result, third-class

   levers produce an output force that is less than the input force. Third-class levers are useful for

   increasing the distance that a load moves because their output forces always move farther than

   their input forces.

5. **Drawing Conclusions** What could you do to any lever to increase its actual mechanical advantage?

   Make the input arm as long as possible and the output arm as short as possible.

   _____

Go Further

Suppose you need to use a nutcracker to crack an especially tough nut. You have the choice of two similar nutcrackers that each have two handles connected at one end. One nutcracker has longer handles than the other one. Which class of lever are the nutcrackers? How can you tell? Which nutcracker would you use? Where would you place the nut relative to the arms? Explain your answer in terms of actual mechanical advantage.

The nutcrackers are second-class levers because the load (nut) is between the input force (user's hand) and the fulcrum (hinge of the nutcracker). The longer nutcracker should be used, with the nut as close as possible to the fulcrum. This increases actual mechanical advantage by increasing the input arm and decreasing the output arm.

Comparing Pulleys

Refer students to pages 417–426, 432, and 433 in their textbooks for a discussion of actual mechanical advantage and simple machines. **SKILLS FOCUS:** Measuring, Calculating **TIME REQUIRED:** 45 minutes

Background Information

One of the most common uses of machines is to increase a force. The force that you exert on a machine is the **input force.** The force that the machine exerts is the **output force.** You can compare the ability of machines to increase input force by determining their actual mechanical advantages. Actual mechanical advantage (AMA) is calculated by dividing the output force by the input force.

$$\text{AMA} = \frac{\text{Output force}}{\text{Input force}}$$

Pulleys are simple machines that are used to lift objects. A pulley consists of a rope wrapped around a wheel. The simplest kind of pulley is a grooved wheel around which a rope is pulled. Pulleys can be used to change the direction of an input force. For example, a pulley attached, or fixed, to the top of a flagpole allows you to raise the flag up by pulling down.

A combination of fixed and movable pulleys is called a pulley system, or block-and-tackle. A pulley system is used to multiply input force so that heavy objects can be lifted. Pulley systems are commonly seen around construction sites.

In this investigation, you will determine the actual mechanical advantage of several different pulleys and pulley systems.

Problem

How do pulleys help to raise objects?

Pre-Lab Discussion

Read the entire investigation. Then, work with a partner to answer the following questions.

1. Observing What is the output force in this investigation?

The output force is the force needed to lift the 1-kg mass.

2. Inferring Why will you record the same output force for all the pulleys in this investigation?

All the pulleys will be used to lift the same mass, so the weight of the 1-kg mass is equal to

the output force of all the pulleys.

3. Calculating How will you calculate the actual mechanical advantage of the pulleys in this investigation?

The actual mechanical advantage will be calculated by dividing the output force by the input force.

4. Predicting How do you expect the actual mechanical advantage to change as more pulleys are added to the pulley system?

The actual mechanical advantage will increase as more pulleys are added to the system.

Materials *(per group)*

2 single pulleys   iron ring

2 double pulleys   10-N spring scale

1-m nylon fishing line   1-kg mass

ring stand

Safety 🖐

Put on safety goggles. Do not wear open-toed shoes or sandals in the laboratory. Note all safety alert symbols next to the steps in the Procedure and review the meaning of each symbol by referring to the Safety Symbols on page xiii.

Procedure

Figure 1

🖐 **1** Find the weight of the 1-kg mass by hanging it from the spring scale. Record this weight in the data table as the output force for all of the pulley arrangements.

2. Set up a single fixed pulley, as shown in Figure 1. **CAUTION:** *Make sure that the ring is over the base of the ring stand to reduce the chance that the equipment will tip over.* Pull down on the spring scale to lift the mass. As you do this, observe the reading on the spring scale. Record this value in the data table as the input force.

3. Set up a single movable pulley, as shown in Figure 2. Lift the mass by pulling up on the spring scale. As you do this, observe the reading on the spring scale. Record this value in the data table as the input force.

4. Set up the pulley systems, as shown in Figure 3. For each pulley system, observe the reading on the spring scale as you pull it to lift the mass. Record the value in the data table as the input force for the pulley system.

Figure 2

Name _____ Class _____ Date _____

Figure 3

Single Fixed Pulley and   Double Fixed Pulley and   Double Fixed Pulley and
Single Movable Pulley   Single Movable Pulley   Double Movable Pulley

5. Calculate the actual mechanical advantage for each pulley
system. To do this, divide the output force by the input force.
Record the actual mechanical advantage of each pulley system
in the data table.

Observations Sample data are shown. The weight of a 1-kg mass is approximately 10 N.

DATA TABLE

Pulleys	Output Force (newtons)	Input Force (newtons)	Actual Mechanical Advantage
Single fixed	10	10	1
Single movable	10	5	2
Single fixed and single movable	10	5	2
Double fixed and single movable	10	3.3	3
Double fixed and double movable	10	2.5	4

Analysis and Conclusions

1. **Analyzing Data** As you added pulleys to the system, what happened to the amount of effort force needed to raise the mass?

   Less effort force was needed as more pulleys were added.

2. **Drawing Conclusions** How did the number of pulleys in the pulley system affect the actual mechanical advantage of the system? Did this result agree with your prediction?

   The sample data supported the prediction that adding pulleys to the pulley system will

   increase the actual mechanical advantage.

3. **Analyzing Data** What type of pulley produced an output force equal in size to the input force?

   A single fixed pulley

4. **Inferring** What is the practical use of a pulley that does not change the size of the input force?

   The pulley changes the direction in which the force is applied.

5. **Inferring** When using any simple machine, you never "get something for nothing." Although a pulley system reduces the amount of input force needed to lift a mass, it does so at a cost. What must be increased as the amount of input force is decreased?

   The distance that the rope must be pulled to lift the mass is increased.

Go Further

In this investigation, you calculated actual mechanical advantage by dividing the output force by the input force. How could you use distances moved by the output and input forces to calculate actual mechanical advantage? Design an experiment to answer this question. Write a detailed plan for your experiment. Your plan should state the hypothesis to be tested, identify the manipulated, responding, and controlled variables, and describe the procedures and safety precautions that you will use. Show your plan to your teacher. When your teacher approves your plan, carry out your experiment and report your results and conclusions. Compare your data with the data you obtained in this investigation. Is one method better for determining mechanical advantage?

Check student plans for safety, practicality, and sound experimental design. Well-designed experimental plans should include detailed procedures that will test a clearly stated hypothesis. An example of an acceptable hypothesis is that measurements of force and distance will produce the same values for mechanical advantage.

In this investigation, students measured the input and output forces to determine the actual mechanical advantage of the pulley systems. Students can compare the distances moved by the input and output forces to determine the ideal mechanical advantage, which neglects the role of friction. If the input force and the output force move the same distance, the pulley system will have an ideal mechanical advantage of 1. If the input force moves a greater distance than the output force moves, the pulley system will have an ideal mechanical advantage greater than 1.

Determining the Effect of Mass on Kinetic Energy

Refer students to pages 446-458 in their textbooks for a discussion of the relationship between kinetic energy and mass and the conversion of potential energy into kinetic energy. **SKILLS FOCUS:** Measuring, Using Tables and Graphs **CLASS TIME:** 45 minutes

Background Information

You wouldn't be afraid to stop a marble rolling down an incline, but if a bowling ball was rolling down the same incline, you'd probably move out of the way. Both objects are rolling because of Earth's gravity, yet the bowling ball has much more energy. The **potential energy** (PE) of an object being pulled by gravity is the product of its mass (m), the acceleration due to gravity (g), and its height (h).

$$PE = mgh$$

Think of a marble and a bowling ball rolling down the same slope from the same starting point. In the absence of friction, they move at the same speed, but they have different amounts of energy. It is a lot easier to see this difference when the potential energy is converted to **kinetic energy** as the object begins to move. As the marble and the bowling ball accelerate to the same speed (v) under the force of gravity, the only difference in their kinetic energies (KE) is due to mass.

$$KE = \frac{1}{2}mv^2$$

In this investigation, you will accelerate four different masses to the same speed. Then, you will compare their kinetic energies.

Problem

How is the energy of a moving object influenced by its mass?

Pre-Lab Discussion

Read the entire investigation. Then, work with a partner to answer the following questions.

1. **Controlling Variables** Identify the manipulated, responding, and controlled variables in this investigation.

   a. Manipulated variable

   Mass of bottle _____

   _____

   b. Responding variable

   Distance that the cup moves _____

   _____

   c. Controlled variables

   Length and steepness of ramp, mass and starting point of cup, starting height of bottle ____

   _____

2. **Applying Concepts** How will the mass of the rolling bottle affect its speed when it collides with the plastic cup? (*Hint:* The bottle accelerates much like a falling body.)

Assuming there is only a small amount of friction acting on the rolling bottle, its speed

should not be significantly affected by a change in mass.

3. **Predicting** How do you expect the mass of the bottle to affect the distance the cup moves?

Increasing the mass of the bottle will increase the distance that the cup is moved.

4. **Applying Concepts** How is work related to the distance that the cup moves?

Work done on the cup moves it along the floor, against the opposing frictional force.

If more work is done on the cup, it moves a greater distance.

5. **Formulating Hypotheses** State a hypothesis about how the kinetic energy of the rolling bottle affects the amount of work done on the cup and the distance the cup moves.

Increasing the kinetic energy of the rolling bottle will increase the amount of work

done on the cup and the distance that it moves.

Materials *(per group)*

2 textbooks
flat board
masking tape
250-mL beaker
balance
plastic bottle that holds about 500–600 mL, with screw cap
plastic cup or margarine container
paper towel
meter stick

The floor should be smooth. The plastic cup should be lightweight and stable so that it will remain upright and slide along the floor. An empty plastic margarine container is suitable.

Safety

Put on safety goggles. Handle the board carefully to avoid splinters. Note all safety alert symbols next to the steps in the Procedure and review the meaning of each symbol by referring to the Safety Symbols on page xiii.

Procedure

Figure 1

1. Stack the two textbooks. Place one end of the board on the stack of books to form a ramp, as shown in Figure 1. Tape the ramp in place so it cannot move.

2. Attach a piece of masking tape across the ramp 15 cm from the bottom of the ramp. Use a pencil to mark the starting point on the masking tape. The bottle will be released from this point in each trial.

3. Using the beaker, carefully pour 100 mL of water into the bottle. Close the bottle tightly and dry the outside of the bottle with the paper towel. Wipe up any spills immediately.

4. Using the balance, measure the total mass of the bottle of water and record it in the data table.

5. Place a small piece of masking tape on the floor in line with the center of the ramp at a distance of 20 cm from the base of the ramp. This is the starting position for the cup in each trial.

6. Place the empty cup at its starting point, with its closest point to the ramp touching the piece of masking tape.

7. Hold the bottle of water lying across the ramp at the starting point, as shown in Figure 1. Allow it to roll down the ramp and collide with the cup. When both the bottle and the cup have stopped moving, use the meter stick to measure the distance the cup moved from its starting point. Record the result (to the nearest centimeter) in the appropriate place in the data table.

8. Repeat Steps 6 and 7 until you have made and recorded five measurements.

9. Using the beaker, add 100 mL of water to the bottle and close it tightly. Measure and record the new mass of the bottle.

10. Repeat Steps 6 and 7 to make five measurements using the new mass.

11. Again, add 100 mL of water to the bottle and close it tightly. Measure and record the new mass.

12. Repeat Steps 6 and 7 to make five additional measurements.

If students make an obvious error in a measurement or if the bottle slides on release, have them discard that measurement and continue until they have made five satisfactory measurements for each bottle mass.

13. Add 100 mL of water to the bottle as before (for a total of 400 mL) and close it tightly. Measure and record the new mass.

14. Repeat Steps 6 and 7 to make five additional measurements.

15. Calculate the average distance that the cup moved for each bottle mass by adding the five distances and dividing by 5. Record your results to the nearest centimeter in the data table.

16. On the grid provided, construct a graph of your data with the mass of the bottle on the horizontal axis and the average distance the cup moved on the vertical axis. Draw a straight line as close as possible to the data points.

Observations Sample data are shown.

DATA TABLE

	Volume of Water			
	100 mL	200 mL	300 mL	400 mL
	Mass of Bottle and Water (g)			
	130	230	330	430
Distance Moved by Cup (cm)				
Trial 1				
Trial 2				
Trial 3				
Trial 4				
Trial 5				
Total Distance (cm)				
Average Distance (cm)	23 cm	41 cm	58 cm	73 cm

Name _____ Class _____ Date _____

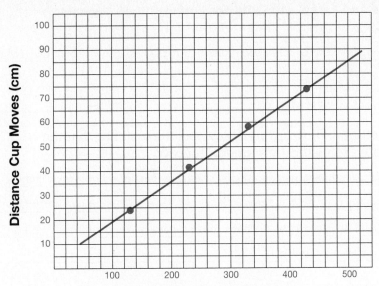

Mass of Bottle and Water (g)

Analysis and Conclusions

1. **Controlling Variables** What procedure was followed to make sure that the bottle would be moving at the same speed each time it collided with the cup? Does this method work? Explain your answer.

A piece of tape was placed on the ramp and marked to identify the starting point, so the bottle

will roll the same distance each time. Since the acceleration due to gravity is constant, objects

that roll the same distance reach the same speed. Assuming that the frictional force on the

rolling bottle is small, the bottle should have the same speed each time.

_____

_____

2. **Inferring** Why is it important that the bottle have approximately the same speed each time it collides with the cup in order to measure the effect of mass on energy?

In order to make any conclusion about the effect of mass on energy, it is necessary to control

speed so only one variable is changed at a time.

_____

_____

3. **Analyzing Data** As the mass of the bottle increased, what happened to the distance that the bottle moved the cup?

As the mass of the bottle increased, the distance it moved the cup increased proportionally.

_____

_____

4. **Relating Cause and Effect** Why did the cup eventually come to a complete stop?

The cup sliding along the floor experienced more friction than the rolling bottle did. The friction

stopped the motion of the cup and the bottle.

5. **Forming Operational Definitions** How was the distance that the cup moved related to the bottle's kinetic energy?

It takes energy or work to move the cup. Kinetic energy is transferred from the rolling

bottle to do work on the cup. Work = Force × Distance. Because the force of friction on the cup

is constant after the initial impact, the distance the cup moves is approximately proportional to

the energy it receives from the bottle.

6. **Evaluating and Revising** Did your experimental results agree with your hypothesis about how the kinetic energy of the bottle affects the amount of work done on the cup? Explain your answer.

The sample data supported the hypothesis that increasing the mass and kinetic energy of the

rolling bottle will increase the amount of work done on the cup. Because of experimental error,

the data points will not form a perfectly straight line.

7. **Applying Concepts** This investigation assumes that the rolling bottle experiences only a small frictional force. How accurate is this assumption? Could this assumption affect the results of the investigation? Explain your answer.

The assumption is fairly accurate because rolling objects experience less friction than sliding

objects do. However, the rolling bottle experiences some friction, which could introduce

experimental error and cause the graph to be a curve instead of a straight line.

Go Further

In this investigation, you examined the relationship between the mass of a rolling bottle and its kinetic energy. Design a procedure to measure how the height of a ramp affects the kinetic energy of a bottle rolling down the ramp. Have your teacher approve your procedure before you carry out the investigation. Propose an explanation for what you find.

Check student plans for safety, practicality, and sound experimental design. Well-designed experimental plans should include detailed procedures that will test a clearly stated hypothesis. An example of an acceptable hypothesis is that a higher ramp will give the bottle more kinetic energy. Students may propose an experimental plan similar to this investigation, except that the height of the ramp would be changed by adding or removing textbooks, while keeping the mass of the bottle constant.

Investigation 15B

Determining the Kinetic Energy of a Pendulum

Refer students to pages 447–458 in their textbooks for a discussion of kinetic and potential energy.
SKILLS FOCUS: Measuring
CLASS TIME: 45 minutes

Introduction

Energy of motion is called **kinetic energy** (KE). An object's kinetic energy depends on its mass (m) and speed (v).

$$KE = \tfrac{1}{2}mv^2$$

Energy of position is potential energy (PE), and it depends on mass, the acceleration due to gravity (g), and the height (h) of the object.

$$PE = mgh$$

The sum of an object's kinetic and potential energies is called its **mechanical energy.**

If you have seen a grandfather clock, you are probably familiar with a pendulum, which consists of a weight that swings back and forth on a rope or string. As the weight, or bob, moves through its arc, its mechanical energy is constantly converted between potential energy and kinetic energy. The kinetic energy increases as the potential energy decreases, and vice versa. If there were no friction, the mechanical energy of the pendulum would remain constant, and the pendulum would continue to swing back and forth, reaching the same height each time. Friction causes the height of a pendulum's swing to slowly decrease until the pendulum eventually stops.

In this investigation, you will perform an experiment to determine when a swinging pendulum has the largest amount of kinetic energy.

Problem

When does a swinging pendulum have the most kinetic energy?

Pre-Lab Discussion

Read the entire investigation. Then, work with a partner to answer the following questions.

1. **Controlling Variables** Identify the manipulated, responding, and controlled variables in this investigation.

   a. Manipulated variable

   Height of the bob at impact with the block

   b. Responding variable

   Distance the block moves along the board

   c. Controlled variables

   Size and mass of block, mass of bob, length of string, height from which bob is released,

   surface on which block moves

2. Predicting At what point in its arc do you expect the bob to have the most kinetic energy? At what point will it have the least kinetic energy? Explain your answers.

The bob will have the most KE at the bottom of its arc, where it moves fastest. The bob will have the

least KE at the top, where its motion stops for an instant.

3. Predicting At what point in its arc do you expect the bob to have the most potential energy? At what point will it have the least potential energy? Explain your answers.

The bob has the most PE at the top of its arc and the least at the bottom because an object's PE

is proportional to its height above a reference point.

4. Predicting Will the block be moved farthest when the bob has the greatest potential energy or the greatest kinetic energy? Explain your answer.

The block will move farthest when the bob has the greatest kinetic energy because at this point, the

bob is moving with maximum speed, so it transfers the most energy to the block.

5. Formulating Hypotheses State a hypothesis that this investigation can be used to test.

An example of an acceptable response is that the kinetic energy of a pendulum is greatest at

the bottom of its swing.

Materials (per group)

1-m string	4 identical bricks,	lightweight wooden block
fishing weight	approximately 8 cm in height	meter stick
flat, smooth board	masking tape	

The fishing weight should have enough mass to move the block at least a few centimeters in each trial.

Safety 🐛

Put on safety goggles. Be careful to stay out of the way of the swinging pendulum bob. Note all safety alert symbols next to the steps in the Procedure and review the meaning of each symbol by referring to the Safety Symbols on page xiii.

Procedure

🐛 **1.** Work with a classmate. Make a pendulum by tying the piece of string to the fishing weight. Hang the pendulum over the edge of a desk or table so that the weight, or bob, just clears a board placed on the floor beneath it. Tape the upper end of the string to the top of the desk or table, as shown in Figure 1.

2. Pull the bob slightly to the side and place a wooden block on the edge of the board, as shown, directly in the path of the pendulum's swing. Hold the bob in place next to the block while your lab partner measures the height of the bob above the floor. Record this value in the data table as the height of the bob at impact.

3. Pull the bob up and to the side until it reaches a height of 30 cm above the floor. Release the bob, allowing it to swing down and strike the wooden block. In the data table, measure and record the distance that the block moved along the board.

4. Replace the block on the edge of the board and repeat Step 3 two more times, releasing the bob from the same point as in the first trial.

5. Place a brick beneath each end of the board. Move the board and bricks sideways so that the bob, when released, will just clear the near end of the board.

Figure 1

6. Place the block on the end of the board as before. Place the bob next to the block and have your partner measure its height above the floor. In the data table, record this as the height of the bob at impact.

7. Raise the bob 30 cm off the floor, as you did in Step 3. Release the bob and again measure and record in the data table the distance that the block moved along the board after impact.

8. Replace the block and repeat Step 7 two more times, releasing the bob from the same point as before.

9. Repeat Steps 5 through 8, this time adding a second brick under each end of the board and moving the board still closer to the release point.

10. Calculate the average distance that the block moved from each position. To do this, add the three distances you recorded and divide the total by 3. In the data table, record the average distances.

Observations

Sample data are shown. Results will depend on the size and mass of the block, the mass of the bob, and the friction between the block and the board.

DATA TABLE

Number of Bricks Supporting the Board	Height of Bob at Impact (cm)	Distance Block Moved Along Board (cm)			
		Trial 1	Trial 2	Trial 3	Average
0	4				35
2	12				24
4	20				15

Analysis and Conclusions

1. **Analyzing Data** How did the height of the bob at impact affect the distance that the block moved along the board?

   The lower the height of the bob at impact, the farther the block moved along the board.

2. **Drawing Conclusions** Based on your data, at what point in its swing do you think a pendulum has the greatest kinetic energy? Explain your answer.

   A pendulum has the greatest kinetic energy at the bottom of its arc. The block moved farthest when the bob struck it closest to the bottom of its arc. This result indicated that the bob's kinetic energy was greatest near the bottom of its arc because at this point it transferred the most energy to the block.

3. **Evaluating and Revising** Did your data support or contradict your hypothesis? Explain your answer.

   Results should support the hypothesis that the kinetic energy of a pendulum is greatest at the bottom of its swing.

4. **Applying Concepts** Because of weathering, a rock on the edge of a cliff may become loose and fall. In terms of kinetic and potential energy, how is the rock at the edge of the cliff similar to a pendulum at the top of its arc?

   In both cases, PE is at a maximum and KE is initially zero.

Go Further

Draw five pictures, in sequence, showing a ball that has been thrown straight upward. Draw it going up (two pictures), at its highest point (one picture), and coming down (two pictures). In each picture, indicate which quantity, KE or PE, is greater. Also, indicate for each picture whether each kind of energy is in the process of increasing, decreasing, or staying the same.

Possible answer: In pictures 1 and 5, KE is high and PE is low. In pictures 2 and 4, KE is low and PE is high. In picture 3, KE is zero and PE is at a maximum. In pictures 1 and 2, KE is decreasing and PE is increasing. In pictures 4 and 5, KE is increasing and PE is decreasing.

Chapter 16   Thermal Energy and Heat   🔍 **Investigation 16A**

Thermal Conduction and Surface Area

Background Information

Refer students to pages 475–480 in their textbooks for a discussion of thermal energy, calorimetry, and conduction. **SKILLS FOCUS:** Predicting, Controlling Variables, Using Tables and Graphs **CLASS TIME:** 45 minutes

The quantity of energy transferred by heat from a body depends on a number of physical properties of the body and its surroundings. For a given substance, the rate at which thermal energy is transferred by conduction depends on temperature difference, cross-sectional area, and a thermal conductivity constant that is unique to the substance. By choosing one of these properties as a manipulated variable and making the other properties controlled variables, the effect of the manipulated variable on thermal conduction can be determined experimentally.

In this investigation, you will study the rates of cooling of three containers of water of equal volume but different surface area.

Problem

How does heat loss depend on surface area?

Pre-Lab Discussion

Read the entire investigation. Then, work with a partner to answer the following questions.

1. **Formulating Hypotheses** How would you expect the rate of thermal energy transfer from the water to depend on the water's surface area? What is your reason for this expectation?

   The water with the greatest surface area will lose thermal energy fastest and so will cool fastest.

   This happens because there are more particles of hot water in contact with cool air when the water's

   surface area is greater, and so more energy is transferred to the air over a given time.

   _____

2. **Controlling Variables** Identify the manipulated, responding, and controlled variables in this investigation.

   a. Manipulated variable

   The surface area of the water

   _____

   b. Responding variable

   The rate of temperature change

   _____

   c. Controlled variables

   The volume of the water, the initial temperature of the water, the room temperature, the

   material the containers are made of

3. **Designing Experiments** Why should plastic containers be used for holding the hot water during the experiment? Why should the containers and the graduated cylinder be warmed first with hot water?

The containers should all be made of a good insulating plastic so that nearly all of the thermal

energy lost from the water is through the water's surface. By warming the containers and

graduated cylinder, the temperature of the water used for the measurements is kept more

nearly constant, thus allowing the water in each container to be at nearly the same

starting temperature.

4. **Using Tables and Graphs** How can you tell which graph indicates the greatest rate of thermal energy transfer?

A steeper negative slope of the line indicates that the water's temperature declines more rapidly

with time. The greater the rate at which temperature drops, the greater is the rate of energy transfer.

Materials (per group)

3 cylindrical plastic containers with different surface diameters

metric ruler

hot tap water

3 Celsius thermometers

100-mL graduated cylinder

grease pencil

clock or watch

graph paper

3 colored pencils

1000-mL beaker (optional)

hot plate (optional)

The hot water used should be roughly between 50°C and 60°C. If hot tap water is not available or if the tap water is cooler than 50°C, provide hot water stored in thermos bottles or use hot plates to heat water.

Safety ⚗ 🔬 ⚠ 🧤 ⚠ 🔥

Put on safety goggles and a lab apron. Be careful to avoid breakage when working with glassware. Use extreme care when working with heated equipment or materials to avoid burns. Observe proper laboratory procedures when using electrical equipment. Note all safety alert symbols next to the steps in the Procedure and review the meaning of each symbol by referring to the Safety Symbols on page xiii.

Procedure

1. Label the plastic containers A, B, and C, using the grease pencil. Label the container with the smallest diameter A and the one with the largest diameter C.

2. Use the ruler to measure the diameter of each container and record this information in Data Table 1. Calculate the cross-sectional surface area, using the formula $Area = (Diameter/2)^2\pi$. Record these values in Data Table 1.

3. Run hot tap water until the water temperature reaches a constant value, about 50°C. Test the water temperature by holding a thermometer bulb in the stream of water. If you do not have a source of hot water, heat 600 mL of water in a beaker on a hot plate. Let the water reach a temperature of 50°C. **CAUTION:** *Use heat-resistant gloves. Be careful not to burn yourself or to break the thermometer or beaker. If using a hot plate, be careful to avoid burns and electrical shock.* Wipe up any spilled water immediately.

4. Warm the labeled containers by filling each of them with about 50 mL of hot water. Also fill the graduated cylinder to warm it. After a few minutes, pour out the water in the containers and the graduated cylinder. Refill the warm graduated cylinder with 100 mL of hot water. Quickly pour the water into container A. Repeat this process, pouring 100 mL of hot water into each of the other two containers.

5. Use the three thermometers to immediately measure the temperature of the water in the containers. Record the maximum temperature values in the second, third, and fourth columns of Data Table 2. The three beginning temperatures should be very similar. Look at a clock or watch and make a note of the time. Record the time in the "Time" column of Data Table 2. **CAUTION:** *Take care not to hit the thermometers against the sides of the containers.*

6. After 1 minute, record the time and the water temperature in each container. Continue to record the temperatures every minute for 15 minutes. Do not stir the water.

7. On a sheet of graph paper, make a graph of the information in Data Table 2. Plot the number of minutes from the start of the experiment on the horizontal axis (x-axis) and water temperature on the vertical axis (y-axis). Use a different-colored pencil for the data for each container. Draw curved lines to connect the data points for each container.

Use this graph to check student graphs.

Temperature changes for water in containers A, B, and C

Observations Sample data are shown.

DATA TABLE 1

	Diameter (cm)	Surface area (cm²)
Container A	10.0	78.5
Container B	15.0	177
Container C	20.0	314

DATA TABLE 2

Time (min)	Temperature of Water in Container A (°C)	Temperature of Water in Container B (°C)	Temperature of Water in Container C (°C)
0	Specific responses will depend on the actual sizes of the containers, the initial temperature of the water, and the temperature of the room. However, for all three samples, temperature values should decrease rapidly at first and then level off. The values for container C should decrease most rapidly.		
1			
2			
3			
4			
5			
6			
7			
8			
9			
10			
11			
12			
13			
14			
15			

Name _____ Class _____ Date _____

Analysis and Conclusions

1. Observing In general, what happened to the temperature of the water in the containers? Describe the three curves on your graph.

The temperature decreases for all three samples. The three curves have a similar shape.

The curves are not linear; the slope changes.

_____

_____

_____

2. Observing From which container of water was thermal energy transferred the fastest? On what evidence do you base your answer?

Thermal energy was transferred most quickly from container C. Container C cooled the fastest and

produced the steepest temperature-time curve.

_____

_____

_____

3. Applying Concepts What happened to the thermal energy that was in the water? Where did it go?

Most of the energy was transferred to the cooler air above the water.

_____

_____

_____

_____

4. Predicting What would have happened, in terms of thermal energy transfer, if the water temperature had originally been 10.0°C? Explain your reasoning.

Thermal energy would have been transferred from the warmer air to the cooler water, and

the temperature of the water would have increased. This would have happened because the

particles in the air would have a greater thermal energy and so would transfer that energy

to the lower-energy water molecules.

_____

_____

_____

_____

_____

_____

5. Drawing Conclusions Based on your findings in this investigation, make a general statement relating thermal energy transfer to surface area. How does this statement compare to the hypothesis you made before the investigation?

Assuming all other factors are equal, the larger the surface area is, the faster that thermal

conduction occurs, and the faster temperature decreases. But there seems to be a limit to this

effect because the cooling curves for containers B and C are very similar.

_____

_____

_____

_____

_____

6. Making Generalizations Two lakes have exactly the same amount of water in them. The surrounding environment is at the same temperature. You can presume the ground beneath each lake is a thermal insulator. Which lake would lose thermal energy at a faster rate—one that was large and shallow or one that was small and deep? Explain your answer.

The large, shallow lake would lose thermal energy at a faster rate because it has a greater

surface area.

_____

_____

_____

_____

_____

_____

Go Further

Plan an investigation to determine how containers made of different materials affect heat loss. Indicate how the containers would differ from the containers used in the current experiment. Show your plan to your teacher. When your teacher approves your plan, carry out your experiment and report your results.

Students may suggest adding lids to containers so that the thermal conductivity of the container, and not of air, is tested. A controlled variable in the new investigation would now be surface area, which should be identical for all containers being used. In this way, the change in temperature with time would depend on the thermal properties of the container rather than differences in surface area.

Chapter 16   Thermal Energy and Heat

Boiling Water in a Paper Cup

Background Information

When a paper cup of water is heated over a flame, the transfer of the thermal energy occurs in three ways—conduction, convection, and radiation. Conduction occurs when there is contact between two materials. In the case of a paper cup containing water, conduction occurs from the paper cup to the water, and through the water itself. Convection occurs when a volume of heated liquid or gas moves from one place to another. When heating water in a paper cup, convection takes place in the air between the burner flame and the bottom of the paper cup, and in the water inside the cup. Radiation conveys energy by electromagnetic waves from a body at a temperature greater than that of its surroundings. In this investigation, the flame transfers thermal energy by radiation.

Because water has a high specific heat, a small amount of water can absorb a fairly large amount of energy without undergoing a large temperature change. An even greater amount of energy must be absorbed by water for it to undergo the phase change from liquid to gas. The temperature at which water boils at sea level is 100°C, and it remains at this temperature until all of the liquid water has boiled. The paper cup would start to burn if the temperature reached 233°C.

In this investigation, you will attempt to boil water in a paper cup over the flame of a Bunsen burner.

Refer students to pages 479–481 in their textbooks for a discussion of the methods of thermal energy transfer. Pages 476 and 477 introduce the concept of specific heat, which will be useful for this activity.

SKILLS FOCUS: Observing, Predicting

CLASS TIME: 30 minutes

Problem

Will the water in a paper cup boil before the cup ignites?

Pre-Lab Discussion

Read the entire investigation. Then, work with a partner to answer the following questions.

1. **Predicting** Predict the result of boiling water through a paper cup. Explain why you believe your prediction is true.

   Many students will predict that the cup will burn. However, the water will boil away, while the paper

   cup will remain unburned. During the transfer of energy to the water, the thin paper cup remains

   at the same temperature as the water it contains. Therefore, the temperature of the paper cup

   remains well below the temperature at which paper ignites and burns.

   _____

   _____

   _____

   _____

   _____

   _____

   _____

2. **Applying Concepts** When water boils, its temperature remains constant. Why doesn't this contradict the law of conservation of energy?

During the phase change from liquid to gas, all of the energy added to the water breaks the

bonds between the water molecules, so the average kinetic energy of the molecules does

not increase. Because temperature is a measure of average kinetic energy, the temperature of

the water does not increase during the phase change. Energy is still conserved, but it is used

in a process that does not increase temperature.

3. **Designing Experiments** Why do you want to be sure that the paper cup does not have a wax coating?

Wax may melt at temperatures below 100°C. The melted wax could get smoky or ignite, which would

be hazardous.

4. **Making Generalizations** Use your prediction to explain why wet wood does not burn.

The energy added to the wet wood is used to vaporize water rather than to ignite the wood.

Only when the water has vaporized and the wood is dry can its temperature increase to the

necessary temperature for burning.

Materials (per group)

paper cup (without wax coating)	DO NOT use plastic or polystyrene cups.	thermometer clamp
ring stand		metal pie tin
support ring		Bunsen burner
wire gauze		matches
thermometer		

Safety 🌀 🔥 🧤 🔥 🔥

Put on safety goggles and a lab apron. Tie back loose hair and clothing when working with flames. Do not reach over an open flame. Be careful when using matches. Use extreme care when working with heated equipment or materials to avoid burns. Make sure that fire suppressant equipment is available. Note all safety alert symbols next to the steps in the Procedure and review the meaning of each symbol by referring to the Safety Symbols on page xiii.

Procedure

🌀 **1.** Set up the equipment as shown in Figure 1. There should be
🔥　　approximately 15 cm between the top of the Bunsen burner and
🧤　　the bottom of the wire gauze.

Name _____ Class _____ Date _____

2. Remove the paper cup. Fill three-fourths of the cup with water and carefully place it back on the center of the wire gauze. Use a thermometer clamp to make sure that the thermometer is suspended in the water so that it does not touch the bottom of the cup.

3. In the data table, record the initial temperature of the water.

🖊 4. Light the Bunsen burner and adjust the flame so that it does not touch the bottom of the wire gauze. **CAUTION:** *Be sure that the flame never touches the wire gauze directly.*

🔬🔥 5. Observe the experiment from the time you start heating the cup of water. What happens before the water boils? What happens to the cup as the water boils? Record your observations next to the data table. **CAUTION:** *Be careful when working with boiling water.*

6. In the data table, record the water temperature every 2 minutes.

7. When the water occupies about one-fourth of the cup's volume, turn off the burner and let the water and the cup cool. **CAUTION:** *Do not handle equipment until it has cooled.*

Figure 1

Observations

DATA TABLE Sample data are shown.

Time (minutes)	Water Temperature (°C)
0	21.3
2	28.0
4	36.5
6	49
8	62.5
10	77
12	89.5
14	98.9
16	98.9
18	95
20	78

Shortly after the burner is lit, small bubbles form in the water. After a few minutes, larger bubbles rise to the water's surface, and the water begins to boil. During this time, the cup remains intact.

_____

_____

_____

_____

_____

_____

Temperature increases with heating time. There may not be a consistent difference between readings as the liquid is heated. Temperature readings may decrease as the water level, reduced through evaporation, falls near and below the thermometer bulb.

Analysis and Conclusions

1. **Analyzing Data** What happened to the temperature of the water in the paper cup?

As a result of thermal energy transfer, the water temperature increased until the water began

to boil. Then, the temperature remained constant.

2. **Observing** What happened to the paper cup?

The paper cup appeared unchanged although its temperature probably increased to equal that of

the water inside it. Water boils at well below the ignition temperature of paper, so the paper cup

did not burn. Convection within the water and conduction between the cup and water kept the

temperature of the water and cup fairly uniform.

3. **Inferring** What determines the temperature of the paper cup?

The water kept the cup at nearly the same temperature as the water itself. The cup's

temperature would not rise above the boiling point of water until all of the water boils.

4. **Drawing Conclusions** Did your observations support or contradict your prediction? Explain your answer.

Students should describe what they observed. Assuming that students predicted that the cup would

be undamaged during the boiling of the water, then, if the cup remained intact while the water

boiled, the prediction was supported. Students should offer explanations for any observations

that contradict the prediction, such as if there is direct contact between the flame and the bottom

of the paper cup.

Go Further

For an additional investigation, determine whether the wire gauze between the flame and the cup prevented the cup from igniting.

As long as the flame does not come in contact with the bottom of the paper cup, then the experimental observations will be the same as before. If the flame was to touch the bottom of the cup, the rate of heating of the bottom of the cup would be fast enough to cause the cup to ignite.

Chapter 17   Mechanical Waves and Sound   Investigation 17A

Measuring the Speed of Sound

Refer students to pages 505 and 506 and 514 and 515 in their textbooks for a discussion of the speed and transmission of sound waves. **SKILLS FOCUS:** Predicting, Measuring, Controlling Variables, Calculating **CLASS TIME:** Part A, 20 minutes; Part B, 20 minutes

Background Information

An echo is reflected sound that can be heard separately from the original sound that produced it. The original sound is heard for about 0.10 second. You will hear an echo clearly if you are far enough away so that it takes more than 0.10 second for the sound to travel to the reflecting surface and back to you. To calculate the speed of sound, you must find your distance from the reflecting surface when you are just far enough away so that you do not hear an echo. It will take 0.10 second for the sound to travel this distance and back.

Sound travels at different speeds through different materials. Temperature also affects how rapidly sound is transmitted. Sound will travel faster in warm air than in cold air. However, the speed of sound in air does not depend upon the frequency of the sound. If it did, you would not be able to listen to music because the high-pitched sounds would arrive at your ear at a different time than the low-pitched sounds would.

The speed of light is much greater than the speed of sound. You will use this principle to calculate the speed of sound. You will perform an experiment similar to one performed by French scientists in 1738. They set up a cannon on a hill and timed the interval between the flash and the sound. Since they knew the distance and the time, they could calculate the speed of sound.

In Part A of this investigation, you will create echoes and measure the distance between you and a reflecting surface in order to determine the speed of sound. Then, in Part B, you will calculate the speed of sound in air by measuring the time between seeing an event and hearing the event.

Problem

What is the speed of sound in air?

Pre-Lab Discussion

Read the entire investigation. Then, work with a partner to answer the following questions.

1. **Comparing and Contrasting** Which method for measuring the speed of sound in air do you think will produce more accurate results—the method used in Part A or the method in Part B? Explain your answer.

   The method in Part B should be more accurate. The time that sound travels is measured with

   reasonable accuracy in Part B. In Part A, the time of travel is based on when the echo is no longer

   heard, which may vary a great deal with the hearing of each observer.

2. Controlling Variables Identify the manipulated and responding variables for both Parts A and B.

For Part A, the manipulated variable is the distance between the observer and the wall, and the

responding variable is the condition when the echo is no longer heard. In Part B, the manipulated

variable is the distance between the observer and the drum, and the responding variable is the time

interval between the time that the striking of the drum is seen and the time that the sound is heard.

_____

_____

3. Evaluating The speed of sound in dry air at a temperature of 20°C is 342 m/s. What sources of error might account for obtaining a different value than this?

The temperature of the air may not be 20°C when the investigation is made. Shorter or longer

response times on the part of the observer will introduce error in the time values and will affect the

calculation of the speed of sound. Wind can also increase or decrease the speed at which sound

travels. Limits in the precision of measuring instruments will also affect the result.

_____

_____

4. Controlling Variables How can the variables that introduce error in the results be controlled?

While the air temperature cannot be restricted to 20°C, its actual temperature can be kept uniform by

performing the experiment within a fairly short time. Because different observers may not hear the

echoes at different spots or may start the clock sooner or later after seeing the drum struck, the

results can be made more consistent with multiple trials, using different observers. By reversing the

positions of the drum and the observers, the effects of wind on the speed of sound would be

cancelled. Taking several measurements and averaging them will improve the precision of the

measurements.

_____

_____

5. Designing Experiments How might you vary the design of the investigation in Part B to test if the speed of sound in air is independent of frequency?

Two drums of very different sizes would produce sounds with very different frequencies. By repeating

the experiment with each drum, the effect of frequency on the speed of sound could be determined.

_____

_____

_____

Materials *(per group)*

2 wooden blocks, each about 20 cm long

metric tape measure or meter stick

drum

stopwatch (that can measure hundredths of a second)

measuring rope, marked off in meters, or a bicycle with a metric odometer

If you carry out the investigation indoors, a room that is at least 25 m on a side, such as a gymnasium, will be necessary. If you work outdoors, students should stand at least 25 m from a high, hard, smooth surface, such as the side of a school building.

Be sure to make arrangements to perform Part B of this investigation outdoors in a very large open area.

Safety 🔧 ✂️ ⚠️

Be careful when handling sharp instruments such as a tape measure. Note all safety alert symbols next to the steps in the Procedure and review the meaning of each symbol by referring to the Safety Symbols on page xiii.

Procedure

Part A: Estimating the Speed of Sound from Echoes

1. In an auditorium or outdoors near a high wall, use a metric tape measure or meter stick to measure a distance of 25 meters from the wall.

2. Stand facing the wall and clap the two wooden blocks together. Listen for an echo. If you can hear one, move closer to the wall by about 1 meter, and repeat. Keep moving closer, 1 meter at a time, until you can no longer hear a separate echo.

3. Measure and record the distance between you and the wall.

Part B: Determining the Speed of Sound From the Delay Between Seeing and Hearing an Event

4. This experiment must be conducted outdoors. Select an area such as an open field or a long, lightly traveled road. Record your observations of the weather conditions.

5. With the measuring rope (or a bicycle equipped with a metric odometer), measure a distance of 100 meters in a straight line.

6. One student should stand at each end of this measured distance, as shown in Figure 1.

7. One student should create a loud, short noise by striking the drum.

100 meters

Figure 1

8. The other student should start the stopwatch precisely when he or she sees the drum being struck. The student should stop the watch precisely when he or she hears the noise.

9. Repeat Steps 8 and 9 three more times. Record the times to a hundredth of a second in the data table.

10. The two students should change places with each other and repeat the experiment. This will help to eliminate any effect the wind might have on the speed at which the sound waves travel. Record your results in the data table.

Observations

Part A

1. What did you observe when you made the sound at a distance of 25 meters from the reflecting surface?

An echo could be heard.

2. At what distance were you no longer able to hear an echo?

The distance should be approximately 17 meters.

Part B

DATA TABLE Sample data are shown.

Trial	Time (first student with stopwatch) (s)	Time (second student with stopwatch) (s)
1	0.25 s	0.30 s
2	0.28 s	0.29 s
3	0.30 s	0.32 s
4	0.31 s	0.25 s

Analysis and Conclusions

1. **Calculating** For Part A, calculate the total distance the sound traveled from you to the reflecting surface and back again.

Approximately 17 m × 2 = 34 m

2. **Calculating** Divide the total round-trip distance by the time, 0.10 s, needed for you to hear the echo and the original clapping sound as just one sound. Express your answer in the correct units.

Approximately 34 m/0.10 s = 340 m/s

3. **Inferring** What type of surface would not have reflected sound
   back to you? Why?

   Irregular soft surfaces, such as curtains, would not reflect sound well. Any soft material would have

   absorbed most of the sound energy instead of reflecting it back.

   _____

   _____

4. **Controlling Variables** For Part B, what were the weather
   conditions in which you measured the speed of sound? Do you
   think the speed would have been different under different
   conditions?

   The conditions could include observation of temperature, clouds, and whether it feels muggy or dry.

   Changes in any of these may result in different speeds of sound. (For example, sound travels slightly

   faster in warm air than in cool air and very slightly slower at high pressure than at low pressure.)

   _____

   _____

   _____

5. **Calculating** Average the eight time values in the data table.
   Calculate the speed of sound by dividing the distance by the
   average time.

   The average time will be approximately 0.29 s. The calculated speed of sound will therefore be

   100 m ÷ 0.29 s = 340 m/s.

   _____

6. **Analyzing Data** What factors might have caused variations in the
   results of your eight trials?

   Answers should take into account wind conditions and the observers' response times for starting and

   stopping the watches.

   _____

7. **Comparing and Contrasting** Compare the values for the speed of
   sound in air calculated in Part A and in Part B. Account for both the
   differences and similarities in the results.

   At 20°C, the two answers should be close to 340 m/s. Differences may be caused by the observers'

   ability to detect echoes, measurements in distance, response times for observers operating

   stopwatches, and the presence of wind. The results will probably be very close because of limits on

   the precision of the measurements, which will restrict the answers to two significant figures.

   _____

   _____

   _____

8. **Applying Concepts** Explain how you can determine the distance from you that lightning strikes if you know the speed of sound and have a stopwatch.

    You can determine the length of time between seeing the flash of lightning and hearing the thunder.

    Sound travels in dry air about 342 m/s. Using this value, you can calculate how far away the

    lightning struck.

    _____

    _____

    _____

9. **Applying Concepts** When fireworks burst in the sky, will you hear the explosion or see the color first? Explain your answer.

    You will see the color first because light travels faster then sound.

    _____

    _____

    _____

10. **Applying Concepts** Sound usually travels faster in liquids than in gases, and faster in some solids than in liquids. Explain why a worker who puts one ear against a long steel pipe would hear two sounds if another worker struck the pipe only once at some distance away.

    The listener would first hear the sound transmitted through the iron and then hear the sound

    transmitted through the air.

    _____

    _____

    _____

Go Further

Suspend an alarm clock inside a bell jar from which air can be evacuated by a vacuum pump. Observe what happens to the sound of the bell or alarm as the air is sucked out. Observe the speed of sound through other materials such as water or iron. Before conducting any experiments, submit your procedure to your teacher for approval.
Students should describe how the sound of the alarm is greatly reduced when the air is removed from the bell jar. Although the reason for this is more complicated than simply the absence of a medium for transmitting sound, students should be aware that the ability to transmit the mechanical energy of the sound has been greatly reduced by creating the vacuum. Similarly, students should explain the faster transmission of sound through liquids and solids as relating to the distance between the particles that make up the liquid or solid and other factors such as the elasticity of the medium.

Chapter 17   Mechanical Waves and Sound   **Investigation 17B**

Sounds in Solids

Refer students to pages 502 and 514–525 in their textbooks for a discussion of longitudinal waves and sound. **SKILLS FOCUS:** Predicting, Comparing and Contrasting, Applying Concepts **CLASS TIME:** 40 minutes

Background Information

Sound is a **longitudinal wave.** As sound travels through a substance, the particles vibrate back and forth parallel to the movement of the sound wave. When the particles vibrate, regions form where they are close together (**compression**) and where they are far apart (**rarefaction**). The sound wave consists of compressions and rarefactions spreading through a substance.

Sound must travel through a **medium.** Sound cannot travel through a vacuum because there are no particles to transmit the pattern of compressions and rarefactions. To transmit sound, the medium must vibrate. The term *vibrate* implies back-and-forth movement. If the particles move forth without moving back again, there is no vibration. Once particles begin forward motion, their inertia would continue to carry them forward unless some force brought them back again. A medium that has strong forces of attraction between the particles tends to be **elastic** because the particles spring back to their original positions after a sound wave passes.

A medium in which the particles are close together so that the vibration in one particle could easily pass to its neighboring particles tends to have greater elasticity than a medium in which the particles are far apart. The particles in metals are arranged very close together in an orderly pattern. This makes the metal rigid. It is very difficult to force the particles closer together. Therefore, a metal is not easily compressed or deformed. A piece of plastic, such as a plastic straw, bends easily. A material is elastic if it is rigid and hard to deform. Metal tends to be more elastic than plastic.

In this investigation, you will compare wood, cardboard, and metal for elasticity to discover how well each transmits sound.

Problem

How well do various materials transmit sound?

Pre-Lab Discussion

Read the entire investigation. Then, work with a partner to answer the following questions.

1. **Comparing and Contrasting** A spring is placed on a tabletop, and one end is held in a fixed position. Two strings are tied to the spring on coils about 1 cm apart, as shown in Figure 1. Then, the spring is given a shove at the left end, causing a wave to travel through it toward the right.

   a. Describe the movement of either string as the wave passes by.

   The string moves forward and then backward and then returns to its original position.

   _____

b. What happens to the distance between the two strings as the wave travels along the spring? Explain your answer.

Strings   Spring

Figure 1

As the string on the left moves to the right, the two

strings move closer together. Then, the first string

moves back to its original position, and the second

string begins to move toward the right, moving the

strings apart. Finally, the second string returns to its original position so that the distance

between the strings is the same as it was originally.

2. **Using Models** How is the behavior of the spring in Question 1 similar to that of a sound wave?

The motion in the spring is a longitudinal wave. The behavior of the spring is similar to that of a sound

wave because the displacement of the strings is parallel to the movement of the wave.

3. **Using Models** Suppose that you made a coil out of cotton and tried to send a wave down the cotton coil in the same way as described in Question 1 with a spring. What would happen? Explain your answer. Use the word *elastic* or *elasticity* in your explanation.

The wave would not spread down the cotton coil because cotton is not elastic. Instead, only part

of the cotton coil would move, and its shape would be deformed.

4. **Inferring** Which substance is probably the most elastic—wood, cardboard, or metal? Which is probably the least elastic? How would you test your prediction?

Metal is probably the most elastic. Cardboard is probably the least elastic. This can be tested by

applying the same force to objects composed of each material and observing whether the objects

are easily deformed (less elastic) or resist change in shape (more elastic).

5. **Predicting** Rank wood, cardboard, and metal from highest to lowest for their ability to conduct sound. Explain your answer.

Metal, wood, cardboard; This ranking is the same as and is based on the materials'

ranking for elasticity.

Materials *(per group)*

clock or watch with second hand (either should produce a ticking sound)

wooden meter stick

metal rod, 1 m long, (iron, steel, or aluminum)

cardboard sheet, 1 m long Cut a strip from a corrugated cardboard box.

Name _____ Class _____ Date _____

Put on safety goggles. Be careful when handling sharp instruments. Note all safety alert symbols next to the steps in the Procedure and review the meaning of each symbol by referring to the Safety Symbols on page xiii.

Procedure

🔥⚒✂⚠ 1. Work with a partner. Check the elasticity of a meter stick by laying it flat on your lab table with about a third of its length hanging over the edge. One student holds the meter stick down on the lab table, and the other flicks the free end to see how easily it bends and how much it vibrates.

2. Repeat Step 1 with a metal rod and a piece of cardboard. Based on your observations, rank the three objects from the most elastic to the least elastic. The harder an object is to bend and the more vigorously it snaps back to its original shape, the more elastic the material is. In the data table, use the numbers 1 to 3 to rank elasticity, with 1 being the most elastic.

3. Hold a ticking watch or clock to your ear. Note the ticking.

4. Hold a wooden meter stick so that one end is pressed gently against your ear. Have your partner hold the watch against the far end of the meter stick. Note whether you can hear any ticking. **CAUTION:** *Use great care when placing the meter sticks and rods near the ear. Pushing these objects against the ear could result in injury.*

Figure 2

5. Repeat Step 5, substituting the metal rod for the meter stick. Note any observations.

6. Repeat Step 5, substituting a piece of cardboard for the meter stick. Note any observations.

7. Change roles with your partner and repeat Steps 3 through 7. Discuss your observations with your partner and record them, again using the numbers 1 (best) to 3 (poorest) to rank how well each medium conducts sound.

Observations Sample data are shown.

DATA TABLE

Medium	Elasticity (1 = most elastic)	Sound Conduction (1 = best conductor)
Meter stick	2	2
Metal rod	1	1
Cardboard	3	3

Analysis and Conclusions

1. **Forming Operational Definitions** What property of sound did you observe to determine if the medium was a good conductor?

   Loudness

2. **Comparing and Contrasting** Compare wood, metal, and cardboard as sound transmitters, based on your observations. How do these compare with your prediction?

   The correct rank is metal (best), wood, cardboard (poorest). Comparisons will depend on the

   initial predictions.

3. **Making Generalizations** Based on your observations, what is the relationship between elasticity and the ability to conduct sound?

   As elasticity increases, so does the ability to conduct sound.

4. **Applying Concepts** Suppose that you are floating outside a spacecraft with another astronaut. You wish to say something to your fellow astronaut, but your two-way radio is not working. How could you transmit a Morse code message by using sound waves?

   To be heard, you should use a medium that could be placed in contact with the two helmets.

   For example, you could place the helmets together or hold both helmets against the metal body

   of the spacecraft.

Go Further

Does elasticity affect the speed of a wave as well as the loudness (intensity) of the sound? Design an experiment to answer this question. Be sure to describe the responding and manipulated variables. Show your plan to your teacher. When your teacher approves your plan, carry out your experiment and report your results and conclusions.

Compare how sound travels through a metal and a wooden fence—both speed and loudness of sound. A student might have a friend tap on a portion of the metal fence, starting a stopwatch as he or she taps. The student would place an ear against the fence a measured distance away, signaling the friend when he or she hears the sound of the tap. Upon the signal, the friend would stop the stopwatch. This procedure could be repeated with a wooden fence. Metal is less compressible (more elastic) than wood, so the sound should travel faster through the metal fence than through the wooden one.

Chapter 18   The Electromagnetic Spectrum and Light   🔍 Investigation 18A

Predicting Spectra

Refer students to pages 546, 547, and 550–553 in their textbooks for a discussion of transparency and color. **SKILL FOCUS:** Predicting, Observing, Drawing Conclusions **CLASS TIME:** 30 minutes

Background Information

Some materials are **transparent** to nearly all frequencies of visible light. This means that these materials transmit most of the light that strikes them. For example, window glass is transparent to nearly all frequencies of visible light. Most materials, however, transmit some frequencies and absorb others. These materials can appear colored.

If you observe the spectrum of light before and after it passes through a material, you can determine which frequencies the material absorbs. You can view the spectrum of light through a prism or an instrument known as a spectroscope. These instruments separate white light into its colors, a process called **dispersion.**

In this investigation, you will predict and observe how the spectrum of white light changes as the light passes through several solutions of different colors. Then, you will use your observations to explain how the color of a material is related to the wavelengths of light that it absorbs.

Problem

How is the color of a solution related to the wavelengths of light that it absorbs?

Pre-Lab Discussion

Read the entire investigation. Then, work with a partner to answer the following questions.

1. **Predicting** Imagine observing a white light through a piece of blue glass.

   a. What color would the light appear to be?

   Blue _____

   b. What color of light would the glass transmit?

   Blue _____

   _____

   c. What colors of light would the glass absorb?

   Red, orange, yellow, green, and violet _____

   _____

2. **Predicting** Describe the spectrum you would see if you passed white light through a piece of blue glass.

   The spectrum would include only blue light. _____

   _____

3. **Controlling Variables** Identify the manipulated, responding, and controlled variables in this investigation.

  a. Manipulated variable _colored solutions_

  b. Responding variable _appearance of spectrum_

  c. Controlled variables _light source, spectroscope_

4. **Formulating Hypotheses** State a hypothesis about how the spectrum of white light changes as the light passes through a colored solution.

Passing white light through a colored solution removes one or more colors.

Materials *(per group)*

lamp and incandescent bulb

spectroscope

colored pencils

stoppered test tube of chlorophyll solution

stoppered test tube of phenolphthalein-sodium
  hydroxide solution

stoppered test tube of potassium
  permanganate solution

Safety 🌀🏠🔦🧤🥼🧹☠️🔥

Put on safety goggles, a lab apron, and plastic gloves. Be careful to avoid breakage when working with glassware. Observe proper laboratory procedures when using electrical equipment. Never touch or taste any chemical unless instructed to do so. The chemicals used in this investigation are toxic and corrosive. Do not open any of the test tubes. Note all safety alert symbols next to the steps in the Procedure and review the meaning of each symbol by referring to the Safety Symbols on page xiii.

Do not allow students to prepare solution To prepare the chlorophyll solution, heat 3(mL isopropyl alcohol to 60°C on a hot pla in a fume hood. Do not heat the alcohol to temperature greater than 60°C. Place fou five dark green plant leaves in the alcohol Add more leaves if necessary until the alcohol becomes deep green. Allow the solution to cool before removing the leave and dispensing the solution into test tube To prepare the phenolphthalein-sodium hydroxide solution, dissolve 1.2 g sodium hydroxide in 300 mL water and add 1% alcoholic phenolphthalein solution one dr at a time until a deep pink color is attaine To prepare the potassium permanganate solution, dissolve 0.3 g potassium permanganate ($KMnO_4$) in 300 mL water. **CAUTION:** *Potassium permanganate is a s irritant and can explode on sudden heatin Alcohol vapors are flammable and can be explosive. Wear safety goggles, a lab apro and plastic gloves when preparing all solutions. Review the safety information ir the MSDS on hazardous chemicals with students before performing this investigat*

Procedure

🔦 1. With the room darkened, turn on the incandescent lamp.
☠️   Observe the light from the bulb. In the data table, draw the
🧹   spectrum that you expect to see when you view the bulb
🥼   through the spectroscope. If necessary, use colored pencils to
   draw the spectrum.

Dim the lights in the classroom by closing window shades or turning off the classroom lights.

2. Now, use the spectroscope to observe the spectrum of the light from the incandescent bulb. In the data table, draw and describe the spectrum that you observed.

Show students how to use the spectroscopes.

🧤 3. Examine the test tube of the chlorophyll solution. Observe the
🔦   light from the incandescent bulb through this test tube. Record
☠️   in the data table the color that you see.

CAUTION: *Do not touch heated bulbs a they can burn skin.*

4. In the data table, draw the spectrum that you expect to see when you view the chlorophyll solution through the spectroscope.

Name _____ Class _____ Date _____

5. Hold the test tube of chlorophyll solution against the far end of the spectroscope so that the light from the bulb passes through the solution before entering the spectroscope. In the data table, draw the spectrum of the chlorophyll solution. Record any differences between this spectrum and the one you observed in Step 2. You may note gaps or differences in the brightness of some colors.

CAUTION: *Handle glass test tubes carefully to avoid breakage and exposure to hazardous chemicals*

6. Repeat Steps 3 through 5 with the test tube of phenolphthalein-sodium hydroxide solution.

7. Repeat Steps 3 through 5 with the test tube of potassium permanganate solution.

8. Return the test tubes to your teacher. Wash your hands thoroughly after carrying out this investigation.

Observations Sample data are shown.

DATA TABLE

Solution	Color	Drawing of Predicted Spectrum	Drawing of Observed Spectrum	Description of Observed Spectrum
None	None			Continuous spectrum of red, orange, yellow, green, blue, and violet
Chlorophyll	Green			Green and yellow are predominant; other colors are nearly absent.
Phenolphthalein-sodium hydroxide	Pink			Green and yellow are absent; violet, orange and red are predominant.
Potassium permanganate	Purple			Green and yellow are absent; blue and red are predominant.

Analysis and Conclusions

1. **Analyzing Data** Did passing white light through the colored solutions add colors to the light or remove colors from the light?

Passing white light through colored solutions removed colors from the light.

_____

_____

2. **Formulating Hypotheses** What happened to the colors of light that did not pass through the solutions? Explain your answer.

The solutions absorbed the colors of light that did not pass through the solutions. The energy of

this light was then converted to thermal energy, or heat.

3. **Inferring** Which colors of light were absorbed in the spectrum of each of the following solutions?

   a. Chlorophyll solution

   Red, orange, blue and violet light were absorbed.

   b. Phenolphthalein-sodium hydroxide solution

   Green and yellow light were absorbed.

   c. Potassium permanganate solution

   Green and yellow light were absorbed.

4. **Drawing Conclusions** What is the relationship between the color of a solution and the colors of light that the solution absorbs?

   A solution that is a primary color of light (green) must absorb at least the other two primary colors

   (red and blue). A solution that is a secondary color of light (magenta) at a minimum must absorb its

   complementary color (green).

5. **Drawing Conclusions** What is the relationship between the color of a solution and the colors of light that the solution transmits?

   Light of the same color as the solution passes through the solution.

6. **Applying Concepts** If you shine a red light through a block of red gelatin, the red beam of light is clearly visible in the gelatin. However, if you shine a red light through a block of blue gelatin, the light is not visible in the gelatin. Explain these observations.

   The red light is visible in the red gelatin because the red gelatin transmits red light and absorbs blue

   and green light. Blue gelatin absorbs red light and transmits blue light. The red light would therefore

   be absorbed by the blue gelatin and would not be seen.

Go Further

The spectroscope that you used in this investigation enabled you to see whether there were any gaps in the spectrum of the light you observed and to judge whether some parts of the spectrum were brighter than others. A more precise instrument called a spectrophotometer enables you to measure the percentage of the light falling on a sample of a solution that the solution absorbs or transmits. The spectrophotometer can make this measurement at any visible wavelength.

Ask your teacher to show you how to use the spectrophotometer. Then, design an experiment to determine whether it is possible to use the spectrophotometer to measure the concentration of a light-absorbing substance in a solution. Write a detailed plan of your experiment. Your plan should state the hypothesis to be tested, identify the manipulated, responding, and controlled variables, and describe the procedures and safety precautions that you will use. Show your plan to your teacher. When your teacher approves your plan, carry out your experiment and report your results and conclusions.

Examine students' plans for sound experimental design and safety. An example of an acceptable hypothesis is that the percentage of the light falling on a solution that is absorbed is proportional to the concentration of the solution. Have students practice using the spectrophotometer to measure the light absorption of a solution of the substance at a range of wavelengths. Then, have students plot the results against wavelength to obtain an absorption spectrum. Students can use this spectrum to select the wavelength at which the substance absorbs the most light. At this wavelength, the percentage of absorption should be proportional to the concentration of the substance. Students can use a set of solutions of known concentrations to calibrate the spectrophotometer to estimate the concentration of the light-absorbing substance.

Chapter 18   The Electromagnetic Spectrum and Light   🔍 **Investigation 18B**

Using Polarized Light

Refer students to pages 548 and 549 in their textbooks for a discussion of polarized light. **SKILL FOCUS:** Measuring, Using Graphs and Tables **CLASS TIME:** 45 minutes

Background Information

Some substances change the direction in which polarized light waves vibrate. These substances are said to be optically active. Sucrose, or table sugar, is optically active. When polarized light passes through a solution of sucrose dissolved in water, the polarization of the light changes—the light waves begin to vibrate in a different direction.

To measure this change, a device called a polarimeter is used. A polarimeter contains two polarizing filters. A container between the two filters holds a sample to be tested for optical activity. If the filters are at right angles to each other, no light can pass through the polarimeter. However, if you place an optically active sample between the filters, it will change the polarization of the light. As a result, some light will pass through the second filter. To measure the optical activity of a sample, you would look through the polarimeter and rotate the second filter until no light is able to pass though the filter. The angle that you rotate the second filter depends on the sample's optical activity.

In this investigation, you will use a polarimeter to determine how the optical activity of a sugar solution is related to the concentration of the solution.

Problem

How is the concentration of a sugar solution related to its optical activity?

Pre-Lab Discussion

Read the entire investigation. Then, work with a partner to answer the following questions.

1. **Inferring** Explain how two polarizing filters can completely block a beam of light.

   The first filter polarizes the light. If the second filter is placed at right angles to the first,

   the second filter will completely block the polarized light that reaches it from the first filter.

   _____

2. **Designing Experiments** Why will you need to be able to change the angle between the polarizing filters in the polarimeter?

   The sugar solution will change the direction in which the polarized light vibrates. The second

   filter must be able to rotate because the distance that the second filter must be rotated to block

   the light measures the optical activity of the solution.

   _____

3. **Applying Concepts** Could you determine the optical activity of a solution if the light passed through the sample before it passed through the two polarizing filters? Explain your answer.

No, the optical activity could not be measured in this way because the light would not be polarized

when it passed through the sample. As a result, the sample would not affect the polarization of the

light or how much light passed through the filters.

4. **Controlling Variables** Identify the manipulated, responding, and controlled variables in this investigation.

   a. Manipulated variable

Sugar concentration

   b. Responding variable

Direction of polarization of light

   c. Controlled variables

Starting position of the filters; distance that light passes through each sample; optical activity

of pure water

5. **Controlling Variables** Why will you need to measure the optical activity of water in Step 9?

The water serves as a control. Any optical activity of the water should be subtracted from the

optical activity of the sugar solutions to determine the optical activity of the sugar in the solutions.

Materials (per group)

2 cardboard tubes	bright light source	**CAUTION:** *Do not permit students to look directly at the sun.*
scissors	red pencil	
transparent tape	paper towels	Polarizing film can be ordered from a scientific supply house or cut from inexpensive polarizing clip-on sunglasses. Use toilet paper rolls for the cardboard tubes. To prepare 20%, 30%, and 40% sugar solutions, dissolve 20 g, 30 g, and 40 g, respectively, of sucrose in 80 mL, 70 mL, and 60 mL water. Make the unknown sugar solution by dissolving 35 g sucrose in 65 mL water.
metric ruler	10 mL 20% sugar solution	
glass vial with cap	10 mL 30% sugar solution	
2 square polarizing filters, approximately 2 cm × 2 cm	10 mL 40% sugar solution	
duct tape	unknown sugar solution	
graph paper with millimeter rulings		

Safety 🔲 🔲

Put on a lab apron. Be careful to avoid breakage when working with glassware. Be careful when handling sharp instruments. Never look directly at the sun. Note all safety alert symbols next to the steps in the Procedure and review the meaning of each symbol by referring to the Safety Symbols on page xiii.

Procedure

Part A: Building a Polarimeter

Figure 1

1. Use scissors to cut a cardboard tube open lengthwise. Then, overlap the cut edges to make a slightly smaller tube that just fits inside the second cardboard tube, as shown in Figure 1. Use transparent tape to hold the cut edges of the smaller tube together. **CAUTION:** *Be careful not to puncture or cut skin when using scissors.*

2. Using a metric ruler to measure, make a pencil mark on the side of the larger tube 4 cm from one end of the tube. Hold the glass vial with the center of its base on this mark. Use a pencil to trace the outline of the base of the vial on the tube.

3. Cut out the circle that you traced on the tube in Step 2. The resulting opening in the tube should be just large enough to allow the vial to fit snugly inside the tube, as shown in Figure 1.

4. Use small pieces of duct tape to carefully mount a polarizing filter over one end of the larger tube. Place tape only on the edges of the filter. To avoid getting any dirt or fingerprints on the polarizing filter, handle the filter only by its edges. If necessary, use small pieces of duct tape to cover any gaps between the edges of the filter and the tube. To hold the pieces of duct tape in place, wrap a piece of duct tape around the end of the tube, as shown in Figure 1.

5. Repeat Step 4 with the second polarizing filter and the smaller tube.

6. Cut a strip of graph paper that is 12 cm long and 1 cm wide. Wrap this strip around the open end of the larger tube, as shown in Figure 1. Use transparent tape to attach the strip of graph paper to the tube.

7. Insert the vial into the hole that you made in Step 3. Then, gently insert the smaller tube into the larger tube as far as the smaller tube will go.

8. Hold the polarimeter in one hand. Use your other hand to cover the vial to prevent it from falling out of the larger tube. Then, look at the bright light source through the polarimeter. As you look at the light through the polarimeter, rotate the smaller tube to make the light as dim as possible. Have a member of your group mark a short red pencil line on the strip of graph paper. Extend this line onto the smaller tube, as shown in Figure 1. **CAUTION:** *Do not aim the polarimeter at the sun.*

Part B: Measuring Optical Activity

9. Remove the vial from the polarimeter. Fill the vial with water and place the cap tightly on the vial. Use a paper towel to remove any water on the outside of the vial. Hold the polarimeter with the opening on top. Carefully put the vial back into the opening. Line up the red lines on both tubes. Look at the bright light source through the polarimeter. Rotate the smaller tube clockwise if necessary until the light is as dim as possible. **CAUTION:** *Immediately wipe up any spilled water. Make sure the vial does not slip out of the polarimeter.*

10. Observe the red pencil lines on the graph paper strip and on the smaller tube. Note that the rulings on the graph paper strip are 1 mm apart. In the data table, record the distance between the two red pencil lines. If the red pencil lines are precisely end to end, record this distance as zero.

11. Carefully remove the vial from the polarimeter. Discard the water in the sink. Rinse out the vial with water and use a paper towel to dry the vial.

12. Repeat Steps 9 through 11 with the 20%, 30%, and 40% sugar solutions. Then, repeat Steps 9 through 11 with the unknown sugar solutions.

13. Make a graph of the data from your observations of the water and the 20%, 30%, and 40% sugar solutions. Plot sugar concentration on the horizontal axis and optical activity on the vertical axis. Draw a straight line as close as possible to all four data points.

14. Find the point on the vertical axis of your graph that corresponds to the optical activity of the unknown sugar solution. Draw a horizontal dotted line from this point to the solid line. Then, draw a vertical dotted line from the point where the two lines meet down to the horizontal axis. The point where the vertical dotted line meets the horizontal axis marks the concentration of the unknown solution. Record this concentration in the data table.

Observations   Sample data are shown.

DATA TABLE

Sugar Concentration (percent)	Optical Activity (mm)
0 (water)	0.0
20	2.1
30	3.0
40	4.2
Unknown 35	3.5

Analysis and Conclusions

1. Analyzing Data What was the relationship between the concentration of the sugar solutions and their optical activities?

The optical activities were directly proportional to the concentration of sugar.

2. Using Graphs Was it reasonable to use your graph to determine the concentration of sugar in the unknown solution? Explain your answer.

Yes, because the unknown value was between two known values, it was reasonable to expect that

the relationship between sugar concentration and optical activity did not change in this range.

3. Evaluating and Revising When would it be unreasonable to use your graph to determine the concentration of an unknown sugar solution? Explain your answer.

If the optical activity of the unknown solution was very different from the range of known values, it

would be unreasonable to assume that the relationship between sugar concentration and optical

activity is the same for the known and unknown solutions.

4. Predicting How do you think the distance that light passes through the sample affects the observed optical activity?

The observed optical activity is directly proportional to the distance that light passes through the

sample.

Go Further

Design an experiment to use your polarimeter to determine the concentration of sugar in liquids such as fruit juices or syrups. Write a detailed plan of your experiment. Your plan should state the hypothesis to be tested, identify the manipulated, responding, and controlled variables, and describe the procedures and safety precautions that you will use. If the liquids you choose to test contain sugar other than sucrose, you will need to make solutions of known concentrations. After your teacher approves your plan, carry out your experiment and report your results and conclusions.

Examine student plans for sound experimental design and safety. Many foods are sweetened with corn syrup, which consists of a 70% solution of glucose in water. Students will need to measure the optical activity of various concentrations of corn syrup. High fructose corn syrup (HFCS) is used to sweeten many foods, especially soft drinks. You can make a solution with the approximate composition of HFCS by dissolving 31.3 g fructose and 43.3 g glucose in 30 mL water. Students can use this solution as a standard for calibrating a polarimeter to measure the concentration of HFCS.

Refraction and Reflection
Refer students to pages 570–575 in their textbooks for a discussion of reflection and refraction. **SKILLS FOCUS:** Inferring, Analyzing Data, Interpreting Diagrams/Photographs **CLASS TIME:** Part A, 25 minutes; Part B, 25 minutes

Background Information

In a vacuum, light travels in a straight line at 3.0×10^8 m/s. The situation is different, however, when light is not in a vacuum. Light can change direction when it passes through, bounces off, or is absorbed by substances. When light rays enter a substance, they change speed and may change direction. This behavior is called **refraction.** When light rays bounce off a surface, or undergo **reflection,** they also change direction. The angle between an incoming ray of light and a line perpendicular to the surface—called the normal line—is the **angle of incidence.** The angle between the reflected ray of light and the normal to the reflecting surface is the **angle of reflection.** If the light enters the substance and is refracted, the angle between the refracted light and the normal is the **angle of refraction.**

In this investigation, you will examine how the direction of light changes during refraction and reflection.

Problem

How do reflection and refraction change the direction of light?

Pre-Lab Discussion

Read the entire investigation. Then, work with a partner to answer the following questions.

1. **Inferring** In what direction will the tennis ball bounce if it is thrown directly at a wall? In what direction will the tennis ball bounce when it hits the wall at an angle? How is the direction influenced by the size of the angle?

   The ball bounces straight back along the same path. When thrown at an angle, the ball's angle of

   incidence equals the angle of reflection. As the angle of incidence increases, so does the angle of

   reflection.

   _____

   _____

2. **Using Analogies** Think of a photon of light as if it were a tennis ball and a mirror as if it were a wall. Use this analogy to describe what happens when light is reflected from a mirror's surface.

   A light ray that approaches a mirror straight on is reflected straight back along its path. When a light

   ray approaches a mirror at an angle, the angle of incidence will always equal the angle of reflection.

   _____

   _____

   _____

3. **Inferring** Consider the tractor shown in Figure 1. The tractor goes straight as long as both belts are going the same speed.

Figure 1

Belt

a. Suppose the tractor exits a road and enters a field such that both belts enter the field at the same time. If the field slows the speed of the belts, how are the speed and direction of motion of the tractor affected as it enters the field?

Both belts slow down equally, and the tractor continues to move in a straight line at

a slower speed.

4. **Inferring** Suppose the tractor exits the road and enters the field at an angle such that one belt enters the field before the other.

a. Describe how the speeds of the belts and the direction of motion are affected as the tractor enters the field at an angle.

The belt entering the field first slows down before the other belt does. This results in a speed

difference between the belts that causes the tractor to change direction.

b. Suppose that the tractor continues through the field in its new direction until it reaches a road parallel to the first. How will the tractor's final direction on the new road compare to its original direction on the first road? Explain your answer.

The new direction will be parallel to the original direction. As the tractor reenters the road, the

opposite speed difference between the belts occurs, turning the tractor back to

its original direction.

5. **Using Analogies** Think of a photon of light as if it were a tractor with belts on each side. Think of the medium that light is traveling through as if it were the surface on which the tractor is traveling. Light moving through air into glass is therefore similar to the tractor moving from the road to the field. Use this analogy to describe what happens when light moves from one medium to another.

As light moves from one medium to another, its speed changes. If the light directly approaches

the boundary between the mediums, its speed changes uniformly and it continues straight ahead. If

the light approaches the boundary at an angle, the change in speed is not uniform, and the light

bends from its original path.

Materials (per group)

cardboard (approximately
  30 cm × 30 cm)

30-cm ruler

4 straight pins

protractor

unlined paper

small mirror

support for mirror (wood block
  and glue, tape, or rubber band)

transparent container with a
  square base (7 cm × 7 cm)

Safety

Be careful when handling sharp instruments. Note all safety alert
symbols next to the steps in the Procedure and review the meaning
of each symbol by referring to the Safety Symbols on page xiii.

Procedure
Part A: Observing Reflection

1. Place the paper on the cardboard. Stand the mirror in the center of the
   paper. Support the mirror by gluing, taping, or tying it with a rubber
   band to a small wooden block. Draw a line along the edge of the mirror.
   Stick a pin in the paper and cardboard about 4 cm in front of the center of
   the mirror. Draw a small circle around the pin position and label it *Object*,
   as shown in Figure 2. **CAUTION:** *Pinpoints can cut or puncture skin, so
   handle pins carefully.*

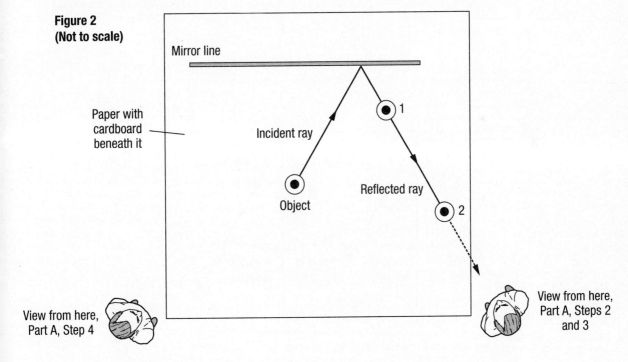

**Figure 2
(Not to scale)**

2. Refer to Figure 2. Position your head near the lower-right corner of
   the paper. Look at the mirror with one eye closed and observe the
   reflection of the pin. Do not look at the real pin. Insert a pin in the
   paper near the mirror so that it hides the reflection of the Object
   pin. Draw a small circle around the pin position and label it *1*.

3. Refer to Figure 2. From the same viewing position, place a second pin in the paper near the mirror so that it hides the pin you placed in position 1 and the reflection of the Object pin. Draw a small circle around the pin position and label it 2.

4. Remove the pins from positions 1 and 2. Use them to repeat Steps 2 and 3 from the lower-left corner of the paper. Draw circles around these pin positions and label them 3 and 4.

5. Remove the mirror and all the pins. Using the ruler, draw a solid line through pin positions 1 and 2 and extend it as far as the mirror line. This line is a reflected ray. Draw a line from the Object pin position to the point where the reflected ray leaves the mirror. This line is the incident ray. Label each ray and draw an arrow on the ray to show its direction.

6. Repeat Step 5 for pin positions 3 and 4.

7. Draw two lines perpendicular to the mirror line at the two points where the incident rays and the reflected rays touch. These lines are the normal lines. Label and measure the angles of incidence and reflection for the rays coming from the left and right corners of the paper, as shown in Figure 3. Record your measurements in Data Table 1.

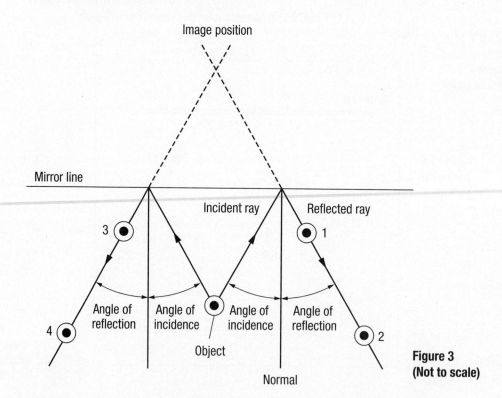

Figure 3
(Not to scale)

8. Using the ruler, draw two dashed lines extending from the two reflected rays beyond the mirror line. Continue these dashed lines just beyond the point where they cross. This point is the position of the Object pin's image in the mirror. Label this point *Image*.

Part B: Observing Refraction

9. Fill a transparent square-based container with tap water. Place a piece of unlined paper on a piece of cardboard. Place the container in the center of the paper and trace a line around the edges.

10. Using the ruler, draw a line on your paper at an angle to one edge of the container. Do not draw this line perpendicular to the edge of the container.

11. Place two pins on the line about 3 cm apart from each other. Draw circles around the base of the pins and label the circles *Pin 1* and *Pin 2*, as shown in Figure 4. Look through the bottom edge of the container until you see Pins 1 and 2 positioned exactly behind each other. (They will look like only one pin.)

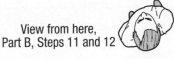

View from here,
Part B, Steps 11 and 12

**Figure 4
(Not to scale)**

12. Place two more pins on the lower part of your paper so that they also seem to line up with Pins 1 and 2. (All four pins should appear to be one pin.) Draw circles around the base of these pins and label them *Pin 3* and *Pin 4*.

13. Remove the pins and the container. Using a ruler, draw a line through the positions of Pins 3 and 4 just to where they meet the line made by the container.

14. The line through Pins 1 and 2 represents a ray of light entering the container and is called the incident ray. Label this ray and draw arrows on it to show its direction.

15. The line through Pins 3 and 4 represents a ray of light leaving the container and going to your eye. It is called the emergent ray. Label this ray and draw arrows on it to show its direction.

16. Using the ruler, connect the incident ray and the emergent ray through the container. This line is called the refracted ray. Label this ray and draw arrows on it to show its direction.

17. Using the protractor, construct normal lines (lines perpendicular to the edge of the container) at the points where the incident and emergent rays touch the container. Extend the normal lines into the container area. You should have formed two angles on each side of the container.

18. Two angles are formed with the normal lines as the incident ray touches the side of the container and as the refracted ray touches the opposite side of the container. These two angles are called angles of incidence. Label these two angles *I*.

19. Two angles are formed with the normal lines as the refracted ray enters the container and again as the emergent ray leaves the opposite side of the container. These two angles are called angles of refraction. Label these two angles *R*.

20. Measure the angles of incidence and the angles of refraction and record your measurements in Data Table 2.

21. Using the ruler and a dashed line, extend the emergent ray backward through the container and beyond it.

Observations   Sample data are shown.

DATA TABLE 1

Side	Angle	
	Incidence	**Reflection**
Left	Answers will vary.	Answers should be the same or close to the angle of incidence.
Right	Answers will vary.	Answers should be the same or close to the angle of incidence.

DATA TABLE 2

Pins	Angle	
	Incidence (I)	**Reflection (R)**
1 and 2	Answers will vary.	Answers will vary.
3 and 4	Answers will vary, but should be the same or close to the angle of refraction for light entering the container.	Answers will vary, but should be the same or close to the angle of incidence for light entering the container.

Analysis and Conclusions

1. Analyzing Data In Part A, how do the distances of the object and image from the mirror compare?

They are approximately the same.

_____

2. Analyzing Data How do the angles of incidence and the angles of reflection in Part A compare in size?

They are approximately the same.

_____

_____

3. **Interpreting Diagrams** Follow the path of one of the incident rays to the mirror and the path of its reflected ray. Repeat for the other incident ray and reflected ray. How does the direction of the incident ray compare to the direction of the reflected ray? As a result, how is the image oriented with respect to the object?

The directions of the incident and reflected rays are opposite. As a result, the image is oriented

opposite (reversed left to right) the object.

4. **Inferring** The image you see in a mirror is formed from many incident and reflected rays. How would the image be affected if there were no relationship between the angles of the incident and reflected rays?

No clear image would be formed.

5. **Relating Cause and Effect** When you look in a plane mirror, the image seems to be "inside" or "behind" the mirror, even though no light rays can pass through the mirror. What kind of image (real or virtual) exists where there are no actual light rays? Explain how the image appears in a place from which no actual light rays are coming.

It is a virtual image. The image appears to be behind the mirror because the reflected rays follow

the same path as light rays coming from an object in that position would.

6. **Analyzing Data** In Part B, as the incident ray enters the container of water, how does it bend with respect to the normal line? As the emergent ray leaves the glass, how does it bend with respect to the normal line?

The refracted ray bends toward the normal line. The emergent ray bends away from the

normal line.

7. **Analyzing Data** In Part B, How does the angle of incidence of the incident ray compare with the angle of refraction for the emerging ray? How does the angle of refraction for the incident ray compare with the angle of incidence for the emerging ray?

They are the same. They are the same.

8. Analyzing Data How do the directions of the emergent ray and the incident ray compare?

They are parallel.

9. Applying Concepts Why does a light ray bend as it passes from air to a container of water or from the container of water to air at an angle?

Light changes speed as it goes from one medium to another. When light approaches the

boundary between mediums at an angle, the change in speed is not uniform and the light bends.

Go Further

Some substances refract light more than others do. Diamond bends light so much that light approaching at even a small angle reflects inside the diamond instead of passing through. This process is called total internal reflection. It is responsible for diamond's characteristic sparkle.

When the pathway of light is disrupted in this way, it can produce some interesting illusions. Try the following experiments:

1. Put a penny on a flat surface and place an empty, transparent cup directly over the penny. Observe the penny through the side of the cup.

2. Completely fill the cup with water and observe the penny through the side of the cup.

3. Carefully remove the cup and use an eyedropper to put several drops of water on the penny.

4. Put the cup containing the water back on the penny. Observe the penny through the side of the cup.

5. What did you observe in each case? How can your observations be explained.

The penny is visible through the cup when it is empty. It is not visible when viewed through the water except when water is placed directly on the penny. In the first example there is no refraction as the light passes basically from air to air. In the second example light from the penny passes from air to water and is refracted at such a large angle that it never reaches the eyes. This makes the penny invisible. Putting water on the penny makes the light rays pass from water to water, resulting in minimum refraction.

Chapter 19   Optics

Harnessing Solar Energy

Refer students to pages 570–573 in their textbooks for a discussion of mirrors and reflection. **SKILLS FOCUS:** Applying Concepts, Inferring, Interpreting Diagrams/Photographs **CLASS TIME:** 45 minutes

Background Information

The sun radiates a tremendous amount of energy. Even from a great distance away, sunlight warms Earth. As the cost of fossil fuels rises, solar energy becomes a more attractive alternative energy source. Some people install solar panels on the roofs of their houses. These devices are often used to heat water that is then used as a hot-water source or to heat the house.

In order to make the greatest use of energy from the sun, it is necessary to focus the sun's rays. This can be accomplished by using a curved, or concave, mirrored surface or a magnifying lens.

In this investigation, you will use a mirror to focus the sun's rays and measure the effect it has on the temperature of a sample of water.

Problem

What happens to the thermal energy of a substance when light rays from the sun are focused on it?

Pre-Lab Discussion

Read the entire investigation. Then, work with a partner to answer the following questions.

1. **Applying Concepts** Suppose parallel rays of light strike a plane mirror at an angle. How will the directions of the reflected rays compare with the directions of the incident rays?

   The rays will still be parallel. Because the light rays are parallel, they all have the same angle

   of incidence, and upon reflection, they all have the same angle of reflection.

2. **Interpreting Diagrams** Two plane mirrors are joined at an angle of 120° and oriented toward two parallel incident rays of light, as shown in Figure 1. Construct the normal lines for each plane mirror, measure the angles of incidence, and draw the reflected rays as dashed lines with arrowheads to show their directions. Are the reflected rays parallel to each other? Explain.

   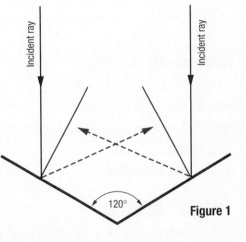

   Figure 1

   Although the two plane mirrors are symmetrically oriented

   to the incoming parallel light rays, the mirrors are not

   parallel to each other. Therefore, when the parallel light

   rays each strike one of the mirrors, they reflect at the same angle, but are reflected

   in different directions.

3. Interpreting Diagrams A spherical concave mirror is shown in Figure 2. Draw dashed lines to represent the reflected rays and use arrowheads to indicate direction. Label the point at which the rays cross as the Focus. How is this concave mirror similar to the V-shaped mirror in Question 2? How does the concave mirror affect the direction of the incident rays?

Both mirrors have surfaces that are not parallel to

each other. The parallel incident rays are reflected

toward each other so that they cross at a common

point called the focus.

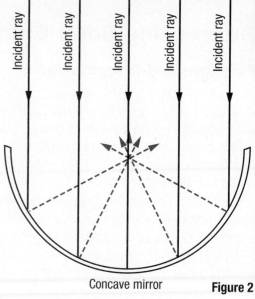

Concave mirror   **Figure 2**

4. Inferring How does the amount of light energy at the focus compare to the amount of energy at any other location near the mirror? Explain.

There is more light energy at the focus than at any other location because all of the incident

light energy converges there.

5. Predicting Two water-filled test tubes are set up so the sun is shining on them. One of the test tubes is positioned to be at the focus of a concave mirror. How would you expect the temperature of the water in the two test tubes to compare after they have each had sun shining on them for an hour? Explain.

The test tube positioned at the focus of the mirror will be warmer because more light rays

are incident upon it.

Materials (per group)

compass   2 thermometers
protractor   2 test tubes
reflector from a large flashlight   2 test-tube clamps
ring stand   triangular file
graduated cylinder   tape

Safety ⬛🔲🔳

Put on safety goggles. Be careful to avoid breakage when working with glassware. Be careful when handling sharp instruments. Note all safety alert symbols next to the steps in the Procedure and review the meaning of each symbol by referring to the Safety Symbols on page xiii.

Procedure

1. Insert one of the test tubes through the hole in the center of a flashlight reflector so that it extends about 1 cm below the bottom of the reflector. The test tube should fit snugly. If the hole is too small, enlarge it with a triangular file. If the test tube is loose, secure it with some tape.

2. Set up a ring stand with two test-tube clamps. Secure the test tube in the reflector and the second test tube in the test-tube clamps, as shown in Figure 3. Place a thermometer into each test tube.

Figure 3

3. Using a graduated cylinder, add 5 mL of water to each test tube. Wait a few minutes. In the data table, record the initial temperature in each test tube.

4. Place the test setup in bright sunlight and position the reflector toward the sun. Tilt the reflector in such a way that a bright spot appears in the water of the test tube. Adjust the position of the other test tube so that it is tilted the same way as the test tube in the reflector.

5. Expose the test tubes to the sun for 5 minutes. Observe the temperatures of the water in each test tube and record the values in the data table.

Observations   Sample data are shown.

DATA TABLE

Test Tube	Initial Temperature (°C)	Final Temperature (°C)
With Reflector	20°C	25°C
Without Reflector	20°C	21°C

Analysis and Conclusions

1. **Comparing and Contrasting** How did the temperature in the two test tubes compare? What caused the difference in temperature? How did this result compare to your earlier prediction?

   The temperature in the test tube with the reflector was higher. This occurred because the

   reflector focuses more light onto the test tube. This result agrees with the earlier prediction.

2. **Controlling Variables** Why did you need to set up two test tubes with the same amount of water in each?

   Two test tubes are needed for comparison because sunlight will heat the water with or

   without the mirror. The amount of the temperature rise depends on the amount of incident

   light and the volume of water. By making the volume of water equal in both test tubes, this

   variable was eliminated as a factor in the results.

3. **Relating Cause and Effect** How did the concave mirror heat the water? What observations support your explanation?

   The concave mirror focuses the incoming light energy on the contents of the test tube. This focused

   light was visible as a bright spot in the test tube.

4. **Applying Concepts** Explain how an apparatus similar to the one you constructed could be used to change the sun's radiant energy into mechanical energy.

   Many answers are possible. One example is to have the sun's rays heat water to run a steam

   engine or turbine.

Go Further

With adult supervision, construct a device to heat water by using a magnifying lens. Use a similar apparatus to the one you used in the investigation. Use two test tubes so that you can evaluate the effect of the lens. Attempt to position the lens in such a way that a large amount of sunlight is focused in a small volume of water. Compare the results of your experiment with the results from this investigation. **CAUTION:** *Focused light from the lens can produce very high temperatures.*

The temperature of the water in the test tube under the magnifying lens will probably be comparable to the temperature of the water in the test tube within the concave mirror.

Constructing a Telephone

Refer students to page 498–523 in their textbooks for a discussion of mechanical waves and sound.
SKILLS FOCUS: Observing, Applying Concepts, Inferring **CLASS TIME:** 20 minutes

Background Information

The operation of the telephone involves energy conversions. In the transmitter of the telephone, sound waves exert a pressure on a flexible film, or diaphragm, that conducts electricity, and which vibrates with the same frequency as the sound waves. The louder the sound waves are, the larger the vibrations of the diaphragm are. In some older telephone transmitters, finely granulated carbon was placed between the diaphragm and a conducting plate. Changes in the diaphragm's vibrations change the distance between the diaphragm and the plate, causing the electric current through the carbon grains to vary. In this way, the variations in intensity and frequency of sound are converted into changes in current. These current changes form electronic signals that travel over wires. In the receiver of the telephone, the electronic signals are converted back into sound waves by a somewhat similar process.

The first telephone conversation took place on March 10, 1876, between the inventor of the telephone, Alexander Graham Bell, and his assistant, Thomas Watson.

In this investigation, you will build a simple device that changes pressure into an electrical signal, which illustrates the operation of a transmitter in older models of telephones.

Problem

How do energy conversions take place within the transmitter of a telephone?

Pre-Lab Discussion

Read the entire investigation. Then, work with a partner to answer the following questions.

1. Observing What process is this investigation meant to test?

This investigation will test how mechanical energy is converted into electrical energy, such as

the energy conversion that takes place within a telephone transmitter.

_____

_____

_____

_____

_____

2. Controlling Variables What is the manipulated variable in this investigation?

Pressure on the copper strips
_____

_____

3. Controlling Variables What is the responding variable in this investigation?

The amount of electric current
_____

_____

4. Predicting What do you predict will occur at the transmitting end of the energy conversion?

Possible answer: Change in the pressure on the copper strips causes change in the resistance of

the circuit, and therefore the amount of current in the circuit.
_____

_____

_____

_____

5. Predicting What do you predict will occur at the receiving end of the energy conversion?

Possible answer: Change in the current causes change in the brightness of the light bulb.
_____

_____

_____

_____

_____

Materials *(per group)*

plastic cup
1.5-V lamp with socket
carbon grains
2 copper strips
2 alligator clips
1.5-V dry cell
3 connecting wires, each 30 cm long

Safety

Put on safety goggles and a lab apron. Be careful to avoid breakage when working with glassware. Observe proper laboratory procedures when using electrical equipment. Note all safety alert symbols next to the steps in the Procedure and review the meaning of each symbol by referring to the Safety Symbols on page xiii.

Procedure

1. Place the two copper strips on opposite sides of the plastic cup. **CAUTION:** *Metal strips can be sharp and can cut skin.*

2. Half-fill the cup with carbon grains.

3. Using an alligator clip, connect one end of a wire to one of the copper strips. Connect the other end of the wire to one side of the lamp socket. **CAUTION:** *Observe proper laboratory procedures when using electrical equipment.* **CAUTION:** *Wire ends can puncture skin.*

4. Using the other alligator clip, connect another wire to the second copper strip. Connect the other end of this wire to one terminal of the dry cell, as shown in Figure 1.

Figure 1

5. Connect a third wire to the other side of the lamp socket. Connect the other end of this wire to the other terminal of the dry cell.

6. Squeeze the lower sides of the plastic cup so that the distance between the copper strips changes. Do not bring the strips into direct contact with each other. Observe how the brightness of the light bulb varies with the pressure applied to the cup.

Observations

The main features that should be observed are as follows: As the pressure on the cup's

sides increased, the copper strips moved closer together. This reduced the resistance in the

circuit, and therefore increased the current. As the current increased, the light bulb burned brighter.

_____

_____

Analysis and Conclusions

1. **Observing** What happened when you squeezed the copper strips together?

   The light bulb became brighter.

2. **Observing** What happened when you stopped squeezing the copper strips together?

   The light bulb became dimmer.

3. **Drawing Conclusions** How did pressure on the carbon grains affect the flow of electricity?

   The greater the pressure that was applied on the carbon grains, the stronger the electric current was.

4. **Inferring** How is the process observed in this investigation comparable to the operation of a telephone transmitter?

   The pressure applied to the sides of the cup is comparable to the pressure applied to the diaphragm

   in a transmitter. The change in the distance between the copper strips is comparable to the change in

   the distance between the conducting plate and diaphragm, while the carbon grains in the cup serve

   the same role as in older transmitters. The variation in the electric current is revealed by the changes

   in the brightness of the light bulb.

Go Further

Using the Internet or the library, perform additional research about telephone transmitters. How similar were old transmitters to the apparatus in the investigation? How are they different now? What materials are currently used in transmitters? What is piezoelectricity, and how are certain crystal used to produce it? Has the basic process of energy conversion changed significantly? Use the results of your research to write a short report.

You may need to provide some guidance to students as they do their research. If possible, provide access to reference books and Internet resources, notably on subjects such as piezoelectricity and capacitors.

Charging Objects

Refer students to pages 602 and 603 in their textbook for a discussion of static electricity and charging. **SKILLS FOCUS:** Predicting; Observing; Recording Data; Inferring; Comparing and Contrasting **CLASS TIME:** 60 minutes

Background Information

An object can become charged in several different ways. When electrons are transferred between objects that are rubbed together, the objects become charged due to friction. An object can sometimes become charged simply by touching it with another charged object. In this case, the object is charged by direct contact, or conduction. An object can also be charged by an object that is already charged, without contact between them. This newly charged object is said to be charged by **induction.** The charge on an object can be detected by using a device called an electroscope.

In this investigation, you will construct an electroscope and use it to explore charging by friction, conduction, and induction.

Problem

How do electrons move when objects become charged?

Pre-Lab Discussion

Read the entire investigation. Then, work with a partner to answer the following questions.

1. **Forming Hypotheses** What hypotheses are to be tested in this investigation?

   Students may hypothesize that objects charged by friction and induction will

   have opposite charges, while objects charged by conduction will have like charges.

   _____

   _____

   _____

   _____

2. **Predicting** When the balloon is rubbed with flannel, in what manner will the balloon become charged?

   Electrons are transferred between objects that are rubbed together. The objects become charged

   by friction.

   _____

3. **Predicting** What type of electron transfer will take place when the electroscope is touched by the balloon?

   The electroscope will be temporarily charged (or electrons will be transferred) by direct contact,

   or conduction.

   _____

4. Predicting When the charged glass rod is held near the electroscope and then moved away, what type of electron transfer will occur?

The electroscope will be temporarily charged (or electrons will be transferred) without contact,

by induction.

5. Drawing Conclusions What is the purpose of this investigation?

That electron transfer takes place between objects in several ways, always resulting in

those objects becoming charged

Materials *(per group)*

scissors	very thin aluminum foil from a gum wrapper	string
cardboard	masking tape	glass rod
glass jar	2 balloons	silk
thick wire	wool flannel	
aluminum foil		

Safety 🔥🔪✋

Put on safety goggles. Be careful to avoid breakage when working with glassware. Be careful when handling sharp instruments. Observe proper laboratory procedures when using electrical equipment. Note all safety alert symbols next to the steps in the Procedure and review the meaning of each symbol by referring to the Safety Symbols on page xiii.

Procedure

Allow two class periods for this investigation. In the first period (Procedure Steps 1–4), students will build and test an electroscope. In the second period (Steps 5–10), they will use the device to detect and identify charges. Carry out the investigation on a dry day.

1. To build an electroscope, cut out a circle of cardboard slightly larger than the opening of the glass jar. Use the point of the scissors to make a small hole in the center of the cardboard. **CAUTION:** *Be careful not to cut yourself when handling sharp instruments.*

2. Push the wire through the hole in the cardboard. Bend one end of the wire to form an L-shaped hook, as shown in Figure 1. Crumple the aluminum foil into a ball and push it onto the other end of the wire. **CAUTION:** *Use care when handling wire; it can cut or puncture skin.*

- Aluminum ball
- Cardboard circle
- Tape
- Jar
- Copper wire
- Thin foil leaves

Figure 1

3. Cut a small strip of thin foil from a gum wrapper. Fold the foil strip in half and hang it over the hook so that the two leaves of foil hang down side by side. Lower the cardboard lid assembly onto the jar and tape it in place. **CAUTION:** *Be careful when handling sharp instruments.* Collect scissors from students when they are finished cutting the foil strips.

4. Inflate the two balloons and tie the ends so that the air does not escape.

5. To test your electroscope, rub one of the inflated balloons with the wool flannel. This will give the balloon a negative charge and the wool a positive charge. Gently touch the rubbed part of the balloon to the aluminum ball of your electroscope. The foil leaves should move apart. (*Hint: If they do not move, remove the lid from the jar and check that the leaves are not stuck together.*) Touch the top of the electroscope with your hand.

6. Tie a piece of string to the end of each balloon. Rub both balloons with the wool flannel. Hang both balloons by their string and bring the rubbed parts of the balloons together. Observe what happens.

7. Hold the wool flannel near one of the hanging balloons. Observe what happens.

8. Touch one of the charged balloons to the top of the electroscope. Record what happens in the data table.

9. Move the balloon away. Record what happens in the data table.

10. Touch the top of the electroscope with your hand and again record what happens in the data table.

11. Rub the glass rod with the silk. Doing this gives a positive charge to the glass and a negative charge to the silk. Touch the glass rod to the electroscope. Record what happens in the data table.

12. Move the glass rod away from the electroscope. Again, record what happens in the data table. Touch the electroscope with your hand.

13. Rub one of the balloons again with the wool. Move the balloon close to but not touching the top of the electroscope. Record what happens in the data table.

14. Move the balloon away from the electroscope. Record what happens in the data table.

15. Rub the glass rod again with the silk. Hold the glass close to but not touching the electroscope. Record what happens in the data table.

16. Move the glass rod away. Record what happens in the data table.

Observations   Sample data are shown.

DATA TABLE

Procedure Step Number	Action	Observation of Electroscope Leaves
8	Rubbed balloon touches electroscope	Move apart
9	After touching, balloon is moved away	Stay apart
10	Hand touches electroscope	Move back together
11	Rubbed glass rod touches electroscope	Move apart
12	Rubbed glass rod is moved away	Stay apart
13	Rubbed balloon held near	Move apart
14	Rubbed balloon moved away	Move back together
15	Rubbed glass held near rod	Move apart
16	Rubbed glass rod is moved away	Move back together

Analysis and Conclusions

1. **Observing** After being rubbed with wool flannel, what happened to the balloons in Step 6 when they were brought near each other?

   The balloons repelled from each other.

2. **Observing** What happens to an electroscope that indicates that a charged object is near?

   The leaves of an electroscope separate when a charged object is near.

3. **Inferring** Recall that rubbing a balloon with flannel gives the balloon a negative charge. Does the balloon gain or lose electrons in this situation? Is this an example of charging by friction, contact, or induction?

   The balloon gains electrons when rubbed with wool flannel. This is an example of charging by

   friction.

4. **Inferring** By what method was the electroscope charged in Step 8? Did the leaves become positively or negatively charged? What happened when the charged glass rod touched the electroscope in Step 11?

   The electroscope was charged by conduction when touched by the balloon. Because electrons

   moved to the electroscope, the leaves became negatively charged. The electroscope lost electrons

   and became positively charged when touched by the glass rod.

5. **Inferring** What happened to the charged electroscope when you touched it with your hand in Step 10? Did the electroscope gain or lose electrons?

   The electrons moved from the electroscope to your hand. The electroscope lost electrons.

6. **Inferring** Why did the electroscope leaves behave as they did when the charged balloon was brought near in Step 13? Did any electrons from the balloon move into the electroscope?

Electrons in the top of the electroscope were repelled from the negatively charged balloon.

They moved to the leaves, giving the leaves a negative charge. Like charges repel, and the leaves

moved apart. No electrons, however, entered the electroscope.

7. **Inferring** Why did the electroscope leaves behave as they did when the charged balloon was moved away in Step 14?

Once the balloon was moved away, the surplus electrons in the leaves moved back to the top and

the leaves moved together. The net charge on the electroscope is still zero.

8. **Classifying** Explain what happened when the charged glass rod was held near and then moved away from the electroscope in Steps 15 and 16. Was the electroscope charged by friction, conduction, or induction?

Electrons in the leaves were attracted to the glass rod and moved to the top. A shortage of electrons

existed in the leaves, leaving both positively charged, and they repelled. Since no contact was made

and therefore no electrons entered the electroscope, this is charging by induction.

9. **Comparing and Contrasting** Compare the three methods of charging in terms of electron movement.

In charging by friction, electrons are rubbed off one object onto another. In charging by friction,

electrons are rubbed off one object onto another. In charging by conduction, electrons move from

one object to another when the objects are in direct contact. In charging by induction, electrons are

rearranged within an object only; electrons do not transfer between objects.

Go Further

Design an experiment to compare how much different substances are charged by friction. Show your plan to your teacher. When your teacher approves your plan, carry out your experiment and report your results and conclusions.

Examine student plans for sound experimental design and safety. Students will need to place a scale on the inner wall of the electroscope to measure the amount that the leaves are separated. Then, they will have to test how the angle between the leaves varies with the distance of a charged object from the top of the electroscope. Controlled variables such as the distance between the electroscope and the charged object, and the number of times the objects are rubbed together need to be described in the experimental design.

Studying Electromagnetic Induction

Background Information

In 1831, Michael Faraday discovered that when a coil of wire is moved in a magnetic field, an electric current is generated, or induced, in the wire. This process is called electromagnetic induction. A current is generated only if the wire is part of a circuit. The current is induced because in the frame of reference of the wire, the magnetic field is changing.

In this investigation, you will move a bar magnet through a coil of wire to induce a current. You will use a simple galvanometer (a second coil of wire wrapped around a compass) to detect the induced current. In this galvanometer, the compass needle responds to the magnetic field produced by the induced current.

Problem

How can you measure an electric current in a a wire using a magnetic compass?

Pre-Lab Discussion

Read the entire investigation. Then, work with a partner to answer the following questions.

1. **Inferring** Why does a compass needle move?

   A compass needle moves so that it aligns with a magnetic field. If the magnetic field changes,

   the compass needle moves to realign.

2. **Inferring** Why does a moving magnet produce a changing magnetic field?

   The field lines of a stationary magnet are also stationary. Therefore, at any one point, the magnetic

   field is constant. But if the magnet moves, then at any one point, the magnetic field can change as

   a stronger or weaker part of the field crosses that point.

3. **Predicting** What will happen when the number of turns in the coil in the 3-m wire is increased? Explain your answer.

   Students may predict that the current will increase. If the current increases, then this should cause

   a greater deflection in the compass needle because a stronger current produces a stronger

   magnetic field.

4. Predicting What will happen when the magnet is moved back and forth inside the coil? Explain your answer.

The current will move first in one direction and then the other because the force on the electrons in

the wire is changing direction. Students may not realize this is an alternating current.

Materials *(per group)*

connecting wire with bare ends, 1 m in length
connecting wire with bare ends, 3 m in length
magnetic compass
bar magnet

Safety ▨

Use caution when connecting wires. Note all safety alert symbols next to the steps in the Procedure and review the meaning of each symbol by referring to the Safety Symbols on page xiii.

Procedure

1. Using a piece of wire 1 m long, wrap a coil with 20 turns of wire around the compass, as shown in Figure 1.

Figure 1

2. Place the compass on a table or other flat surface. Rotate the compass to align the compass needle with the wire.

3. In the middle of the 3-m length of wire, wind a coil with ten turns of wire around your finger. The coil should be large enough for the bar magnet to fit through.

▨ 4. Connect the two coils of wire by twisting the bare ends of the wires together, as shown in Figure 2. **CAUTION:** *Be careful when handling the sharp ends of wires; they can puncture skin.* The second coil should be at least 1 m away from the compass so that the magnet does not directly affect the compass needle. Hold the compass in a horizontal position so the needle moves freely.

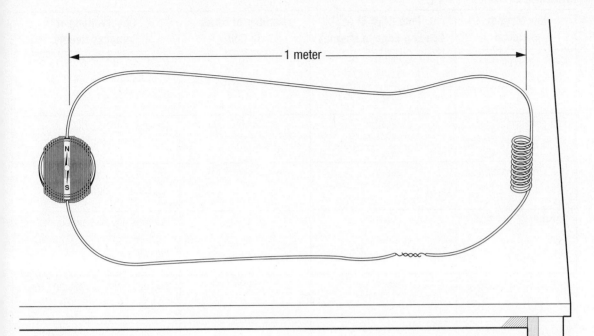

Figure 2

5. Slowly push the north pole of the bar magnet into the coil of wire. Have a partner observe what happens to the compass needle. Record your observations in the data table.

6. Have your partner observe what happens to the compass needle as you slowly pull the magnet out of the coil of wire. Record your observations in the data table.

7. Add ten more loops of wire to the coil in the 3-m wire. Then, repeat Steps 5 and 6.

8. Repeat Steps 5 and 6, but this time make the south pole of the magnet the leading edge.

9. Repeat Steps 5 and 6, but this time move the magnet quickly instead of slowly.

10. Try pushing and pulling the magnet continuously into and out of the coil. Record your observations in the data table.

Name _____ Class _____ Date _____

Observations

Note that the actual directions (clockwise or counterclockwise) that students record will depend on the direction in which they wind the turns of the coil that surrounds the comp...

DATA TABLE

How Magnet Is Moved	Pole (N or S) at Leading Edge of Magnet	Number of Turns in Coil	Observations of Compass Needle
Push inward slowly	North	10	Compass needle deflects and then returns to its original position.
Pull outward slowly	North	10	Compass needle deflects in opposite direction.
Push inward slowly	North	20	Compass needle deflects by a greater amount.
Pull outward slowly	North	20	Compass needle deflects by a greater amount in opposite direction.
Push inward slowly	South	20	The deflection is reversed by using the opposite pole.
Pull outward slowly	South	20	The deflection is reversed by using the opposite pole.
Push inward quickly	South	20	The deflection is even greater.
Pull outward quickly	South	20	The deflection is even greater in the opposite direction.
Push and pull continuously	South	20	The compass needle vibrates back and forth.

Analysis and Conclusions

1. **Observing** Explain what you observed happening when you moved a magnet in a coil of wire.

When the magnet was moved into or out of the coil of wire, the wire crossed magnetic field lines

surrounding the magnet. This changing magnetic field caused an electric current to be induced in

the wire, as shown by the deflection of the compass needle.

_____

_____

2. **Drawing Conclusions** How does the number of turns in the coil affect the current in the wire?

The more turns in the coil there are, the greater is the current in the wire.

3. **Drawing Conclusions** How did changing the pole of the magnet affect the direction of the current in the wire? How can you tell?

Changing the pole of the magnet reversed the direction of the current. The compass needle was

deflected in the opposite direction.

4. **Predicting** Would a current be induced in the wire if you did not move the magnet? Why or why not?

No, because the magnetic field lines would not be crossed if there was no motion.

5. **Predicting** Would a current be induced if you moved the coil of wire instead of the magnet? Why or why not?

Yes, because the magnetic field lines are crossed if either the magnet or the wire is moved.

6. **Inferring** What kind of current was induced in Step 10? Explain your answer.

An alternating current was induced. The compass needle continually reversed because the direction

of current continuously reversed.

Go Further

What do you think would happen if you made a coil of wire by first winding ten turns of wire in one direction and then winding ten turns in the opposite direction? Try it and find out.

The current may start but then suddenly stop. Depending on how the coil is wound, the magnet may move into the first part of the coil and induce a current. As soon as it is moving through both coils, however, there will be no current because the effects from the two coils will cancel.

Making a Compass

Refer students to pages 630–633 in their textbook for a discussion of magnet fields and magnetic materials. **SKILLS FOCUS:** Predicting, Observing, Inferring **CLASS TIME:** 25 minutes

Background Information

A compass is basically a floating magnet used to find directions. It responds to the magnetic poles of Earth. The north-seeking pole of the floating magnet points in the northern direction and is therefore called the north pole of the compass. The south-seeking pole of the floating magnet points in the southern direction and is therefore called the south pole of the compass.

The Earth's magnetic pole in the northern hemisphere is located in the Hudson Bay region of northern Canada, nearly 1800 km from the geographical North Pole. The magnetic pole in the southern hemisphere is south of Australia.

In this investigation, you will use a permanent magnet and a needle to make a floating compass. You will then test your compass by comparing it to a standard compass.

Problem

How accurate is a classroom compass that you make?

Pre-Lab Discussion

Read the entire investigation. Then, work with a partner to answer the following questions.

1. **Predicting** What do you expect to happen when you hold the north pole of a bar magnet near a compass needle?

   The south pole of the compass needle will be attracted to the north pole of the magnet.

   _____

   _____

2. **Predicting** In what direction do you expect the magnetized needle to point when you magnetize it with the south pole of the bar magnet? Explain your answer.

   Students may predict that the needle will point north. The south pole of the bar magnet aligns

   the atoms in the needle so that the tip of the needle closest to the magnet becomes a north

   magnetic pole.

   _____

3. **Designing Experiments** Why is it important to stroke the needle with the magnet in only one direction?

   By stroking in only one direction, the atoms in the needle will magnetically align in one direction.

   In this way, the needle becomes magnetized.

   _____

4. **Applying Concepts** How do the properties of magnets make it possible to use compasses?

The poles of a magnet are attracted to the opposite magnetic poles of Earth. Because the

geographical positions of Earth's magnetic poles are known, magnets can be used in compasses

to determine direction.

_____

_____

_____

_____

_____

5. **Applying Concepts** Why might the use of a compass mislead you if you were seeking geographic north?

Earth's magnetic poles are not at the geographic poles. If a compass is to be used to find

geographic north or south, an angle between the magnetic poles and the geographic poles must

be taken into account.

_____

_____

_____

_____

Materials (per group)
magnetic compass
permanent bar magnet
file
cork strip or disk, 3 cm in length or diameter
grease pencil
petri dish or other shallow dish
2 needles

Safety 🔲 ✂ ✂
Be careful to avoid breakage when working with glassware. Be careful when handling sharp instruments. Note all safety alert symbols next to the steps in the Procedure and review the meaning of each symbol by referring to the Safety Symbols on page xiii.

Procedure
🔲 1. Use the grease pencil to label one point on the side of a petri dish with the letter N. Label the point on the opposite side S. Label with an E the point that is to the right when the S is closest to you. Label with a W the point that is on the left of S. Make an intermediate marking at each of the four positions midway between the pairs of letters.

2. Obtain a bar magnet. If its north and south poles are not marked (with an *N* and an *S*), place one end near the north-pointing end of a magnetic compass. If the compass needle is deflected, the end of the bar magnet is its north pole. If the compass needle is attracted, the end of the bar magnet is its south pole.

✂ 3. Use the file to make a straight, shallow groove lengthwise on the cork strip or disk. **CAUTION:** *Be careful when handling sharp instruments.*

✂ 4. Hold the needle at its eye end (the end with the opening in it). Stroke the needle at least ten times along the south pole of the bar magnet. The strokes should all be in the same direction and should all start near the eye end of the needle. Do not use a back-and-forth motion. Instead, lift the needle each time you bring it back to its starting position for the next stroke.

5. Move the bar magnet at least a meter from where you are working so that it will not interfere with your observations.

6. Fill the labeled petri dish halfway with water. Float the cork groove side up in the water so that it floats freely.

7. Lay the stroked needle inside the groove in the cork. Observe what happens. Rotate the cork by 90° in either direction. Again, observe what happens.

8. Repeat Steps 4 through 7, using a different needle and stroking the needle along the bar magnet's north pole. You must stroke the new needle in exactly the same direction as in Step 4.

9. To check the accuracy of your floating compass, compare its orientation with that of the standard magnetic compass. Turn the dish so that the *N* and *S* markings you made are oriented like those on the standard compass.

If the needle is stroked by accident in the opposite direction, the opposite pole is produced.

Observations

1. What happened when you floated the cork with the needle that was stroked along the magnet's south pole? What happened when you tried to turn the cork in other directions?

   The needle and cork turned so that the tip of the needle pointed north. The cork returned to this

   orientation after it was turned.

   _____

   _____

2. What happened when you floated the cork with the needle that was stroked along the magnet's north pole? What happened when you tried to turn the cork in other directions?

   The needle and cork turned so that the tip of the needle pointed south. The cork returned to this

   orientation after it was turned.

   _____

Analysis and Conclusions

1. **Observing** Which needle for the floating compass lined up in the same way as the needle of a standard magnetic compass?

   The needle stroked by the south pole of the bar magnet lined up the same way.

2. **Inferring** How could you use your floating compass to find east? To find southwest?

   When the dish is turned so that the north pole of the needle points toward the N marked on the dish,

   east will be directly to the right, and southwest will be in the direction of the mark between the W

   and S markings.

3. **Inferring** What does the magnetic polarity of your compass tell about the polarity of Earth's magnetic poles?

   Earth's magnetic poles are opposite their geographical locations. Because the north magnetic pole

   of the compass points north, the Earth's magnetic pole near geographical north must be a south

   magnetic pole. Similarly, the pole near Earth's south geographical pole is a north magnetic pole.

Go Further

Try to improve on the design of your compass. For example, you can find ways to reduce friction in the compass so that the needle aligns with Earth's magnetic field more easily. Think of other designs that do not require the use of liquid in a petri dish. Write a description of your improved design. When your teacher has approved your design, carry it out and test it, using all necessary safety procedures. Report your observations and conclusions.

Review student designs for appropriateness and difficulty before students begin testing. Suggestions that can help students are to reduce surface contact between the water and the needle, the use of less viscous fluids in the petri dish, or eliminating fluid resistance by devising ways of suspending a magnet in air.

Chapter 22   Earth's Interior

Investigation 22A

Identifying Rocks

Refer students to pages 670–675 in their textbooks for a general discussion of rocks. **SKILLS:** Observing, Classifying, Using Tables and Graphs **CLASS TIME:** 45 minutes

Background Information

A rock is a solid combination of one or more minerals or other materials. Geologists classify rocks into three major groups (igneous, sedimentary, and metamorphic) based on how the rocks form. To identify rocks, geologists observe a rock's texture—the size, shape, and arrangement of the crystals and other particles that make up the rock.

Igneous rock forms from magma that cools either underground (intrusive rock) or on Earth's surface (extrusive rock). Intrusive rocks cool slowly, allowing crystals to grow larger and giving the rock a coarse-grained texture. Extrusive rocks cool quickly and have a fine-grained, or even glassy, texture.

Sedimentary rock forms from sediment that is squeezed and cemented together. Sedimentary rocks that form from the broken fragments of other rocks are called clastic rocks. The fragments might be fairly large, such as pebbles, somewhat smaller, such as grains of sand, or very small, such as grains of clay. Other kinds of sedimentary rock include chemical rocks, which form when minerals precipitate out of solution, and organic rocks, which form when the shells and skeletons of marine animals become compacted and cemented together over time.

Metamorphic rock forms from rock that has been changed by temperature, pressure, or chemical reactions. Metamorphic rocks may be foliated, in which the particles are arranged in parallel bands, or nonfoliated, in which the particles are not arranged in bands.

In this investigation, you will learn how to identify the three major types of rocks as well as some rock types within each major category.

Problem

What are the identifying properties of rocks?

Pre-Lab Discussion

Read the entire investigation. Then, work with a partner to answer the following questions.

1. Inferring What is the purpose of this investigation?

The purpose of this investigation is to categorize and identify the major types of rocks.

_____

_____

_____

_____

_____

2. **Observing** What property distinguishes the two main types of igneous rock? Explain your answer.

Grain size distinguishes intrusive igneous rock from extrusive igneous rock. Intrusive rocks

have larger grains than do extrusive rocks.

3. **Drawing Conclusions** Chalk is made of tiny fragments of marine animals. What kind of rock is chalk?

Chalk is an organic sedimentary rock.

4. **Drawing Conclusions** If you have a rock that has parallel bands in it, what kind of rock might you have? Might it be another type of rock? Explain your answer.

It might be a foliated metamorphic rock. However, it might be a sedimentary rock, which

also sometimes has bands. Other observations would have to be made to identify the rock.

Materials (per group)

igneous rocks

sedimentary rocks

metamorphic rocks

Hand lens

Dropper bottle of dilute
  hydrochloric acid (HCl)

Paper towels

Safety 🗣️👓✂️🧪

Put on safety goggles and wear plastic disposable gloves when handling chemicals, as they may irritate the skin or stain skin or clothing. Never touch or taste a chemical unless instructed to do so. Note all safety alert symbols next to the steps in the Procedure and review the meaning of each symbol by referring to the Safety Symbols on page xiii.

Provide students with a variety of rock specimens from all three major types. Examples: igneous—basalt, granite, and obsidian; sedimentary—limestone, sandstone, and shale; metamorphic—marble, slate, and schist. Choose specimens so that at least most of them will be identifiable by using the key in Figure 1. You may have to help students identify the specimens that are more difficult.

If so, discuss the properties of that specimen or the subtleties that make identification difficult. Identify each specimen with a letter either by using masking tape and a marker or by painting a small solid white circle on the rock and marking the circle. Prepare a 1M solution of HCl by slowly adding 82 mL of concentrated (12M) HCl to 500 mL of distilled water in a flask. Then fill the flask with distilled water to the 1000 mL mark.

Name _____ Class _____ Date _____

Procedure

1. Choose one of the rock samples provided by your teacher. Observe its texture, color, and other properties.

2. Use the key in Figure 1 to identify the sample. Begin by reading the first question. Answer yes or no based on your observations.

3. After Yes or No, you will find a phrase telling you to proceed to another question. Continue working through the key in this way until you come to a phrase that identifies your rock sample. In the data table, record the route that you take through the key, using the numbers of the questions. Then, record the type of rock you have identified.

4. Work through the key for each of your samples to identify them.

5. Check your identifications with the true identifications from your teacher.

Figure 1 Key to Identification of Some Rocks

1. Does the rock contain visible interlocking crystals?	Yes: Go to Step 2.
	No: Go to Step 4.
2. Are all of the crystals the same color and shape?	Yes: nonfoliated metamorphic (possibly marble or quartzite)
	No: Go to Step 3.
3. Are all of the crystals in a mixed "salt-and-pepper" pattern?	Yes: intrusive igneous (possibly granite or diorite)
	No: foliated metamorphic (possibly schist or gneiss)
4. Does the rock contain many small holes or have a uniform dark appearance?	Yes: extrusive igneous (possibly pumice or basalt)
	No: Go to Step 5.
5. Is the rock glassy, like broken black or brown glass?	Yes: extrusive igneous (obsidian)
	No: Go to Step 6.
6. Is the rock made of strong, flat sheets that can be split in layers?	Yes: foliated metamorphic (slate)
	No: Go to Step 7.
7. Does the rock contain pebbles, sand, or smaller particles cemented together?	Yes: clastic sedimentary (possibly conglomerate or sandstone)
	No: Go to Step 8.
8. Does the rock fizz when dilute HCl is added to it?	Yes: chemical or organic sedimentary (limestone or chalk)
	No: Ask your teacher for help.

Note: Answer Question 8 by placing the rock on a paper towel, then placing a single drop of HCl on the rock. **CAUTION:** *Wear safety goggles and disposable gloves when using the HCl.*

Observations Data will vary depending on samples chosen.

Letter of Sample	Route Taken	Identity of Rock Sample

Analysis and Conclusions

1. **Evaluating and Revising** How difficult was it to use the key to identify your rock samples? What problems did you encounter?

   Answers will depend partly on how clearly the samples represent the rock type. Students

   may encounter difficulty if samples appear to exhibit properties of more than one rock type or

   have subtle properties.

   _____

   _____

   _____

   _____

   _____

   _____

2. **Evaluating and Revising** For each sample that you incorrectly identified, retrace the route you took through the key. Do you need to correct your route? If so, write it below. If not, why might you have incorrectly identified the sample?

   If the route was correct, yet the rock is incorrectly identified, it might be because the key does

   not provide enough information for identification of that sample.

   _____

   _____

   _____

   _____

   _____

   _____

   _____

   _____

3. **Generalizing** How helpful is a rock's color in identifying the rock? Explain your answer.

   Color is not very helpful for identification. Often, more than one kind of rock has the same color.

   Also, a particular kind of rock often has more than one color.

   _____

   _____

   _____

   _____

   _____

   _____

4. **Comparing and Contrasting** Which two of the rock samples were the easiest to identify? What properties made them easy to identify?

Answers may include rocks that have distinguishing properties such as the glassy

texture of obsidian, the fizzing of HCl in contact with limestone, or the bands or layers

of a foliated metamorphic rock.

_____

_____

_____

_____

_____

_____

_____

_____

_____

_____

Go Further

Collect several rock samples from the area around your home or school and attempt to identify them by using the key in this investigation.

Students should be able to find a variety of rocks. Suggest that they look in different places to get the greatest variety, such as road sides, along a creek, in a field, and so on.

🔍 **Investigation 22B**

Recovering Oil

Refer students to pages 267 and 667 in their textbooks for general discussions of petroleum and density. **SKILLS FOCUS:** Predicting, Inferring, Comparing and Contrasting **CLASS TIME:** 45 minutes

Background Information

Crude oil, or petroleum, is usually found beneath nonporous rock in underground deposits. The petroleum can be recovered by a well pipe lowered to the deposit through a drilled hole. In some cases, the petroleum is automatically pushed up by the pressure of underground water. In other cases, however, pressure must be applied by methods involving pumping water into the petroleum deposit. This method works because petroleum is less dense than water and so will float on top of it.

In this investigation, you will use various methods to recover the maximum amount of oil from a pump bottle.

Problem

How does water affect the recovery of oil from a petroleum deposit?

Pre-Lab Discussion

Read the entire investigation. Then, work with a partner to answer the following questions.

1. **Predicting** What do you expect to happen when you add water to the bottle after the first attempt to remove the oil has been made? Do you expect more oil to be brought up after adding cold water or hot water? Explain your answer.

   Additional oil will be brought up along with the added water. Hot water will make the oil more fluid,
   _____
   so more oil should be brought up after adding hot water.
   _____
   _____

2. **Applying Concepts** Would you expect more oil to be removed by using hot water or cold water? Explain your answer.

   Hot water should remove more water. The higher temperature of the water will increase the
   _____
   temperature of the oil, making it flow more easily and so removing it from small places between
   _____
   the rocks.
   _____
   _____
   _____

3. **Applying Concepts** How does adding water increase pressure within a petroleum deposit?

   By adding water to the oil in the deposit, the total amount of fluid within the deposit increases.
   _____
   Because the volume of the deposit does not expand, this added material will cause an increase
   _____
   in pressure.
   _____
   _____

4. Inferring What properties of oil makes water the preferred substance for pushing oil up to Earth's surface?

Oil is less dense than water and so will float on the water. The oil will therefore be pushed to the

top levels of the deposit.

_____

_____

_____

5. Controlling Variables Why must the investigation be repeated with hot water after it has been performed with cold water?

By performing the investigation first with cold water and again with hot water, all variables

except water temperature will be controlled. Therefore, the effect of water temperature can be more

clearly observed.

_____

_____

_____

Materials *(per group)* Collect the oil to reuse in the next class.

plastic bottle with spray pump
plastic tubing to fit the pump nozzle
pebbles (enough to half-fill the plastic bottle)
2 graduated cylinders
200 mL of vegetable or mineral oil

4 250-mL beakers
cold tap water
hot tap water
paper towels
clock or watch

Safety

Be careful to avoid breakage when working with glassware. Use extreme care when working with hot water to avoid burns. Wash your hands thoroughly after carrying out this investigation. Note all safety alert symbols next to the steps in the Procedure and review the meaning of each symbol by referring to the Safety Symbols on page xiii.

Procedure

1. Build a model of an oil pump, as shown in Figure 1. Remove the spray pump top of the spray bottle and half-fill the spray bottle with clean pebbles.

Figure 1

2. Use a graduated cylinder to measure 100 mL of vegetable or mineral oil and pour the oil into the bottle. **CAUTION:** *Be careful to avoid breakage when working with glassware. Be careful not to spill any oil onto your clothing. Immediately wipe up any spilled water or oil.*

3. Place the spray-pump top back onto the bottle while working its tube down through the pebbles. Attach the plastic tubing to the nozzle and place the other end of the tubing into a 250-mL beaker.

4. Use the spray pump to remove as much oil as you can from the bottle within 5 minutes. Use the graduated cylinder to measure the amount of oil removed. Record this information in the data table.

5. Measure 80 mL of cold tap water in the second graduated cylinder and add this water to the spray bottle. Attempt to pump as much liquid as possible into the second beaker within 5 minutes. Let the mixture stand for 1 or 2 minutes so that the oil and water separate. Carefully pour into the first graduated cylinder the oil layer that is on top of the water in the beaker. Record in the data table how much oil you collected.

6. Rinse the bottle and pebbles with hot water to remove any excess oil and wipe them dry with paper towels. Place the used oil in a container designated by your teacher. Clean the first graduated cylinder and add 100 mL of fresh oil.

7. Repeat Steps 1 through 5, but in Step 5, use 80 mL of hot tap water instead of cold water. Record in the data table the amount of oil collected. Place the used oil in a container designated by your teacher. The water with traces of oil can be poured down the sink. **CAUTION:** *Use extreme care when working with hot water to avoid burns. Wash your hands thoroughly after carrying out this investigation.*

Observations   Sample data are shown.

DATA TABLE

	Oil Added to Bottle (mL)	Oil Removed Before Adding Water (mL)	Oil Removed After Adding Water (mL)
Cold water	99.0–101.0	50.0–65.0	15.0–20.0
Hot water	99.0–101.0	50.0–65.0	25.0–30.0

Analysis and Conclusions

1. **Analyzing Data** How did your results compare with your prediction?

   The prediction that hot water would remove more oil than cold water was confirmed by the results.

   _____

   _____

   _____

2. **Observing** Why were you unable to remove all the oil from the bottle when you pumped it in Step 4?

   Some of the oil clung to the pebbles.

   _____

   _____

   _____

3. **Applying Concepts** Explain the effect of adding cold water.

   Cold water removed some of the oil that was around the pebbles, allowing more oil to be pumped.

   _____

   _____

   _____

4. **Applying Concepts** Explain the effect of adding hot water.

   As well as removing oil around the pebbles, hot water rendered the oil more fluid and more easily

   separated and pumped.

   _____

   _____

Go Further

Repeat the investigation, using different kinds of oil to determine how the density and thickness, or viscosity, of the oil affects recovery. Show your plan to your teacher. When your teacher approves your plan, carry out your experiment and report your results.

Review student designs for appropriateness and difficulty before students begin testing. If samples of motor oil are used, be sure that the investigation is performed under your supervision and that all oil is collected and taken to a garage for proper disposal.

Using a Contour Map to Create a Landform

Refer students to pages 706–708 and 713–717 in their textbooks for a discussion of fresh water motion, deposition, and erosion. **SKILLS FOCUS:** Measuring, Inferring, Using Models, Interpreting Diagrams/Photographs **CLASS TIME:** 60 minutes

Background Information

Water is responsible for shaping much of Earth. For example, the southeastern part of the United States is part of a coastal plain that was deposited by water. The coastal plain is a flat, fertile plain that gently slopes down to the coast from the mountains farther inland. Much of the coastal plain is underlain with limestone and other water-deposited rocks. The surface soil tends to be chiefly sand or clay. These conditions produce a somewhat flat landscape except where interrupted by unusual rock formations, tectonic uplift, or depressions such as **sinkholes.**

One of the tools that scientists use to study the landscape and its history is a contour map. Contour maps are also called topographic maps. The high and low elevations created by mountains, hills, and valleys cannot be observed on a typical map. Contour maps show differences in elevation, or height above sea level, and outline the shapes, or contours, of the landscape by using contour lines. A contour line connects the points on a map that have the same elevation. The contour interval is the difference in elevation between one contour line and the next contour line.

In this investigation, you will interpret the contour lines of a topographic map and use them to create a three-dimensional model, or landform, of the region shown on the map.

Problem

How can you use a contour map to create a landform?

Pre-Lab Discussion

Read the entire investigation. Then, work with a partner to answer the following questions.

1. **Using Models** What is the advantage of creating a landform from a topographic map?

   A landform makes it easier to visualize elevation and, therefore, to interpret the form of the land
   _____
   in three dimensions.
   _____
   _____
   _____
   _____
   _____
   _____
   _____

2. Applying Concepts Why does the land vary so much throughout the United States?

The processes of erosion and deposition, as well as the interactions between tectonic plates,

have had different effects on the land in various parts of United States. These processes have

resulted in the great geographical variety observed.

_____

_____

_____

3. Applying Concepts How does a topographic map illustrate the elevation of the land?

Contour maps show differences in elevation through the use of contour lines. A contour line

connects points on a map that have the same elevation.

_____

_____

_____

_____

4. Applying Concepts What do all contour intervals on a single topographic map have in common? Why is this done?

Contour intervals indicate the change in elevation between contour lines on a given topographic map.

In this way, the scale for elevation can be made constant for a given map, just as the distance scale

for the other two dimensions is constant.

_____

_____

_____

_____

_____

5. Using Models What do narrow contour intervals indicate? What do wide contour intervals indicate? Explain your answers.

A narrow contour interval indicates a relatively steep change in elevation. This is because the

change in elevation indicated by the contour interval occurs over a small lateral distance. A wide

contour interval indicates a relatively small change in elevation. This is because the change in

elevation indicated by the contour interval occurs over a large lateral distance.

_____

_____

_____

_____

_____

Materials (per group)

transparent plastic box with lid
nonpermanent marking pen
enlarged photocopy of a regional contour map
modeling clay
meter ruler

Make an enlarged photocopy of either the Northeast, Southeast, or Midwest contour map shown in Figure 3 for each group of students. The copy should be slightly smaller than the box lid used in the Procedure.

Procedure

1. Place the contour map provided by your teacher inside the lid of the plastic box so that the map can be seen through the top side of the lid. Secure the map to the lid by using small pieces of masking tape near the corners. Using a nonpermanent marking pen, trace the contour map onto the box lid. Then, remove the contour map from the lid.

2. Using the marking pen and a ruler, make a centimeter scale on one of the vertical sides of the transparent box. Start by making a mark at the bottom edge of the box. Then, continue to make marks at centimeter intervals upward along the side of the box until you reach the top of the box, as in Figure 1.

3. Find the lowest elevation on the regional contour map. Write this elevation next to the bottom edge of the box.

4. Find the contour interval for your regional map. Each centimeter mark on the side of the box will represent the same vertical distance as the contour interval. Next to each cm mark, write the elevation in meters.

5. Using modeling clay, construct the first layer of the landform shown in your regional contour map. Start at the lowest elevation and work your way up to the next contour interval.

6. When you have finished the first layer of the landform, check it for accuracy. Do this by placing the lid with the contour map on top of the box. Looking down through the lid, compare the landform with the corresponding contour lines shown on the map, as in Figure 2.

7. Repeat Steps 5 and 6 for each layer of the landform until all of the contour lines of the map have a corresponding level on the landform.

Figure 1

258 m
252 m
246 m
240 m

Figure 2

Observations

1. Describe the shape of the landform you made.

Answers will vary depending on the accuracy of student models and the map used,

but they should resemble one or two low mounds.

_____

_____

2. How many meters above sea level is the base of the landform?

Answers will vary depending on the map used. The base for the Southeast map is at 24 m,

the Northeast map is 730 m, and the Midwest map is 240 m.

_____

_____

3. What is the contour interval of the contour map you used to make the landform?

Answers will vary depending on the map used. The contour interval for the Southeast map is 3 m,

the Northeast map is 30 m, and the Midwest map is 6 m.

_____

_____

Analysis and Conclusions

1. Analyzing Data What does your landform indicate about the region modeled?

Answers will vary depending on the map used. The Southeast and Midwest maps indicate fairly

flat topography with gradual changes in elevation. The regions modeled are fairly flat plains. The

map of the Northeast indicates a much steeper landform. The region modeled is hilly.

_____

_____

2. Drawing Conclusions What might you conclude about the type of region that you modeled? Explain your answer.

Answers will vary depending on the map used. The Southeast and Midwest maps indicate gently

sloping land, which is typical of floodplains. The Northeast map indicates a hilly region, which

could be formed from material that has not been affected by weathering or erosion or

or could be associated with tectonic uplift throughout the region.

_____

_____

_____

3. **Using Models** Look at the contour maps in Figure 3. How does the feature in the map for the Southwest differ from the features depicted in the other maps?

The map for the Southwest shows a feature that is higher at the edges and drops in elevation

toward the center. This is a map of a canyon or gorge. The other maps indicate hills or rising

areas of plains.

_____

_____

_____

_____

_____

4. **Inferring** Compare the contour map for the Southeast with the contour map for the Southwest. Do you think the feature in the map for the Southwest was also formed by water? Explain your answer.

Students should note that the Grand Canyon was also formed by water but the processes were

different—deposition versus erosion.

_____

_____

_____

_____

_____

Go Further

Repeat the investigation, using one of the two other maps shown in Figure 3 or find a contour map of a different region and model it with a landform. Be sure to choose a region that does not cover too large an area or does not have too great an elevation change so that your landform will still be reasonably accurate. First, show your selected map to your teacher. When your teacher approves your plan, carry out the investigation.

Be sure that students choose a small enough area to construct an accurate model. Have them avoid regions with extreme and irregular changes in elevation. Be sure that the map is enlarged sufficiently so that the contour intervals can be easily seen and measured.

Southwest—Grand Canyon, Arizona
Contour interval: 50 meters

1250

1000
750
River   750
1000

1250

0   1 km

Northeast—Vermont
Contour interval: 30 meters

820

730

0   1 km

N
W — E
S

Southeast—Florida
Contour interval: 3 meters

27

33   30

0   1 km

Midwest—Wisconsin
Contour interval: 6 meters

240

0   1 km

Figure 3

Chapter 23   Earth's Surface   **Investigation 23B**

Beach Erosion

Refer students to pages 728 and 729 in their textbooks for a discussion of wave erosion and deposition. **SKILLS FOCUS:** Observing, Inferring, Using Models **CLASS TIME:** 40 minutes

Background Information

Ocean waves are examples of kinetic energy transferred through the medium of water. If ocean waves hit a beach at an angle, some of their kinetic energy is transferred to sand and pebbles, causing them to move. Some of the energy is reflected back through the water at right angles to the incoming waves, and some energy is dissipated by heat because of friction.

The kinetic energy transferred to the rocks and sand on the shore causes them to move not in the direction of either the incoming or reflected waves, but in a direction perpendicular to the shore. This is part of the process called **longshore drift.** Sand and small rocks move away from the shore at right angles to the shore as they obtain kinetic energy from the waves. Eventually, the sand and rocks are far from the shore, and so the incoming waves they encounter simply push them along in the direction of the wave. This direction is back toward the shore, but further along than where the rocks and sand originally were. Once they reach a new location on the shore, the rocks and sand once again move away from the shore at right angles. This cycle is repeated so that over time, the sand and small rocks on a beach can move long distances along the shore.

In this investigation, you will create a shoreline model with a beach and rocks. By simulating ocean waves, you will observe how the sand and rocks are moved by the energy from the waves.

Problem

How does the energy in ocean waves affect the material on the shore?

Pre-Lab Discussion

Read the entire investigation. Then, work with a partner to answer the following questions.

1. **Applying Concepts** What happens to the kinetic energy of a wave as the wave comes ashore?

   Some of the kinetic energy is transferred to sand and pebbles, causing them to move. Some of

   the energy is dissipated by heat. The remainder of the kinetic energy is reflected back through

   the water at right angles to the incoming waves.

   _____

2. **Inferring** From your answer to Question 1, what can you infer about the amount of kinetic energy of the waves reflected from the shore compared to the amount of kinetic energy of the incoming waves?

   The reflected waves will have less kinetic energy than the incoming waves will have.

   _____

3. **Controlling Variables** What are the manipulated and responding variables in this investigation?

The number of waves or length of time that the waves strike the shore is the manipulated variable.

The motion of the sand and rocks is the responding variable.

4. **Controlling Variables** What variables must be kept constant in this investigation so that the results will be meaningful?

The intensity and angle of the waves should be kept as constant as possible so that changes on

the simulated shoreline are the result of the number of waves, rather than the incoming angle or

intensity of the waves.

5. **Predicting** If you perform this investigation long enough, what do you expect will happen?

Much of the sand at one end of the simulated beach will undergo longshore drift and gradually

will move to the other end of the pan.

Materials *(per group)*

large rectangular aluminum baking dish   water
fine sand   ruler or flat stick 10–12 cm long
5 very small pebbles, each about 1 cm in diameter newspaper
clock or watch

Safety

Put on safety goggles and a lab apron. Note all safety alert symbols next to the steps in the Procedure and review the meaning of each symbol by referring to the Safety Symbols on page xiii.

Procedure

1. Mix the sand with a little water so that it will hold its shape. Use the sand to create a shoreline along one side of the baking dish. Make the sand deeper along the edge of the pan and taper it, as shown in the side view in Figure 1.

Figure 1

2. Place the dish on a sheet of newspaper so that any water that is spilled over the sides will be absorbed. Add water to the dish very slowly so that you do not disturb the sand. Leave 4 or 5 cm of beach above the water line. **CAUTION:** *Wipe up any spilled liquids immediately to avoid slips and falls.*

3. Place a small pebble every few centimeters along the simulated beach.

4. Set the ruler on edge in the water, as shown in Figure 1. Gently rock the top edge of the ruler back and forth to create waves. Try to keep the intensity with which you rock the ruler steady and uniform so that the waves are nearly the same throughout the investigation. Observe the movement of the sand and pebbles. Record your observations.

5. Restore the pebbles and sand to their original positions. Repeat Step 4 for three minutes.

Observations

Answers will vary, depending on how vigorous the waves are and how long the investigation

is performed. Assuming that the waves are directed along the length and slightly to the right side

of the dish, over time sand should be seen to drift away from the shore toward the water

and then back toward the shore and to the right of its original location. Stronger waves should

move the pebbles slightly in the same manner, though not as far.

Analysis and Conclusions

1. **Observing** In what direction did the reflected waves move with respect to the incoming waves? How did the intensity of the reflected waves compare to the intensity of the incoming waves?

The reflected waves were at right angles to the incoming wave, and they were less intense.

2. **Interpreting Diagrams** The diagram in Figure 2 shows how a pebble on the shore moves as an incoming wave strikes the beach at an angle. Draw the path that the pebble will take as the next three waves hit the beach.

Student art should show the pebble moved toward the shore in the same direction as the next incoming wave. If after this wave the pebble is on the shore, the next wave will move the pebble away from the shore in a perpendicular direction as shown in the diagram. The third wave will move the pebble toward the shore in the same direction as the wave. If the pebble is not shown on the shore after the first wave, the second wave will move it toward the shore in the same direction as the wave.

Figure 2

3. **Drawing Conclusions** Based on your investigation, in what direction will beach erosion occur?

Beach erosion will occur in the direction of the wave component that moves along the shore. In

this investigation, this was toward the right side of the dish.

Go Further

Plan an experiment to show how the angle and intensity of the incoming waves affect longshore drift. Vary the procedure of this investigation accordingly, making sure to account for all controlled, manipulated, and responding variables. Show your plan to your teacher. When your teacher approves your plan, carry out your experiment and report your results.

Student plans for observing drift dependence on incoming wave angle should indicate that wave angle changes while wave intensity and time of observation are kept as constant as possible. Students should make observations for at least four different wave angles. For observing drift dependence on wave intensity, wave angle and time of observation should be kept constant. Observations should be made for at least four levels of wave intensity.

🔍 **Investigation 24A**

Recipe for a Cloud

Background Information

The scientific study of clouds was begun in 1803 by Luke Howard, a British meteorologist. However, it was not until the late 1800s that clouds were classified according to their different forms.

Clouds consist of tiny water droplets or ice crystals. These droplets or crystals form when water vapor in the atmosphere condenses. Condensation occurs when air pressure decreases so that the water vapor in the air expands and cools. Therefore, factors such as atmospheric pressure and the relative humidity of the air determine when clouds form and what form they take.

For a cloud to form, there must be a surface of some kind for water vapor to condense on, and so form the small water droplets or (if it is cold enough) ice crystals that make up the cloud. In most cases, small particles of dust provide the surfaces for such condensation. By artificially adding small particles, such as salt or dry ice crystals, to clouds at certain temperatures, condensation can be stimulated, causing rain. Such a process is called cloud seeding.

In this investigation, you will examine how the temperature and humidity of air, as well as the presence or absence of tiny particles in the air, affects the formation of cloud droplets.

Problem

Under what basic conditions do clouds form?

Pre-Lab Discussion

Read the entire investigation. Then, work with a partner to answer the following questions.

1. **Formulating Hypotheses** Write a hypothesis about how you expect pressure, humidity, and the presence of tiny particles in the air to affect cloud formation.

   For clouds to form, there must be enough water vapor in the air (high humidity), low enough

   temperatures (reduced air pressure), and some particles upon which condensation can occur.

2. **Designing Experiments** Why is it important to this investigation to use a container in which the pressure can be easily and significantly changed?

   The pressure must be changed significantly so that the water vapor in the air will expand and cool

   significantly. This will allow the vapor to condense on any small particles that are in the air.

3. **Controlled Variables** For the first half of the investigation, in which cold water is used, what are the manipulated and controlled variables?

Air pressure is the manipulated variable, and humidity and the absence of particles are the

controlled variables. Then, particles are introduced in the investigation as a controlled variable,

humidity is still kept controlled, and pressure is again the manipulated variable.

4. **Controlled Variables** What controlled variable is changed in the second half of the investigation, in which hot water is used?

The temperature of the water changes the humidity, which is a controlled variable throughout

the second half of the investigation.

5. **Predicting** Do you expect to observe cloud formation before smoke is added to the container or after it is added? Explain your answer.

Students may think that cloud formation may occur without smoke added to the container

because the temperature may drop sufficiently to cause condensation or because there

may be unidentified particles in the air that can promote condensation. Cloud formation will

occur because the change in temperature will allow water vapor to condense, and the smoke

particles will provide surfaces on which condensation can occur.

Materials (per group)
graduated cylinder
gallon glass pickle jar
plastic freezer storage bag (26 cm × 26 cm)
rubber band (15 cm circumference; 0.5 cm width)
cold tap water
hot tap water
safety matches

Safety 🔥🔪🥽🔥
Put on safety goggles. Be careful to avoid breakage when working with glassware. Be careful when using matches. Do not reach over an open flame. Tie back loose hair and clothing when working with flames. Note all safety alert symbols next to the steps in the Procedure and review the meaning of each symbol by referring to the Safety Symbols on page xiii.

Procedure

1. Use the graduated cylinder to measure 40 mL of cold water. Pour the water into the jar. Place the plastic bag into the jar so that the top edges of the bag lie just outside the rim of the jar, as shown in Figure 1. **CAUTION:** *Wipe up any spilled liquids immediately to avoid slips and falls.*

1-gallon pickle jar

Plastic freezer bag

Water

Figure 1

2. Secure the top of the bag to the outer rim of the jar using the rubber band, as shown in Figure 2.

Top edge of plastic bag

Rubber band

Figure 2

3. Place your hand inside the bag, grab the bag's bottom edge, and rapidly pull the bag out of the jar. Observe the inside of the jar while pulling the bag out. Record your observations in the data table provided on the following page.

4. Remove the rubber band and plastic bag. Light a match, allow it to burn for about 3 seconds, then drop the match into the jar. Quickly place the plastic bag inside the jar, again securing its top edge around the rim of the jar with the rubber band.

5. Repeat Step 3. Again, observe the inside of the jar as you pull the bag rapidly out of the jar. Record your observations in the data table.

6. Remove the plastic bag and rinse out the bottle. Throw away the burnt match as directed by your teacher.

7. Repeat Steps 1 through 6, this time using 40 mL of hot tap water. **CAUTION:** *Be careful not to burn yourself when using hot water.*

Observations   Sample data are shown.

DATA TABLE

Water Type	Smoke	Cloud Formation
Cold	Absent	No
Cold	Present	Yes
Hot	Absent	No
Hot	Present	Yes

If clouds formed under more than one set of conditions, did you observe any difference between the clouds?

Answers will depend on whether or not clouds formed in the absence of smoke. The most

common result is that, in the presence of smoke particles, the hot water will produce

a somewhat denser cloud than the cold water.

_____

_____

_____

_____

Analysis and Conclusions

1. **Inferring** What effect did pulling the plastic bag out of the jar have on the water vapor inside the jar?

    It reduced the air pressure so that the water vapor rapidly expanded. As it did so, the water

    vapor's temperature decreased temporarily, and it was able to condense on particles in the air

    in those cases where particles of smoke were added to the container.

    _____

    _____

2. **Drawing Conclusions** What conditions proved most important for forming clouds?

The most important condition was the presence of smoke particles for water to condense on.

Cloud formation was slightly better for hot water than for cold water, but both provided sufficient

humidity for clouds to form in the presence of smoke.

3. **Drawing Conclusions** Did your results support or contradict your hypothesis? Explain your answer.

Results of the investigation showed that a small quantity of water and a rapid decrease in

pressure can produce the necessary humidity and temperature decrease needed to form clouds,

provided there are some particles on which the water vapor can condense. These results confirmed

the hypothesis.

4. **Designing Experiments** What improvements could you make to the apparatus to provide quantitative information?

One improvement may consist of a thermometer attached to the inner wall of the jar.

While one student pulls on the plastic bag and reduces pressure, the other student can

observe the thermometer to determine the minimum temperature reached within the jar

when the pressure is reduced. Another improvement might consist of replacing the plastic bag

with a lid that can be screwed in place and which has an opening through which a known quantity

of smoke can be added. The pressure within the jar could be steadily lowered by a vacuum pump

so that the exact pressure at which condensation occurs could be measured.

5. **Using Models** Relate each ingredient in your cloud-making procedure to the process of making clouds in nature.

The decrease in pressure and temperature in the bottle correspond to such decreases when

air rises and expands. The high humidity and subsequent condensation in the bottle correspond

to the humidity needed to cause condensation at a given temperature in the atmosphere. The

particles of smoke correspond to small particles in the atmosphere around which water

vapor can condense.

6. **Making Generalizations** A topic of discussion in astronomy is terraforming, the process by which other planets can be modified so that their climates are like those on Earth. One important feature of terraforming is starting and maintaining a water cycle in the planet's atmosphere. What conditions would be necessary for rain to be stimulated and maintained on a terraformed planet?

Features that should be included in answers are 1) enough water on the planet's surface so

that it can evaporate and enter the atmosphere, 2) sufficient changes in the atmospheric

pressure so that water vapor can condense to form rain, 3) particles in the atmosphere

so that condensation can take place when humidity and temperature are satisfactory.

_____

_____

_____

_____

_____

_____

Go Further

Plan an investigation to determine the way that different changes in pressure and different particles sources may affect cloud formation. You can plan your design, using the same equipment used in the investigation or using some or all of the improvements listed in your answer to Question 4 of Analysis and Conclusions. Identify which variables are to be manipulated and which are to be controlled throughout the investigation. Show your plan to your teacher. When your teacher approves your plan, carry out your experiment and report your results and conclusions.

Student designs may include a number of features to make the investigation more quantifiable. A spray bottle, for example, may be used to introduce a known quantity of water mist or smoke into the jar. A thermometer may be used to estimate the minimum temperature reached when pressure is lowered. Substances such as chalk dust or talcum powder might be used to induce cloud formation. Be sure that the manipulated and controlled variables are clearly defined in the plan and that all aspects of the plan are safe to perform.

Chapter 24   Weather and Climate   🔍 **Investigation 24B**

Modeling Global Warming

Refer students to pages 779–782 in their textbooks for a discussion of factors affecting climate and global warming.

Background Information

SKILLS FOCUS: Observing; Inferring; Comparing and Contrasting
CLASS TIME: 50 minutes

Some atmospheric gases keep Earth much warmer than it would be otherwise. Energy from the sun is transferred to Earth through radiation and is absorbed by the surface of Earth. Then, some of this energy is transferred back toward space through the process of radiation. Carbon dioxide, water vapor, and other gases in the atmosphere absorb some of this radiated energy, making the atmosphere warmer. The warm atmosphere re-radiates this energy, some of which is directed back toward Earth's surface. This entire process is called the greenhouse effect.

In this investigation, you will describe how carbon dioxide affects the temperature of the atmosphere. You will also understand more about the process that results in the greenhouse effect.

Problem

Does carbon dioxide really affect the atmosphere's temperature?

Pre-Lab Discussion

Read the entire investigation. Then, work with a partner to answer the following questions.

1. **Posing Questions** Write a question that summarizes the purpose of this investigation.

   How does carbon dioxide affect the temperature of the atmosphere?

   _____

   _____

2. **Controlling Variables** What is the manipulated variable in this investigation?

   The presence or absence of carbon dioxide, which in turn is dependent on the presence

   or absence of baking soda

   _____

   _____

3. **Controlling Variables** What are the controlled variables in this investigation?

   The amount of light shone on the two bottles and the size of the bottles

   _____

   _____

   _____

4. Controlling Variables What is the responding variable in this investigation?

The temperature in the bottle

_____

_____

_____

_____

_____

5. Predicting Predict the outcome of this investigation.

The bottle of carbon dioxide will undergo a larger temperature increase than the bottle of air

during the same period of time.

_____

_____

_____

_____

Materials (per group)

2 clear 2-L plastic bottles

2 one-hole rubber stoppers with a Celsius non-mercury
  thermometer inserted into each   Wrap each thermometer in a thick towel for your protection when
                                        gently inserting it in the stopper.

funnel

plastic spoon

baking soda

vinegar

25-mL graduated cylinder

bright incandescent lamp or flood lamp

Safety 🥽🦺🧤🔥⚡

Put on safety goggles and a lab apron. Be careful to avoid breakage
when working with glassware. Use extreme care when working with
heated equipment or materials to avoid burns. Observe proper
laboratory procedures when using electrical equipment. Note all
safety alert symbols next to the steps in the Procedure and review
the meaning of each symbol by referring to the Safety Symbols on
page xiii.

Procedure

🥽 **1.** Fill a bottle with carbon dioxide by adding baking soda and
🦺   vinegar to the bottle. **CAUTION:** *Leave the bottle open until the
     bubbling stops.*   Show students how to fill a bottle with carbon dioxide in Step 1. They must insert a
                        funnel in the bottle and put one spoonful of baking soda into the funnel. Then, they
                        should pour 20 mL of vinegar into the funnel and remove the funnel.

2. Put a one-hole stopper containing a thermometer in the bottle
   of carbon dioxide. Put the other stopper with its thermometer in
   the bottle of air. In the data table, record the initial temperature
   for each bottle.

3. Shine a lamp on both bottles at the same angle from a distance
   of 30 cm. In the data table, record the temperature of each bottle
   every two minutes for 20 minutes. **CAUTION:** *Lamps can get very
   hot. Be sure not to come too close to the lamps when they are in use.*

Observations

DATA TABLE

Elapsed Time (minutes)	Temperature in Bottle With Air (°C)	Temperature in Bottle With Carbon Dioxide (°C)
0		
2		
4		
6		
8		
10		
12		
14		
16		
18		
20		

Analysis and Conclusions

1. **Comparing and Contrasting** What was the difference in the temperatures of the two bottles at the end of the experiment?

   Results will vary, but the temperature of the bottle of carbon dioxide will be higher than the

   temperature of the bottle of air.

   _____

2. **Inferring** What can you infer about how carbon dioxide affects air temperature?

   Carbon dioxide in the air causes the air temperature to rise more quickly when the air is illuminated.

   _____

   _____

3. **Drawing Conclusions** What do your observations suggest about the effect of carbon dioxide on global warming?

   The bottle of carbon dioxide became warmer than the bottle of air. This observation supports the

   idea that the presence of carbon dioxide in air helps to warm the atmosphere.

   _____

   _____

4. **Applying Concepts** How do you think your conclusions for this investigation could be applied to situations that you observe in your everyday life?

   Further research into the ways that the greenhouse effect influences climate would help

   understand changes in climate and suggest ways to limit those changes.

   _____

   _____

Go Further

Conduct this investigation on a larger scale. Set up terrariums next to sunlit windows in two large, clear, wide-mouth bottles. Place plants in only one of the terrariums. Record the temperature of each terrarium at the same time of day over several days. Write a report of your observations and your conclusions based on your analysis of the data. Remind students that plants consume carbon dioxide. Have students consider this when they explain their observations. The greenhouse effect will be more pronounced in the terrarium without plants. Plants absorb carbon dioxide, which in turn reduces the temperature of the terrarium.

Chapter 25   The Solar System

Deflecting an Asteroid

Refer students to page 809 in their textbooks for a discussion of asteroids. **SKILLS FOCUS:** Predicting, Observing, Making Analogies, Controlling Variables, Using Models **CLASS TIME:** 45 minutes

Background Information

Although asteroids and comets often have well-defined orbits, these orbits can be disturbed by the gravitational forces of massive bodies that the asteroids or comets encounter. Such gravitational disturbances, or perturbations, cause the asteroid or comet to change direction and follow a new orbital path.

The perturbation of an asteroid or comet depends on its speed and how close it approaches the more massive body. Sometimes the perturbations are strong enough that the asteroid or comet is captured by the more massive body. In these cases, the asteroid or comet orbits or collides with the larger object.

In this investigation, you will simulate the perturbation of an asteroid's motion by observing how a magnet deflects a steel ball bearing from its path.

Problem

How does the amount an object is deflected from its path depend on its speed and its distance from a perturbing force?

Pre-Lab Discussion

Read the entire investigation. Then, work with a partner to answer the following questions.

1. **Formulating Hypotheses** Write a hypothesis about how you expect the speed of the ball bearing and the distance of the magnet from the ball bearing's path to affect the deflection of the ball bearing.

   For a given magnet distance, the faster the ball bearing moves, the less it will be deflected. For a

   given ball bearing speed, the closer the magnet is to the ball bearing's path, the greater the ball

   bearing will be deflected.

   _____

   _____

   _____

   _____

2. **Using Models** What force is being modeled in this investigation by the magnet?

   The gravitational force exerted by a massive body on an asteroid is the force being modeled.

   _____

   _____

   _____

3. **Controlling Variables** What are the manipulated and controlled variables in this investigation?

For the first part of the investigation, the height of the tube and thus the speed of the ball bearing are

the manipulated variables. The distance between the ball bearing and the magnet is the controlled

variable. For the second part of the investigation, the distance of the magnet from the ball bearing's

path is the manipulated variable, and the tube height (ball bearing speed) is the controlled variable.

_____

_____

_____

_____

4. **Controlling Variables** What is the responding variable in this investigation?

The responding variable is the deflection of the ball bearing from the target.

_____

_____

_____

_____

5. **Predicting** Assuming that all other conditions are the same, how would placing the magnet near the target produce different results from placing it near the end of the tube? Explain your answer.

The deflection of the ball bearing will be greater when the magnet is placed near the end of the

tube than if it is placed near the target. Assuming the angle of deflection is the same in both cases,

the ball bearing travels farther to the side as it travels farther forward.

_____

_____

_____

Materials *(per group)*
cardboard tube, 30 cm long
steel ball bearing, 1.5 cm in diameter
magnet (preferably a strong alnico or rare-earth type)
3 books, each about 3 cm thick
wooden block, at least 6 cm long on each side
meter stick
paper strip, 60 cm × 4 cm
masking tape
pencil

Procedure

1. Set up the materials, as shown in Figure 1. Center the block (target) in the middle of the paper strip and tape the edges of the strip to the table surface.

Figure 1

2. Place the cardboard tube so that one end is supported on the top edge of one of the books and the other end is on the table. The target block should be in a direct line with the tube so that a ball bearing rolled down the tube will strike the center of the block, as shown by the undeflected path in Figure 1.

3. The distance from the end of the cardboard tube to the target block should be between 50 and 75 cm. Measure the actual distance and record the value in the data table.

4. Measure the height of the tube above the table (that is, the thickness of the book). Record the value in the data table.

5. Place the magnet 6 cm to the side of the lower end of the cardboard tube. Roll the ball bearing down the tube and observe how it deviates from the straight path it followed before the magnet was introduced. Adjust the position of the magnet so that the ball bearing is deflected enough to miss the target. (*Hint:* Depending on how strong the magnet is, you may have to try positioning the magnet farther or closer to the side of the tube so as to keep the ball bearing from attaching itself to the magnet or from not causing any deflection at all).

6. Repeat the trial, marking on the paper strip the point where the ball bearing crosses the strip. Measure the distance from the center of the block to the mark and record the value in the data table.

7. Place a second book on top of the first book, measure the tube height, and record the value in the data table. Repeat Step 6 and record your observations in the data table.

8. Place a third book on top of the first two books, measure the tube height, and record the value in the data table. Repeat Step 6 and record your observations in the data table.

9. Repeat Steps 6 through 8, after halving the distance between the magnet and the end of the tube. Record your observations in the data table.

10. Repeat Steps 6 through 8, placing the magnet against the end of the tube. Record your observations in the data table.

Observations Sample data are shown.

DATA TABLE

Distance of Magnet From Tube (cm)	Tube Height (cm)	Distance Between Tube and Target (cm)	Deflection Distance (cm)
6.0	3.5	55.0	2.3
6.0	7.0	55.0	1.5
6.0	10.5	55.0	0.75
3.0	3.5	55.0	4.5
3.0	7.0	55.0	3.0
3.0	10.5	55.0	1.5
0.0	3.5	55.0	9.0
0.0	7.0	55.0	6.0
0.0	10.5	55.0	3.0

Analysis and Conclusions

1. **Observing** What effect did raising the height of the tube have on the deflection of the ball bearing?

   It caused the ball bearing to move faster and so reduced the amount that the ball bearing

   was deflected.

2. **Applying Concepts** How does the speed of the ball bearing relate to the amount of deflection? Explain your answer.

   The faster the ball bearing moves, the farther it goes forward in a given time. During that same

   time, the force causing the deflection accelerates the ball bearing, causing it to travel a certain

   distance sideways. The greater the forward speed of the ball bearing, the shorter is the time for

   deflection and the smaller is the distance of deflection.

3. **Observing** What effect did moving the magnet closer to the opening of the tube have on the deflection of the ball bearing?

   It caused the deflection of the ball bearing to increase.

4. **Drawing Conclusions** Did your results support or contradict your hypothesis? Explain your answer.

   The results confirmed that, for a given magnet distance, the faster the ball bearing moves, the less

   it will be deflected. The results also confirmed that, for a given ball bearing speed, the closer the

   magnet is to the ball bearing's path, the greater the ball bearing is deflected.

5. **Designing Experiments** How might you redesign the experiment so that the deflecting force was provided by gravity instead of by magnetism?

   A direct means of using gravity for deflection would be to design a test surface that tilts

   to one side or the other of the undeflected path. As the ball bearing rolls forward, it also rolls

   down the plane to the side, and thus is deflected by gravity. The greater the tilt of the plane,

   the greater is the deflection. Students may also suggest using a bowl rather than a flat surface.

6. Designing Experiments How would the design improvement you
have suggested in Question 5 allow you to test spherical objects
with different masses?

The use of magnetism for deflection limits the spheres to ferromagnetic materials. By

designing a deflection method that uses gravity, any material can be used. This provides a

wider range of densities for the rolling spheres so that spheres of the same size but much

different mass can be tested. Note, however, that friction may vary for different materials,

so this variable would need to be controlled.

7. Inferring From you observations, infer why a small gravitational
force could cause an asteroid to travel far off course as it moves
through the solar system.

A small force might pull an asteroid only a short distance in one direction, but as

the asteroid continued to travel, it would move farther from its original path.

8. Inferring A concern about asteroids is that they might collide with
Earth, causing tremendous destruction. Why is this concern greater
for asteroids moving at high speeds than for those moving at
lowers speeds?

Asteroids that move at higher speeds have greater kinetic energies than those moving at lower

speeds. This energy is given up during impact, and so the collision is more destructive. Also, it

would be more difficult to deflect a fast-moving asteroid by human intervention, as any

force acting on the asteroid will deflect it less than if the asteroid was moving at a slower speed.

Go Further

Design an experiment to determine how the mass of an asteroid affects
the deflection by a given force. Your plan can use the same materials used
in this investigation or some or all of the improvements you suggested
in Question 5. Specify which variables are to be manipulated and which
need to be controlled throughout the experiment. Submit your procedure
and design to your teacher for approval before conducting your
experiment. Record your observations and report your results.

Check to be sure that the manipulated and controlled variables are clearly defined in
the plan and that all aspects of the plan will produce measurable results. Be sure that
the experimental design is safe to perform.

Exploring Orbits

Refer students to pages 790–795 in their textbooks for a discussion of planetary orbits. **SKILLS FOCUS:** Measuring, Inferring, Comparing and Contrasting **CLASS TIME:** 45 minutes

Background Information

All bodies that move in closed orbits around the sun follow a path described by an **ellipse.** An ellipse is an oval-shaped figure that is characterized by two quantities. The first of these quantities is the width of the ellipse, which is called the major axis.

Along the major axis and on either side of the center of the ellipse are two points called the foci. For elliptical orbits, the sun is at one focus. The distance between the foci is called the focal length of the ellipse, as shown below. This distance determines the eccentricity of the ellipse. Eccentricity is an indicator of how elongated an ellipse is. Ellipses can be very elongated, or they can be nearly circular. The planets of the solar system have orbits with different major axes and eccentricities.

In this investigation, you will draw some elliptical shapes, calculate the eccentricity of these ellipses, and compare them to the orbital eccentricities of Earth and other planets in the solar system.

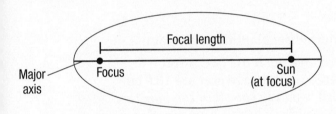

Problem

What do the elliptical orbits of the planets look like?

Pre-Lab Discussion

Read the entire investigation. Then, work with a partner to answer the following questions.

1. **Predicting** Predict the shapes of the planets' orbits (more circular or more flattened).

   Many students may predict that the planets' orbits are flattened ellipses.

2. **Applying Concepts** What is the one thing that the elliptical orbits of all planets, asteroids, and most comets have in common?

   The sun is at one focus of all these elliptical orbits.

3. **Controlling Variables** What is the manipulated variable for the various ellipses drawn?

   The focal length is the manipulated variable.

4. Controlling Variables What are the responding variables for the various ellipses drawn?

The eccentricity and the major axis are responding variables.

5. Designing Experiments What purpose do the two pushpins serve in this investigation?

The pushpins mark the foci of the ellipses.

Materials (per group)

3 sheets of paper

heavy corrugated cardboard

2 pushpins

metric ruler

string, 30 cm in length

colored pencils

tape

calculator

Safety ✄

Be careful when handling sharp instruments. Note all safety alert symbols next to the steps in the Procedure and review the meaning of each symbol by referring to the Safety Symbols on page xiii.

Procedure

✄ 1. Fold a sheet of paper in half lengthwise. Flatten it out again.

2. Place the paper on the cardboard and push the two pins on the crease so that they are centered on the page and are 10.0 cm apart. **CAUTION:** *Be careful when handling pins; they can puncture skin.* (*Hint:* As the focal length for ellipses in this investigation becomes smaller, you may have to tape additional sheets of paper above and below to show the entire ellipse).

3. Label one of the pushpins as the sun.

4. Take the string, tie it in a loop, and place it around the pins. Using one of the colored pencils, gently pull the string taut. Keep the string taut without pulling the pins out of the cardboard and carefully drag the pencil around the pins to draw an ellipse, as shown in Figure 1.

5. Remove the pin that is not labeled as the sun. In its place, draw a noticeable dot the same color as the ellipse.

6. Use the metric ruler to measure the length of the major axis and focal length. Record these values in the data table.

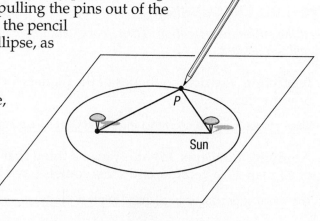

Figure 1

7. Reposition the second pin so that it is now 8.0 cm from the other pin. Repeat Steps 4 through 6, using a different colored pencil.

8. Repeat Step 7, using distances of 6.0 cm, 4.0 cm, and 2.0 cm between the pins.

9. The eccentricity for each ellipse is calculated by dividing the focal length by the length of the major axis:

$$\text{Eccentricity} = \frac{\text{Focal length}}{\text{Major axis}}$$

Calculate the eccentricity for each ellipse and record the values in the data table.

10. Label each ellipse on your diagram with its matching eccentricity.

Observations   Sample data are shown.

DATA TABLE

Ellipse (color)	Major Axis (cm)	Focal Length (cm)	Eccentricity
Black	20.0	10.0	0.500
Red	22.0	8.0	0.36
Blue	24.0	6.0	0.25
Green	26.0	4.0	0.15
Purple	28.0	2.0	0.071

Analysis and Conclusions

1. **Drawing Conclusions** Did the investigation results confirm your prediction? Explain why or why not.

   If students predicted the orbits to be flattened ellipses, they will not find the prediction to be

   confirmed. Even the orbits of Mars and Mercury are only slightly flattened.

   _____

   _____

2. **Compare and Contrast** Compare the following values for planetary eccentricities to those you calculated for your ellipses. What can you state about the orbits of the various planets?

Planet	Eccentricity
Mercury	0.206
Venus	0.007
Earth	0.017
Mars	0.093
Jupiter	0.048
Saturn	0.056
Uranus	0.047
Neptune	0.009
Pluto	0.250

   Most planets have nearly circular orbits. The planets with greater eccentricities have more elongated

   orbits. The most elongated orbits are for Pluto and Mercury. Venus and Neptune have the least

   elongated orbits.

Go Further

Research the orbits of various smaller bodies in the solar system, such as asteroids or comets. Use the materials from this investigation and researched values for the major axis and eccentricity to produce drawings of these objects' orbits. Include in your report all values used and your drawings.

Review student information before students begin drawing the orbits to be sure that eccentricities are not too small (not much less than 0.10) nor too large (greater than 0.90).

Chapter 26   Exploring the Universe

Measuring the Diameter of the Sun

Refer students to pages 828–833 in their textbooks for a discussion of the sun.
SKILLS FOCUS: Observing, Measuring, Calculating **CLASS TIME:** 45 minutes

Background Information

The sun is approximately 150,000,000 km from Earth. To understand how far away this is, consider the fact that light travels approximately 300,000 km/s. At this incredible speed, it takes the light from the sun a little over 8 minutes to reach Earth.

Even though the sun is very far away, it is still possible to make an accurate measurement of its size. This can be done by making two simple measurements and then setting up and solving a proportion problem. You can estimate the diameter of the sun by solving the following proportion problem.

$$\frac{\text{Diameter of sun}}{\text{Distance to sun}} = \frac{\text{Diameter of sun's image}}{\text{Distance between two cards}}$$

If you can determine three of the terms in a proportion problem, the fourth term, such as the diameter of the sun, can be solved mathematically.

In this investigation, you will construct a simple device and use it to collect data that will enable you to calculate the diameter of the sun.

Problem

What is the diameter of the sun, and how can it be determined?

Pre-Lab Discussion

Read the entire investigation. Then, work with a partner to answer the following questions.

1. **Inferring** What is the purpose of this investigation?

   The purpose is to calculate distances mathematically, using three of the four proportional terms and

   calculating for the fourth. With this method, estimation of the sun's diameter is solved

   mathematically.

2. **Calculating** To prepare for this calculation, solve for x in the following proportion problems.

   a. $\dfrac{x}{5} = \dfrac{100,000}{20}$

   $x = 25,000$ _____

   _____

   b. $\dfrac{5}{x} = \dfrac{200,000}{50}$

   $x = 0.00125$ _____

   _____

Name _____ Class _____ Date _____

3. Inferring Why is it important to never look directly at the sun?

Looking directly at the sun can be very harmful to the eyes and can cause blindness because of the

high-energy ultraviolet radiation that the sun emits.

4. Applying Concepts In what way is the process of proportional relationships practical for determining the diameter of the sun?

Student answers should indicate that the image of the sun on the card is a scaled down version

of the actual sun, so the physical relationships present in the sun are also present in the scaled

image except that the values are smaller.

5. Predicting Would you expect error in the value you calculate for the sun's diameter? Explain your answer.

All measurements will have some error.

Materials *(per group)*
2 index cards (10 cm × 15 cm)   metric ruler
drawing compass   tape
meter stick

Safety
Be careful when handling sharp instruments. Never look directly at the sun. Note all safety symbols next to the steps in the Procedure and review the meaning of each symbol by referring to the Safety Symbols on page xiii.

Procedure
Part A: Measuring Distances and Calculating Ratios

1. In Figure 1, measure the base of each of the two triangles. Record your measurements in Data Table 1.

2. Measure the altitude (distance from tip to base) of each of the two triangles. Record your measurements in Data Table 1.

3. Determine the ratio between the base of the large triangle and the base of the small triangle. Record this ratio in Data Table 1.

4. Determine the ratio between the altitude of the large triangle and the altitude of the small triangle. Record this ratio in Data Table 1.

5. Think about how these two ratios compare. In Part B of this lab, you will use a similar procedure to determine the diameter of the sun. The base of the small triangle will represent the diameter of the image of the sun on a card. The altitude of the small triangle will represent the distance between the two cards

in the device you will construct. The altitude of the large triangle will represent the distance from Earth to the sun. The base of the large triangle will represent the diameter of the sun, which you will determine. **CAUTION:** *Never look directly at the sun.*

Figure 1

Part B: Determining the Diameter of the Sun

6. Using scissors, cut I-shaped slits in each card in the positions shown in Figure 2. The meter stick should be able to slide through the slits, but the slits should be small enough so that the meter stick fits snugly. **CAUTION:** *Be careful when handling sharp instruments.*

Figure 2

7. With the tip of the compass, punch a pinhole in one of the cards, in the position shown in Figure 2. Tape this card to the meter stick at the 5-cm mark so that it is perpendicular to the meter stick. **CAUTION:** *Be careful when handling sharp instruments.*

8. On the other card, draw two parallel lines exactly 0.8 cm (8 mm) apart, directly above the slit, as shown in Figure 2. Slide this card onto the meter stick. Do not tape this card to the meter stick.

9. While outdoors on a sunny day, position the meter stick so that the taped card is directly facing the sun and casts a shadow over the movable card. **CAUTION:** *Never look directly at the sun.* You should be able to see a bright circle on the movable card caused by the sun's rays passing through the pinhole on the first card.

Do not attempt this investigation if it is cloudy or windy outside.

10. The bright circle on the second card is an image of the sun. Slide the movable card until the image of the sun fits exactly between the two parallel lines you drew earlier.

11. Make sure that both cards are perpendicular to the meter stick. You will know they are perpendicular when the bright circle, the sun's image, is as close to a circle as possible. Tape the second card in place. Measure the distance between the two cards. Record all data in Data Table 2.

Observations Sample data are shown.

DATA TABLE 1

Base of small triangle (Triangle 1)	0.85 cm
Altitude of small triangle (Triangle 1)	2.90 cm
Base of large triangle (Triangle 2)	2.60 cm
Altitude of large triangle (Triangle 2)	8.90 cm
Ratio of base of large triangle to base of small triangle	3.05:1
Ratio of altitude of large triangle to altitude of small triangle	3.07:1

DATA TABLE 2

Distance between two cards (cm)	80 cm
Diameter of sun's image (cm)	0.8 cm

Analysis and Conclusions

1. **Calculate** Using the formula below, calculate the diameter of the sun. Show your work.

$$\frac{\text{Diameter of sun (km)}}{\text{Distance to sun (km)}} = \frac{\text{Diameter of sun's image (cm)}}{\text{Distance between two cards (cm)}}$$

$$\frac{x \text{ km}}{150{,}000{,}000 \text{ km}} = \frac{0.8 \text{ cm}}{80 \text{ cm}}$$

$$x = 1{,}500{,}000 \text{ km}$$

2. **Calculate** The actual diameter of the sun is 1,391,000 km. Using the formula below, determine the amount of error in your calculated value for the sun's diameter. Show your work.

$$\text{Percentage of error} = \frac{\text{Difference between your value and the correct value}}{\text{Correct value}} \times 100$$

Sample answer: % error = [(1,500,000 – 1391,000)/1,391,000] × 100 = 7.8%

3. **Analyze Data** What could account for your error in calculating the sun's diameter?

Students used an average value for the distance between the sun and Earth; in fact, the

distance varies from a maximum of 152,086,000 km to a minimum of 147,097,000 km. There may

also be error involved in accurately measuring the diameter of the sun's image or the

distance between the cards.

4. **Apply Concepts** How might the technique used in this investigation be useful in making other astronomical measurements?

If the light is bright enough, the diameter of the moon could be measured. With a light-gathering

instrument such as a telescope, the diameters of planets could be measured.

5. **Relate Cause and Effect** How might clouds in the sky affect the accuracy of your measurement in this investigation?

If a cloud partially covers the sun, the image might appear smaller in diameter than it normally

would. Total cloud cover would probably make the image too faint to be seen and measured

properly.

Go Further

A sunspot moves along the sun's equator. If the sunspot takes 14 days to move from one side of the sun to the other, calculate how fast the sunspot is moving. Explain why this value is also the speed at which the sun's surface is moving at the equator.

1. Using the actual value for the diameter of the sun and the formula below, calculate the circumference of the sun. The value of p (pi) is approximately 3.14.

$$\text{Circumference} = \pi \times \text{Diameter}$$

C = 3.14 × 1,391,000 km = 4,368,000 km

2. The sunspot moved only halfway around the sun, so to calculate the distance it traveled in 14 days, divide the value for the circumference by 2.

Distance C ÷ 2 = 14,368,000 km ÷ 2 = 2,184,000 km

3. To calculate the distance traveled by the sunspot in one day, divide the distance you calculated in Step 2 by 14.

Speed = distance/time = 2,184,000 km/14 days = 156,000 km/day

4. The sunspot is part of the sun's surface, so it moves as the sun moves. Therefore, the speed of the sunspot is the same as the speed at which the sun's surface is moving at the equator.

Modeling Rotation of Neutron Stars

Background Information

SKILLS: Measuring, Recording Data, Observing, Calculating, Inferring

Angular momentum measures an object's tendency to continue to spin. If the mass of the spinning object is being pulled closer to the axis of the spin (shrinking in size), then the speed of the spin must increase in order to conserve momentum. For example, when a spinning skater pulls in his arms, he spins faster because his mass is less spread out.

Stars also spin on an axis. When a supergiant with 15 times the sun's mass collapses into a neutron star, much of the star's mass is lost in a supernova explosion. Although the mass decreases somewhat, the diameter of the star drastically decreases. A star that is a supergiant may have a diameter of several million kilometers and may rotate on its axis about once a month. The neutron star into which a supergiant develops may be only a few kilometers across but may rotate thousands of times per second.

In this investigation, you will use a rotating square of cardboard and weights to model the effect of mass distribution on rotation rate.

Problem

Why do neutron stars rotate so rapidly?

Pre-Lab Discussion

Read the entire investigation. Then, work with a partner to answer the following questions.

1. Inferring What is the purpose of this investigation?

The purpose is to answer the question of why neutron stars rotate with such great speed.

_____

_____

2. Observing After a supergiant becomes a neutron star, what is its size and mass, and what happens to its rotation speed?

The neutron star into which a supergiant develops may be only a few kilometers across but may

rotate thousands of times per second.

_____

3. Inferring How will this investigation answer the question of why neutron stars rotate with such great speed?

In this investigation, a rotating square of cardboard and two weights are used to model the effect

of mass distribution on rotation rate. The rotating cardboard square and weights are a model for

the supergiant and the neutron star. The model can show the effect of mass on the speed of rotation.

4. Predicting What would you predict would be the outcome of this investigation?

The rate of rotation will increase as the masses are placed closer to the center.

Materials *(per group)*
pencil with eraser

square of stiff cardboard, at least 35 cm wide

pushpin

masking tape

2 identical small weights

centimeter ruler

clock or watch with second hand

Provide small stones or balance weights to use as weights. As the mass of the weights increases, they ma pull the pushpin out of the eraser while rotating. Students may have to experiment with which size of weights works best for their cardboard. Corrugated cardboard works best. Odd shaped weights can be difficult to tape down. A nickel weighs 5 g. Students ca use multiple nickels to increase the mass of the weight

Note that if a smaller square is used, it is more difficult get variance in the number of spins for a given weight.

Safety ⬛ ✂ ⬛
Put on safety goggles. Be careful when handling sharp objects. Make sure that weights stay attached and do not fly off and hit anyone. Note all safety alert symbols next to the steps in the Procedure and review the meaning of each symbol by referring to the Safety Symbols on page xiii.

Procedure
⬛ ✂ **1.** Draw lines along the two diagonals of the cardboard square, as shown in Figure 1. Punch a hole through the center of the cardboard with the pushpin. Then, push the pushpin into the eraser end of the pencil. Check that the cardboard is able to spin freely. If it sticks, use the pushpin to widen the hole. **CAUTION:** *Be careful when handling sharp objects.*

2. Measure Attach a piece of masking tape to one corner of the square. Then, attach the two weights to the cardboard so that each weight is 30 cm from the center, as shown in Figure 1. The weights should both lie along one of the two diagonals that pass through the center. The card is still balanced because the weights are equidistant from the center.

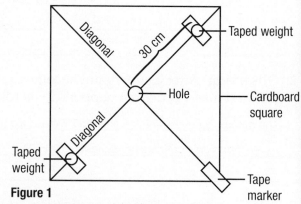

Figure 1

⬛ **3.** Hold the pencil in front of you and perpendicular to your body so that the square of cardboard rotates below eye level and parallel to your body. Try to give each spin of the square the same force. **CAUTION:** *Make sure that weights stay attached and do not fly off and hit anyone.*

To make sure the forces are the same, have students attach a paper clip to the free corner of the square and hook a weight to the paper clip. Be sure to cushion the floor under the weight because it will fall off as the square rotates.

4. Spin the square. Watch the taped corner as it goes by and count the number of times it passes in 5 seconds. (If the square slows down during this time, adjust the pushpin so that it turns with less friction. Then, try again.) In Data Table 1, record the number of rotations.

5. Move the weights inward toward the center so that each is 20 cm from the center and tape them down. Spin and count the rotations. Make sure that you apply the same force you did before. In Data Table 1, record the number of rotations.

6. Repeat Step 5, but this time, tape the weights so that each is only 10 cm from the center. In Data Table 1, record the number of rotations.

Observations

DATA TABLE 1

Distance of Weights from Center of Square	Number of Rotations (spins)
30 cm	10 (for a 25-g weight)
20 cm	13
10 cm	22

Analysis and Conclusions

1. **Calculate** Calculate the rotation rate for each case by dividing the number of spins by 5 seconds.

Results will vary widely, but rates should increase as the radius decreases so that angular momentum is conserved. For example, angular momentum = mvr, so if the radius is halved, the speed doubles, assuming the initial angular momentum is always the same in each trial.

2. Infer Explain why the rate of rotation of a neutron star is so great compared to that of the star from which it was formed.

A neutron star is much smaller but retains a great deal of mass. The size of the star decreases

dramatically. The effect of decreasing mass is therefore much less than the effect of decreasing size.

Both effects cause the rotation rate to increase.

_____

_____

_____

3. Infer Suggest reasons why this model might not give accurate results.

A star is a fluid, and rotating fluids behave differently than solids. Also, a star loses mass when

it becomes a neutron star.

Go Further

What happens to the rotation rate when mass decreases? Repeat Step 5 two more times, but for the first repetition, use weights that are about one-half the mass of the initial weights used. For the second repetition, use weights that are one-fourth the mass of the initial weights used. Create a data table in which to record your results.

Students could compare the number of rotations of the cardboard square at three different masses located the same distance from the center.

The tape is sometimes difficult for students to see when the square is spinning very fast, so there may be a wide variance from the theoretical number of spins.

DATA TABLE Sample data are given.

Mass of Weights Taped at 20 cm	Number of Rotations (spins) From Center of Cardboard Square
25 g	13
15 g	22
5 g	38

Chapter 1   Science Skills   **Consumer Lab**

Determining the Thickness of Aluminum Foil

See pages 26 and 27 in the
Teacher's Edition for more
information.

*Many products such as aluminum foil are too thin to measure easily.
However, it is important for manufacturers to know how thick these
products are. They wouldn't be useful if they were made too thick or too
thin. In this lab, you will use the same method that manufacturers use to
determine the thickness of aluminum foil.*

Problem How can you determine the thickness of aluminum foil?

Materials
- metric ruler
- aluminum foil
- scissors
- balance
- graph paper

Skills Measuring, Calculating, Using Graphs

Procedure ✎
1. Cut out three squares of aluminum foil with sides of the following
   lengths: 50 mm, 100 mm, and 200 mm.
2. To determine the area of the 50-mm foil square, measure the length
   of one of its sides and then square it. Record the length and area in
   the data table.

DATA TABLE

Length (mm)	Area (mm²)	Mass (g)	Volume (mm³)	Thickness (mm)
50.0	2500	0.10	36.9	0.015
100.0	10,000	0.40	148	0.015
200.0	40,000	1.60	590	0.0148

Density of aluminum = _____ 0.00271 _____ g/mm³				

3. Place the foil square on the balance to determine the mass of the foil. Record the mass of the foil square in the data table.

4. You will need the density of aluminum foil to calculate the volume of the foil square from its mass. The density of aluminum foil is 2.71 g/cm^3. Convert cm^3 to mm^3 and record the density of aluminum foil (in g/mm^3) on the line provided at the bottom of the data table.

5. To determine the volume of the foil square, divide its mass by its density in g/mm^3. Record the volume in the data table.

6. To determine the thickness of the foil square, divide its volume by its area. Record this thickness in the data table.

7. Repeat Steps 2 through 6, using the 100-mm foil square.

8. Repeat Steps 2 through 6, using the 200-mm foil square.

9. Construct a graph of your data on a separate sheet of graph paper. Plot length on the horizontal axis and thickness on the vertical axis. Draw a straight line connecting all three points.

Analyze and Conclude

1. **Measuring** How many significant figures were there in your measurement of the length of each square of aluminum foil?

There were three significant figures for the 50-mm square and four for the 100-mm and

200-mm squares.

2. **Using Graphs** What effect, if any, did the length of the square have on your estimate of the thickness of the foil?

The length of the square had no effect on the estimated thickness of the foil.

3. **Comparing** Which estimate of thickness was most precise? Explain your answer.

The thickness calculated for the 200-mm square is most precise because it has the most significant

figures (three). The precision of a calculated answer is limited by the least precise measurement used

in the calculation. For the 200-mm square, the least precise measurement (mass) has three significant

figures. For the 50-mm and 100-mm squares, the least precise measurement (mass) has only two

significant figures.

4. **Controlling Variables** What factors limited the precision of your measurements?

Precision was limited by the spacing of the smallest markings on the ruler and the balance.

Chapter 2   Properties of Matter   **Forensics Lab**

Using Properties to Identify Materials

See pages 60 and 61 in the Teacher's Edition for more information.

Forensic chemists test the physical and chemical properties of materials found at a crime scene. They also do similar tests on the materials found on a suspect's skin or clothing. These materials are often complex mixtures, such as soil, which contain many substances. In this lab, you will compare the properties of three known materials with two samples of "evidence." These samples represent evidence from a crime scene and evidence from a suspect's shoe. Although your materials and equipment are less complex than those used by forensic chemists, your overall method will be similar to the methods they use.

Problem   Can the properties of materials that appear similar be used to tell them apart?

Materials
- 2 spot plates
- glass-marking pencil
- 5 laboratory spatulas
- cornstarch
- baking soda
- baking powder
- wash bottle of water
- vinegar
- iodine solution
- sample from crime scene
- sample from suspect's shoe

Skills   Observing, Inferring, Predicting

Procedure 🗳️ 🔥 🧪 🧤 ♨️

Part A: Properties of Known Substances

1. Use a glass-marking pencil to label 15 wells A through O on the spot plates. Make a mark next to each well, not in the well.

2. Use a spatula to place a small amount of cornstarch in wells A, B, and C. In the data table, record any physical properties of the cornstarch that you observe.

DATA TABLE

Sample	Description	Result of Adding Water	Result of Adding Vinegar	Result of Adding Iodine
Cornstarch	White powder	No change	No change	Blue-black
Baking soda	White powder	Dissolves	Bubbles	No change
Baking powder	White powder	Partly dissolves bubbles	Bubbles	Bubbles
Crime scene sample	White powder	Partly dissolves bubbles	Bubbles	Bubbles
Sample from suspect's shoe	White powder	Dissolves	Bubbles	Bubbles

3. Use a clean spatula to place a small amount of baking soda in wells D, E, and F. Record any physical properties of baking soda that you observe.

4. Using a clean spatula, place a small amount of baking powder in wells G, H, and I. Record any physical properties of baking powder that you observe.

5. Fill wells A, D, and G with water. Record any observed changes.

6. Fill wells, B, E, and H with vinegar. Record any observed changes.

7. Add one drop of iodine solution to wells C, F, and I. Record any changes that you observe. **CAUTION:** *Iodine solution is corrosive and poisonous. It can stain skin and clothing. Rinse any iodine spills with water.*

Part B: Properties of Unknown Substances

8. **Predicting** Look at the sample from the crime scene and the sample from the suspect's shoe. Based on your observations, predict whether testing will show that the samples are identical.

_____

_____

9. Use a clean spatula to place a small amount of the sample from the crime scene in wells J, K, and L. In the data table, record any physical properties of the sample that you observe.

10. Use a clean laboratory spatula to place a small amount of the sample from the suspect's shoe in wells M, N, and O. In the data table, record any physical properties of the sample that you observe.

11. Fill wells J and M with water. In the data table, record your observations.

12. Fill wells K and N with vinegar. In the data table, record your observations.

13. Add 1 drop of iodine solution to wells L and O. In the data table, record your observations.

14. Rinse all materials off the spot plates and flush them down the drain with at least ten times as much water. Dispose of your plastic gloves as directed by your teacher. **CAUTION:** *Wash your hands thoroughly with soap or detergent before leaving the laboratory.*

Analyze and Conclude

1. **Analyzing Data** Were you able to use the ability to dissolve in water to distinguish all three materials? Explain your answer.

   The ability to dissolve in water distinguished only cornstarch from baking soda and baking powder,

   but not baking soda from baking powder.

   _____

2. **Drawing Conclusions** Are the samples from the suspect's shoe and from the crime scene identical?

   The results did not indicate that the sample from the suspect's shoe (baking soda) has the same

   properties as the sample from the crime scene (baking powder).

3. **Evaluating and Revising** Did the data you collected support your prediction? Explain your answer.

   Yes or no (depending on the prediction made). Students should use evidence from the water and

   iodine solution tests to support their answers.

   _____

Chapter 3   States of Matter   **Exploration Lab**

Investigating Changes in Temperature During Heating of Solids

See pages 92 and 93 in the Teacher's Edition for more information.

Lauric acid is a solid that is found in coconuts and processed foods that are made with coconut oil. Lauric acid is also used to make some soaps and cosmetics. In this lab, you will measure the temperature of ice and of lauric acid as these solids are heated and melt. You will graph the data you collect and compare the heating curves for ice and lauric acid.

Problem   What happens to the temperature of a substance during a phase change?

Materials

- 500-mL beaker
- crushed ice
- thermometer
- hot plate
- clock or watch with second hand
- test tube of lauric acid with thermometer
- glass stirring rod
- graph paper

Skills   Measuring, Using Graphs

Procedure
Part A: Heating Ice

1. Fill a 500-mL beaker halfway with crushed ice. **CAUTION:** *Use care when handling glassware to avoid breakage. Wipe up any spilled ice immediately to avoid slips and falls.*

2. Place the beaker on a hot plate. Don't turn the hot plate on yet. Insert a thermometer into the ice. It takes several seconds for the thermometer to adjust to the temperature of its surroundings. Wait 20 seconds and then measure the temperature of the ice. Record this temperature next to the 0 minutes entry in the data table.

DATA TABLE

Time (minutes)	Temperature of Water (°C)	Temperature of Lauric Acid (°C)
0		
1		

3. Turn the hot plate to a low setting. **CAUTION:** *Be careful not to touch the hot plate because contact with the hot plate could cause a burn.*

4. Observe and record the temperature at one-minute intervals until all the ice has changed to liquid water. Circle the temperature at which you first observe liquid water and the temperature at which all the ice has changed to liquid water.

5. After all the ice has melted, make five more measurements of the temperature at one-minute intervals. Turn off the hot plate.

6. On a separate sheet of graph paper, graph your data with time on the horizontal axis and temperature on the vertical axis.

Part B: Heating Lauric Acid

7. Empty the water from the beaker into the sink. Fill the beaker halfway with cool tap water.

8. Place a test tube containing lauric acid and a thermometer into the beaker. If necessary, add or remove water from the beaker so that the surface of the water is above the surface of the lauric acid but below the opening of the test tube.

9. Place the beaker on the hot plate. After 20 seconds, measure the temperature of the lauric acid. Record this temperature next to the 0 minutes entry in the data table.

10. Repeat Steps 3 through 6, using the lauric acid instead of the ice. To keep the temperature the same throughout the water bath, use the glass stirring rod to stir the water after you take each temperature measurement.

Analyze and Conclude

1. **Using Graphs** Describe the shape of your graph for ice.

   The graph rises quickly to 0°C and remains horizontal at that temperature for a number of

   minutes. Then, it begins to rise again.

2. **Analyzing Data** What happened to the temperature of the ice-water mixture during the phase change?

   The temperature remained constant until the phase change was completed.

3. **Drawing Conclusions** What happened to the energy that was transferred from the hot plate to the ice during the phase change?

   At first, the energy absorbed by the ice was used to overcome the forces of attraction holding

   water molecules in fixed positions. After all of the ice had melted, the energy absorbed increased

   the kinetic energy of the molecules in the liquid water.

4. **Comparing and Contrasting** Compare the shapes of the ice and lauric acid graphs. Compare the melting points of ice and lauric acid.

   The two graphs had similar shapes. However, ice melted at 0°C and lauric acid melted at

   about 43°C.

Chapter 4   Atomic Structure   **Forensics Lab**

Using Flame Tests
See page 119 in the Teacher's Edition for more information.

*Forensic scientists use various approaches to distinguish substances.
In this lab, you will observe the flame colors of several substances
and use the data to determine the identity of an unknown substance.*

Problem How can the color of a flame be used to distinguish
substances?

Materials
- solutions of calcium chloride, boric acid, potassium chloride,
  copper(II) sulfate, sodium chloride, and an unknown
- Bunsen burner
- nichrome wire loop
- dilute solution of hydrochloric acid
- wash bottle with distilled water

Skills Observing, Predicting, Using Data Tables

Procedure 🔒 🧤 🥽 ✳ 🔥
Part A: Observing Flame Colors

1. Light the Bunsen burner. **CAUTION:** *Put on safety goggles and a lab
   apron. Tie back loose hair and clothing before working with a flame.*

2. Dip the wire loop into the calcium chloride solution and then place
   the loop in the flame. Observe and record the color of the flame in
   the data table.

DATA TABLE

Solution	Flame Color
Calcium chloride	Orange
Potassium chloride	Violet
Boric acid	Light green
Copper(II) sulfate	Green
Sodium chloride	Yellow-orange
Unknown	
Identity of unknown	

3. Clean the loop by dipping it into hydrochloric acid. Then, while holding the loop over a sink, rinse away the acid with distilled water. **CAUTION:** *Keep hydrochloric acid away from your skin and clothing. Do not breathe in its vapor.*

4. Repeat Steps 2 and 3 with each of the other solutions. Be careful not to transfer any solution from one container to another. **CAUTION:** *These chemicals are poisonous. Do not let them get on your skin.*

Part B: Examining an Unknown Solution

5. Obtain the unknown solution from your teacher.

6. Repeat Steps 2 and 3, using the unknown solution. Compare your observations with the other data that you recorded to identify the unknown. **CAUTION:** *Wash your hands thoroughly before leaving the laboratory.*

Analyze and Conclude

1. **Comparing and Contrasting** Is there a relationship between the color of the flame and the color of the solution?

   There is no relationship between flame color and solution color.

   _____

   _____

   _____

2. **Formulating Hypotheses** How do these substances produce light of different colors?

   When the compounds are placed in the flame, atoms absorb energy and electrons move to

   higher energy levels. As these electrons move back to lower energy levels, they release energy

   as visible light. The color of light produced depends on the difference in energy between two

   specific energy levels in an atom.

   _____

   _____

   _____

3. **Drawing Conclusions** A forensic scientist does a flame test on a substance that was found at a crime scene. What might the scientist conclude if the flame turns green?

   The green flame indicates that the substance may contain copper, barium, or boron.

   _____

   _____

   _____

Predicting the Density of an Element

See pages 150 and 151 in the Teacher's Edition for more information.

Density is a useful property for identifying and classifying elements. In this exploration, you will determine the densities of three elements in Group 4A— silicon, tin, and lead. Then, you will use your data to predict the density of another element in Group 4A—germanium.

Problem Can the densities of elements within a group be used to help predict the density of another element in the group?

Materials
- unlined white paper
- scissors
- metric ruler
- balance
- forceps
- silicon
- tin
- lead shot
- 50-mL graduated cylinder
- graph paper
- periodic table

Skills Measuring, Observing, Using Graphs, Calculating

Procedure 🐚 🏠 🔦 ✋ ✂

Part A: Measuring Mass

DATA TABLE

Element	Mass of Paper (g)	Mass of Paper and Element (g)	Mass of Element (g)	Volume of Water (cm³)	Volume of Water and Element (cm³)	Volume of Element (cm³)	Density of Element (g/cm³)
Silicon							
Tin							
Lead							

1. Cut out three 10-cm × 10-cm pieces of paper from a sheet of unlined white paper. Label one piece of paper Silicon, the second Tin, and the third Lead. Find the mass of each piece of paper and record it in the data table.

2. Using forceps, place the silicon onto the paper labeled Silicon. Find the mass of the silicon and the paper. Record this mass in the data table. Then, subtract the mass of the paper from the mass of the silicon and paper. Record the mass of silicon in the data table. Set the paper containing the silicon aside for now.

3. Repeat Step 2 to find the masses of tin and lead.

Part B: Measuring Volume

4. Place 25 mL of water in the graduated cylinder. Measure the volume of the water to the nearest 0.1 mL. Record the volume (in cm^3) in the data table. (*Hint:* 1 mL = 1 cm^3)

5. Tilt the graduated cylinder and carefully pour the silicon from the paper into the graduated cylinder. Make sure that the silicon is completely covered by the water. Measure and record the volume of the water and silicon in the data table. Then, subtract the volume of water from the volume of the water and silicon. Record the result in the data table.

6. Repeat Steps 4 and 5 to find the volumes of tin and lead.

Part C: Calculating Density

7. To calculate the density of silicon, divide its mass by its volume.

$$\text{Density} \quad = \quad \frac{\text{Mass}}{\text{Volume}}$$

Record the density of silicon in the data table.

8. Repeat Step 7 to find the densities of tin and lead.

9. Make a line graph that shows the relationship between the densities of silicon, tin, and lead and the periods in which they are located in the periodic table. Place the number of the period (from 1 to 7) on the horizontal axis and the density (in g/cm^3) on the vertical axis. Draw a straight line that comes as close as possible to all three points.

10. Germanium is in Period 4. To estimate the density of germanium, draw a dotted vertical line from the 4 on the horizontal axis to the solid line. Then, draw a dotted horizontal line from the solid line to the vertical axis. Read and record the density of germanium.

_____

_____

11. Wash your hands with warm water and soap before you leave the laboratory.

Name _____ Class _____ Date _____

Analyze and Conclude

1. Classifying List lead, silicon, and tin in order of increasing density.

Silicon, tin, and lead _____

_____

_____

2. Comparing and Contrasting How does your estimate of the density of germanium compare with the actual density of germanium, which is 5.5 g/cm³?

A typical student estimate for the density of germanium is 4.6 g/cm³, which is a rough

approximation of the actual value of 5.5 g/cm³.

_____

_____

3. Calculating Use the formula for percent error (PE) to calculate a percent error for your estimate of the density of germanium.

$$PE = \frac{Estimated\ value - Accepted\ value}{Accepted\ value} \times 100$$

Student estimates are likely to be approximately 16% lower than the actual value.

_____

_____

4. Drawing Conclusions How does the density of the elements change from silicon to lead in Group 4A?

From silicon to lead, the density of the element increases.

_____

_____

Chapter 6   Chemical Bonds   Consumer Lab

Improving the Dyeing of Nonpolar Fabrics
See pages 184 and 185 in the Teacher's Edition for more information.

Most natural fibers, such as cotton and wool, consist of large molecules that have regions with a partial positive or partial negative charge. These polar molecules have a strong attraction for dyes that contain either polar molecules or ions.

The molecules in some manufactured fibers, such as nylon, are nonpolar molecules. These synthetic fibers are difficult to dye. Molecules of other synthetic fibers, such as polyester and rayon, have only a few polar regions. As you might suspect, polyester and rayon have intermediate attractions for dyes. In this lab, you will investigate a process for improving a fiber's ability to absorb and retain dye.

Problem How can you increase the dye-holding capacity of nonpolar fibers?

Materials
- tongs
- 2 fabric test strips
- hot dye bath containing methyl orange
- clock or watch
- paper towels
- scissors
- soap
- hot iron(II) sulfate solution

Skills Observing, Drawing Conclusions

Procedure 🔬 🧤 🖐 ⚗ ☠
Part A: Dyeing Without Treatment

1. Use the tongs to immerse a fabric test strip in the methyl orange dye bath. **CAUTION:** *The dye bath is hot. Do not touch the glass. The dye will stain skin and clothing.*

2. After 7 minutes, remove the strip from the dye bath. Allow as much of the dye solution as possible to drip back into the bath. Rinse off the excess dye with water in the sink.

3. Place the strip on a paper towel to dry. Be careful to avoid splashes when transferring the strip between the dye bath and paper towel. Record your observations in the data table.

DATA TABLE

Dye Treatment	Dyeing of Fibers	Colorfastness of Fibers
Methyl orange	Intensity of color varies; wool is strongest, synthetics weakest	Wool and cotton are colorfast; synthetic fibers are not.
Iron sulfate and methyl orange	Intensity of color varies, but increase in intensity is strongest in synthetics.	All fibers are colorfast.

4. After the fabric strip is dry, test it for colorfastness, or the ability to hold dye. Cut the strip in half lengthwise and wash one half of the strip in the sink with soap and water.

5. Allow the washed half-strip to dry and then compare the washed half to the unwashed half. Record your observations in the data table. Staple the half-strips to a sheet of paper and label each half-strip to indicate how you treated it.

Part B: Dyeing With Treatment

6. Use the tongs to place the second fabric strip in the iron(II) sulfate solution for 25 minutes. Then, use the tongs to lift the strip and allow it to drain into the iron(II) sulfate solution. Wring the strip as dry as possible over the solution. **CAUTION:** *The strip will be hot. Allow it to cool before touching it. Wear plastic gloves.*

7. Repeat Steps 1 through 3, using the strip that you treated with iron(II) sulfate.

8. To test the strip for colorfastness, repeat Steps 4 and 5.

9. Clean up your work area and wash your hands thoroughly with warm water and soap before leaving the laboratory.

Analyze and Conclude

1. **Comparing and Contrasting** How did the color of the untreated strip compare with the color of the treated strip?

   Treatment increased the intensity of the colors for synthetic fibers.

2. **Comparing and Contrasting** How did the colorfastness of the untreated strip compare to the colorfastness of the treated strip?

   In general, treatment improved colorfastness, especially in synthetic fabrics.

3. **Applying Concepts** Silk blouses and shirts can be purchased in many intense colors. Why do you think silk is able to hold a variety of intense dyes?

   Silk is a natural fiber. Like most natural fibers, it has many polar regions that allow the dye to

   attach to the fibers.

4. **Drawing Conclusions** How does iron(II) sulfate affect the ability of a fabric to absorb dyes? (*Hint:* What kind of compound is iron(II) sulfate?)

   Iron(II) sulfate is an ionic compound. Treatment with this compound adds ionic sites to the fabric,

   increasing its ability to bind dyes.

5. **Predicting** A care label might read *Wash in cold water only.* What might happen to the color of a piece of clothing with this label if you washed the clothing in hot water?

   The hot water would remove more dye than would cold water, and the colors would run.

Manipulating Chemical Equilibrium

See pages 220 and 221 in the Teacher's Edition for more information.

Chemical reactions tend to go to equilibrium. It is possible to shift the equilibrium by changing the conditions under which the reaction occurs. Factors that can affect chemical equilibrium include the concentration of reactants and products, temperature, and pressure. In this lab, you will observe a chemical reaction and use your observations to predict how one factor will shift the equilibrium of the reaction. Then, you will perform an experiment to test your prediction.

Problem How can you change the equilibrium of a chemical reaction?

Materials

- iodine-starch solution
- 150-mL beaker
- 4 dropper pipets
- spot plate
- ascorbic acid (vitamin C) solution
- chlorine bleach (sodium hypochlorite, NaOCl) solution

Skills Formulating Hypotheses, Designing Experiments, Observing

Procedure 🗒 🗒 🖐 ⚗ ☠

Part A: Observing a Reversible Reaction

1. Pour 50 mL of iodine-starch solution into the 150-mL beaker. The dark color of this solution is caused by the presence of iodine molecules (I_2) within the grains of starch. **CAUTION:** *Handle iodine solutions with care. Iodine is toxic.*

2. Use a dropper pipet to transfer 3 drops of iodine-starch solution from the beaker to one well on the spot plate.

3. Use another clean dropper pipet to add 1 drop of ascorbic acid solution to the iodine-starch solution on the spot plate. Continue to add ascorbic acid solution to the mixture on the spot plate, 1 drop at a time, until the mixture becomes clear. When an iodine molecule reacts with ascorbic acid, the iodine molecule is reduced and breaks down into two colorless iodide ions ($2I^-$).

4. Use the third clean dropper pipet to transfer one drop of colorless iodide solution to a second well on the spot plate.

5. Use the last clean dropper pipet to add bleach solution to the drop of colorless iodide solution, one drop at a time. Continue until the dark color of the iodine-starch solution reappears. **CAUTION:** *Bleach can damage skin and clothing.* The chlorine bleach (NaOCl) oxidizes iodide ions (I^-), converting them to iodine molecules (I_2).

6. Write a chemical equation showing the equilibrium between iodine molecules and iodide ions. This equation does not need to be balanced. Label the two sides of your equation to indicate which substance appears dark and which appears colorless.

$$I_2 \rightleftharpoons 2I^-$$

dark   colorless

Part B: Design Your Experiment

7. Predicting Select one of the solutions used earlier that affects the equilibrium between iodine molecules and iodide ions. Record your prediction of the change you will observe in an iodine-starch solution as you add the solution that you selected.

Students may select either ascorbic acid solution or chlorine bleach solution. Students may predict

that adding ascorbic acid to a dark iodine-starch solution will produce a clear solution or that

adding chlorine bleach to a clear iodine-starch solution will produce a dark solution.

8. Designing Experiments Design an experiment to test your prediction. Your experimental plan should describe in detail how you will perform your experiment.

In their experimental designs, students should understand that the color of the resulting mixture is

the responding variable and that the type of solution added (ascorbic acid solution or chlorine

bleach solution) is the manipulated variable.

9. Construct a data table like the sample data table shown in which to record your observations. (*Hint:* Your data table may not be exactly like the sample data table.)

SAMPLE DATA TABLE

Initial Solution	Solution Added	Quantity Added	Color of Resulting Mixture
Dark iodine-starch solution	Ascorbic acid solution	27 drops	Clear
Clear iodine-starch solution	Chlorine bleach solution	70 drops	Dark

10. Perform your experiment only after your teacher has approved
your plan. Record your observations in your data table.
CAUTION: *Wash your hands with soap or detergent before leaving the
laboratory.*

Analyze and Conclude

1. **Analyzing Data** What factor did you investigate? How did it
affect the equilibrium between iodine molecules and iodide ions?

Students should observe that increasing the quantity of chlorine bleach shifts the equilibrium

toward iodine molecules, and increasing the quantity of ascorbic acid shifts the equilibrium toward

iodide ions.

_____

_____

2. **Predicting** How would you expect the equilibrium to change if
you added more iodide ions to the mixture? Explain your answer.

Adding iodide ions would shift the equilibrium toward the formation of more iodine.

_____

_____

3. **Calculating** When chlorine bleach (sodium hypochlorite,
NAOCl) oxidizes iodide ions to iodine molecules, sodium
hypochlorite is reduced to sodium chloride (NaCl) and water
(H_2O). Write a balanced chemical equation for this reaction,
beginning with the reactants sodium hypochlorite, iodide ions,
and hydrogen ions (H^+).

$NaOCl + 2I^- + 2H^+ \rightarrow I_2 + NaCl + H_2O$

_____

_____

4. **Drawing Conclusions** How does the addition of more product
affect the chemical equilibrium of a reaction?

Adding more product shifts the equilibrium toward the reactants in a reaction.

_____

_____

Chapter 8   Solutions, Acids, and Bases

Preparing a Salt by Neutralization

See pages 254 and 255 in the Teacher's Edition for more information.

In this lab, you will prepare table salt by reacting hydrochloric acid (HCl) with sodium hydroxide (NaOH). To be sure that all of the acid and base have reacted, you will use phenolphthalein. You will first have to test the colors of this indicator with a known acid and base. After the acid and base have reacted, you will measure the pH of the solution with pH paper. Finally, you will evaporate the water and collect the sodium chloride.

Problem How can you produce a salt by neutralization?

Materials
- 3 dropper pipets
- labels
- 10-mL graduated cylinder
- test tube rack
- 2 10-mL test tubes
- distilled water
- hydrochloric acid
- sodium hydroxide solution
- 3 stirring rods
- phenolphthalein solution
- 2 25-mL beaker
- pH paper
- large watch glass
- 100-mL beaker
- hot plate

Skills Observing, Measuring, Analyzing Data

Procedure
Part A: Preparing for the Experiment

1. Place about 10 mL of distilled water in a 25-mL beaker. Set the graduated cylinder on the table and add distilled water to the 5-mL mark. Be sure that the *bottom* of the meniscus is on the 5-mL line.

2. To determine the number of drops in 1 mL, use a clean dropper pipet to add 1 mL of water to the graduated cylinder. Hold the dropper pipet straight up and down with the tip of the dropper pipet just inside the mouth of the cylinder. As your partner watches the liquid level in the cylinder, add drops of water one at a time while counting the drops. Continue adding drops until the liquid level reaches 6 mL. In the data table, record the number of drops in 1 mL.

3. Label one clean dropper pipet *Hydrochloric acid (HCl)* and the other *Sodium hydroxide (NaOH)*.

4. Using the HCl dropper pipet, add 3 mL of hydrochloric acid to a clean test tube. **CAUTION:** *Hydrochloric acid is corrosive. In case of spills, clean thoroughly with water.* Add 2 to 3 drops of phenolphthalein to the test tube. Use a clean stirring rod to mix the hydrochloric acid and indicator. Record your observations.

DATA TABLE

Material(s)	Observation	
1 mL	22	drops
HCl + phenolphthalein	Clear	(color)
NaOH + phenolphthalein	Pink	(color)
Drops of HCl used	88	drops
mL of HCl used	4	mL
Drops of NaOH used	88	drops
mL of NaOH used	4	mL
pH of final solution	7	

5. Using the dropper pipet labeled NaOH, add 3 mL of sodium hydroxide solution to a clean test tube. **CAUTION:** *Sodium hydroxide is corrosive. In case of spills, clean thoroughly with water.* Add 2 to 3 drops of phenolphthalein to the test tube. Use a clean stirring rod to mix the sodium hydroxide solution and indicator. Record your observations.

Part B: Making the Salt

6. Using the HCl dropper pipet, add 4 mL of hydrochloric acid to a clean 25-mL beaker. Record the number of drops you used. Add 2 to 3 drops of phenolphthalein to the beaker.

7. Use the NaOH dropper pipet to add sodium hydroxide drop by drop to the beaker of hydrochloric acid and phenolphthalein, stirring constantly. Count the drops as you add them. As a pink color remains longer, add the drops more slowly.

8. Continue to add and count the drops of sodium hydroxide until a light pink color remains for at least 30 seconds. (*Hint:* If you add too much sodium hydroxide, add a few more drops of hydrochloric acid until the color disappears.) Record any additional drops of hydrochloric acid that you added. Then, carefully add sodium hydroxide until 1 drop produces a lasting pink color. Record the total number of drops of sodium hydroxide used.

9. Use a piece of pH paper to determine the pH of the final solution. Record the pH. If the pH is higher than 7.0, add hydrochloric acid drop by drop, testing the pH with pH paper after each drop, until the pH is equal to 7.0. Record the pH and the total number of drops of HCl you added.

10. Use the solution in the beaker to fill the watch glass halfway.

11. Fill the 100-mL beaker about half full of water. Place the beaker on top of the hot plate.

12. Set the watch glass on top of the beaker.

13. Turn on the hot plate to a low setting. Adjust the heat as the water in the beaker warms. The water should simmer, but not boil. **CAUTION:** *Do not touch the hot plate or the beaker.* Heat until a solid is visible at the edges of the water in the watch glass and the water is nearly evaporated. Turn off the heat.

14. Allow the remaining water to evaporate. Observe the contents of the watch glass. Record your observations.

A white solid deposits on the watch glass.

15. When the watch glass has cooled, dispose of the contents as directed by your teacher. Clean up your equipment. Wash your hands with soap and water.

Analyze and Conclude

1. **Comparing and Contrasting** What was the total amount of hydrochloric acid used to make the neutral solution? What was the total amount of sodium hydroxide? How do the amounts compare?

See the data table. Students should recognize that they used the same volume of base as the volume

of acid they began with (assuming the concentrations of the acid and the base are the same).

_____

_____

2. **Drawing Conclusions** What do you conclude about the concentrations of hydrochloric acid and sodium hydroxide in the solutions?

The concentrations are the same.

_____

3. **Predicting** If the acid had been twice as concentrated as the base, how would your data have changed?

It would have taken twice as much base to reach the color change.

_____

Comparing Vitamin C in Fruit Juices

See page 285 in the Teacher's Edition for more information.

Various brands of juices often claim to be good sources of vitamin C, but which juices are the best sources? Vitamin C is an organic acid called ascorbic acid. Like other organic acids, vitamin C reacts with indicators to produce a color change. This reaction can be used to determine the amount of vitamin C present in foods, such as fruit juices. In this lab, you will add an indicator to a sample of apple juice. The indicator will change color when all the vitamin C has reacted. Then, you will test and compare the vitamin C content in other juices with the results for apple juice.

Problem Which juice provides the most vitamin C?

Materials
- apple juice
- a variety of other fruit juices
- test tubes and rack
- 10-mL graduated cylinder
- methylene blue indicator
- dropper pipet
- stirring rods
- graph paper

Skills Observing, Measuring, Analyzing Data

Procedure
Part A: Measuring Vitamin C in Apple Juice

1. Use a graduated cylinder to measure 10 mL of apple juice. Pour the juice into a test tube.

2. Add a drop of methylene blue indicator to the test tube. Stir until the color of the indicator disappears.

3. Add more indicator, one drop at a time, stirring after each addition. Count the drops that you add. Stop adding the indicator when the last drop of indicator does not change color. Record the number of drops that you used in the data table.

DATA TABLE

Type of Juice	Number of Drops
Apple	

Part B: Measuring Vitamin C in Other Juices

4. Formulate and record a hypothesis about which juice will have the greatest amount of vitamin C. You will need to decide which variables must be kept the same, as well as how to account for bits of solid in some juices.

_____

_____

5. List the steps in your procedure and write the names of each of the juices to be tested in the left column of the data table.

_____

_____

_____

_____

_____

_____

_____

6. Have your teacher check your procedure before you begin your experiment.

Analyze and Conclude

1. **Using Graphs** Make a bar graph of your data. Which juice required the most drops of indicator? Which required the least?

The graph and answers will vary depending on the samples tested.

_____

_____

2. **Drawing Conclusions** Based on your data, which juice contained the most vitamin C? How did you reach this conclusion?

The juice that required the most drops of methylene blue indicator is the one that contained the

most vitamin C.

3. **Evaluating and Revising** What unexpected problems did you encounter? Explain how you could revise your procedure to avoid these problems.

Acceptable answers include that juices with large amounts of pulp were a problem. Students

may suggest filtering those samples, but removing the pulp removes some of the vitamin C.

(Students could process the samples in a blender instead.) Students may also state that dark juices,

such as prune juice or grape juice, obscure the color change. Students might suggest diluting all

samples with the same amount of distilled water.

Chapter 10   Nuclear Chemistry   Exploration Lab

Modeling a Chain Reaction
See pages 316 and 317 in the Teacher's Edition for more information.

In a nuclear fission chain reaction, a nucleus is struck by a neutron, which causes the nucleus to split into two smaller nuclei and to release other neutrons. If these neutrons strike other nuclei, a chain reaction can occur. In this lab, you will model a nuclear fission chain reaction, using dominoes.

Problem How can you make a model of a nuclear fission chain reaction?

Materials
- 20 dominoes
- watch with a second hand, or stopwatch
- metric ruler

Skills Observing, Using Models

Procedure

1. Stand 15 dominoes in a single straight row in such a way that the distance between them is about one-half of their height. Knock over the first domino. Measure and record the time it takes for all the dominoes to fall.

_____

2. Repeat Step 1 two more times. Then, average the three time measurements to get a more accurate time.

0.7–0.9s
_____

3. Arrange 15 dominoes, as shown below, so that each domino will knock over two others. Observe what happens when you knock over the first domino. Measure and record how long it takes for the whole set of dominoes to fall over.

_____

Figure 1

4. Repeat Step 3 two more times. Average the three time measurements to get a more accurate time.

0.5–0.7s

_____

5. Set up 15 dominoes again as you did in Step 3. This time, however, hold a metric ruler on end, in the middle of the arrangement of dominoes. Knock over the first domino. Observe what happens.

The ruler prevents some of the dominoes from falling.

_____

6. Set up 15 dominoes as you did in Step 3, but this time, place 5 additional dominoes behind and at right angles to 5 randomly chosen dominoes for support, as shown below. The 5 supported dominoes represent atoms of a different isotope that must be struck with more energy to undergo fission.

Figure 2

7. Knock over the first domino. Measure and record the time it takes for the dominoes to fall and how many dominoes fall.

7–10 dominoes fall

_____

_____

8. Repeat Steps 6 and 7 two more times. Then, average the three time measurements to get a more accurate time.

0.4–0.5s

_____

_____

9. Repeat Steps 6 through 8, but this time, place supporting dominoes behind only 3 dominoes.

   10–12 dominoes fall; 0.3–0.4s _____

   _____

   _____

10. Repeat Steps 6 through 8, but this time, place a supporting domino behind only 1 domino.

    12–14 dominoes fall; 0.3–0.4s _____

    _____

    _____

Analyze and Conclude

1. **Calculating** What was the average fall time for the arrangement of dominoes in Steps 1 and 2? In Steps 3 and 4?

   The time should be shorter in Steps 3 and 4. _____

   _____

   _____

2. **Applying Concepts** What type of reaction was modeled in Steps 3 and 4?

   A nuclear fission chain reaction was modeled in Steps 3 and 4. _____

   _____

   _____

3. **Using Models** In your falling-dominoes model of nuclear fission chain reactions, what did a standing domino represent? What did the fall of a domino represent?

   A standing domino represented the nucleus of an atom. The fall of a domino represented

   the fission of the nucleus and the release of neutrons. _____

   _____

   _____

   _____

4. **Using Models** In your falling-dominoes model of nuclear fission chain reactions, what did the striking of one domino by another represent? What did the metric ruler represent?

   The striking of one domino by another represented the striking of a nucleus of a nearby atom

   by a neutron. The ruler represented a control rod. _____

   _____

   _____

   _____

5. **Analyzing Data** Before a sample of an easily fissionable isotope is used, it is refined by removing less fissionable isotopes of the same element. On the basis of your observations in Steps 6 through 10, explain why this refinement is necessary.

Atoms of the less-easily fissionable isotopes can absorb some of the energy released during

the fission of other atoms, which can interfere with development of a chain reaction.

_____

_____

_____

6. **Inferring** What factors do you think would affect the rate of a nuclear fission chain reaction?

The number of neutrons released when a nucleus undergoes fission and the number of other

atoms that are nearby and available for the released neutrons to strike affect the rate of the

reaction.

_____

_____

7. **Drawing Conclusions** What do you think would happen to the nuclear fission chain reaction if control rods were not present?

The reaction would go out of control, perhaps leading to a meltdown or an explosion.

_____

_____

_____

8. **Evaluating and Revising** What are some of the limitations of using falling dominoes to model a nuclear fission chain reaction? Suggest how you might revise this model to make it more representative of a chain reaction.

One limitation of the model in Step 3 is that it treats each fission reaction as the same. In reality,

the fission of a nucleus does not always release exactly two neutrons. The model could be revised

by using dominoes of varying sizes and/or colors to represent differing numbers of neutrons

released during fission.

_____

_____

_____

_____

Chapter 11   Motion

Investigating the Velocity of a Sinking Marble

In this lab, you will graph the motion of a marble falling through shampoo.

See page 349 in the Teacher's Edition for more information

Problem What does a distance-time graph look like for a marble falling through shampoo?

Materials

- clear shampoo
- 100-mL graduated cylinder
- 2 small marbles
- stopwatch
- forceps
- masking tape
- metric ruler
- 10-mL graduated cylinder
- long glass stirring rod
- dropper pipet
- graph paper

Skills Measuring, Observing, Using Tables and Graphs

Procedure 🧤 🔬 ⚡

1. Wrap a small amount of masking tape around the tips of the forceps. This will allow you to grip the marble with it.

2. Measure the distance between the 10-mL gradations on the 100-mL graduated cylinder. Record the new distance in the first row of the data table.

DATA TABLE

Distance (mm)	First Marble Time (s)	Second Marble Time (s)

3. Multiply this distance by 2 and write the result in the second row of the data table. For the third row, multiply the distance by 3. Continue until you have written distances in 10 rows.

4. Slowly pour 100 mL of clear shampoo into the 100-mL graduated cylinder.

5. Be ready to observe the marble as it falls through the shampoo. Grasp the marble with the forceps and hold the marble just above the shampoo-filled graduated cylinder.

6. Say "Go!" as you drop the marble into the shampoo. At the same moment, your partner should start the stopwatch.

7. Each time the lower edge of the marble reaches a 10-mL mark on the cylinder, say "Now." Your partner should note and record the time on the stopwatch.

8. Continue calling out "Now" each time the marble reaches a 10-mL mark until it comes to rest on the bottom of the cylinder. Say "Stop!"

9. Use the 10-mL graduated cylinder to add about 8 mL of water to the 100-mL graduated cylinder. Use the glass stirring rod to mix the water and shampoo gently but thoroughly.

10. With the dropper pipet, remove enough liquid from the graduated cylinder to decrease the volume to 100 mL.

11. Repeat Steps 5 through 8, using another marble.

12. Wash all supplies as instructed by your teacher.

Analyze and Conclude

1. **Using Tables and Graphs** Use the data you collected to make a distance-time graph for each of the two marbles.

   The graph should be a nearly straight line for both marbles. The graph for the second marble will

   be steeper.

2. **Observing** Explain the motion of the marbles as they fell through the shampoo. How did you show this motion on your graph?

   At first, the marbles fell at a nearly constant velocity, which is shown as a straight line on the

   distance-time graph. The second marble fell faster than the first marble. As the marbles

   approached the bottom of the cylinder, the viscosity of the shampoo caused them to slow down.

3. **Inferring** Based on your graph, were the marbles accelerating? Explain your answers.

   Answers will depend on the viscosity of the shampoo. In most cases, the marbles did not

   accelerate because of the resistance from the viscous shampoo.

4. **Calculating** Use the data table to calculate the average speed of each marble.

   The speeds will depend on the type of shampoo used. Typical speeds are 2.5 mm/s and 6.0 mm/s

   for marbles falling in shampoo and diluted shampoo, respectively.

Investigating a Balloon Jet

See page 383 in the Teacher's Edition for more information.

In this lab, you will examine the relationships among force, mass, and motion.

Problem How does a jet-powered device move?

Materials
- string, 3 m in length
- drinking straw
- 4 long balloons
- masking tape
- stopwatch
- meter stick
- 2 threaded nuts
- 2 chairs

Skills Applying Concepts

Procedure

1. Insert the string through the straw and tie each end of the string to the back of a separate chair. Pull the chairs apart until the string is tight and horizontal.

2. Blow up the balloon and then hold the balloon's opening closed. In the data table, record the length of the balloon. Have a classmate attach the balloon lengthwise to the straw, using tape.

3. While continuing to hold the balloon's opening closed, slide the balloon jet to the end of the string.

4. Release the balloon. Measure the time during which the balloon jet moves. Measure the distance that the balloon jet travels along the string. Record the distance and time values in the data table for 0 Nuts Used, Trial 1.

DATA TABLE

Number of Nuts Used	Trial Number	Time (seconds)	Distance (centimeters)	Average Velocity (cm/s)
0	1			
0	2			
2	1			
2	2			
Length of inflated balloon (centimeters)				

5. Repeat Steps 2 through 4 with a new balloon. Make sure to inflate the balloon to the same size as in Step 2. Record your results in the data table for 0 Nuts Used, Trial 2.

6. Repeat Steps 2 through 5 twice more with a new balloon. This time, tape two nuts to the balloon before releasing it. Record your results in the data table for 2 Nuts Used, Trials 1 and 2.

7. Calculate and record the average velocity for each trial. The average velocity is equal to the distance divided by the time.

Analyze and Conclude

1. **Applying Concepts** Use Newton's second and third laws to explain the motion of the balloon jet.

A balloon jet's movement depends on Newton's third law of motion. The pressurized air inside the

sealed balloon pushes outward in all directions, but as long as the air can't go anywhere,

neither can the balloon. As soon as the air inside the balloon is allowed to escape, the force

of the air on the opened end of the balloon no longer balances the force of air on the opposite

end. The reaction to this action is the movement of the balloon in the opposite direction.

Newton's second law of motion predicts that the balloon will accelerate at a rate that is

directly proportional to the force of the compressed air and inversely proportional to the

balloon's mass.

_____

_____

_____

_____

_____

_____

_____

2. **Analyzing Data** How did adding mass (nuts) to the balloon jet affect its motion?

Adding nuts increased the mass of the balloon jet, which reduced its acceleration.

_____

_____

_____

_____

_____

_____

Determining Buoyant Force
See page 405 in the Teacher's Edition for more information.

In this lab, you will analyze recorded data to determine the buoyant forces acting on objects.

Problem
How does the buoyant force determine whether an object sinks?

Materials
- string
- rock
- spring scale
- can
- plastic tub
- sponge
- paper towels
- 100-g standard mass
- wooden block tied to a fishing weight
- 250-mL graduated cylinder

Skills
Measuring, Calculating

Procedure 🔧✂️

1. Tie one end of the string around the rock. Tie the other end to the spring scale. Suspend the rock from the spring scale and measure and record its weight in air in the data table.

DATA TABLE Sample data are shown.

Object	Weight in Air (N)	Apparent Weight in Water (N)	Buoyant Force (weight in air – apparent weight in water, N)	Volume of Displaced Water (mL)	Weight of Displaced Water (N)
Rock	0.3	0.2	0.1	5.0	0.049
100-g standard mass	1.0	0.75	0.25	10.0	0.098
Wood block with fishing weight	1.8	1.5	0.3	25.0	0.24

2. Place the can in an upright position in the plastic tub. Completely fill the can with water. Wipe up any water that has spilled into the tub. **CAUTION:** *Wipe up any water that spills on the floor to avoid slips and falls.*

3. Lower the rock into the water until it is completely submerged. Record in the data table the apparent weight in water of the submerged rock. Remove the rock from the can.

4. Without spilling any water, carefully remove the can from the tub. Pour the water from the tub into the graduated cylinder. Record in the data table the volume of displaced water .

5. Repeat Steps 1 through 4, first with the 100-g standard mass and then with the wooden block that is tied to a fishing weight.

6. To determine the buoyant force on each object, subtract its apparent weight in water from its weight in air. In the data table, record these values.

7. Calculate the weight of the water that each object displaces. (*Hint:* 1.0 mL of water has a weight of 0.0098 N.) In the data table, record these weights.

Analyze and Conclude

1. **Observing** What force is responsible for the difference between the weight of each object in the air and its apparent weight in water?

The difference is equal to the buoyant force that the water exerts on the object.

_____

_____

_____

2. **Analyzing Data** How is the buoyant force related to the weight of water displaced?

They are equal.

_____

_____

_____

3. **Forming Operational Definitions** Define buoyant force and describe two ways you can measure it or calculate it.

Buoyant force is an upward force exerted on an object by water when the object is

submerged in water. The buoyant force on an object is equal to the difference between

its weight in air and its apparent weight in water. It is also equal to the weight of the water

the object displaces.

_____

_____

4. **Drawing Conclusions** Explain what causes an object to sink or to float, using the terms *buoyancy, weight, force, density,* and *gravity.*

An object will float when the upward force of buoyancy is greater than or equal to the downward

force of gravity (the weight of the object). For the buoyant force to counteract the gravitational

force, the object must weigh as much as or less than the volume of water it displaces. For this

reason, floating objects have low densities.

_____

_____

_____

_____

_____

_____

_____

Chapter 14   Machines   **Consumer Lab**

Determining Mechanical Advantage

See pages 438 and 439 in the Teacher's Edition for more information.

Many complex machines have an adjustable mechanical advantage. In this lab, you will learn how adjusting the mechanical advantage of a bicycle affects the bicycle's performance.

Problem How does mechanical advantage affect the performance of a bicycle?

Materials
- board with 2 nails
- 4 thread spools, 3 with different diameters
- rubber band
- masking tape
- multispeed bicycle (one or more per class)
- meter stick
- thick leather glove

Skills Measuring, Calculating

Procedure

Part A: Modeling the Mechanical Advantage of a Bicycle

1. Use a piece of masking tape to label each nail on the board. Label one nail *Pedals* and the other nail *Wheel*. To model the pedals and rear wheel of a bicycle, place a spool on each nail in the board and join the spools with a rubber band, as shown in Figure 1.

Figure 1

2. Use a pencil to make a reference mark on the edge of each spool. These marks will help you observe the motion of the spools as they turn.

3. **Measuring** Use a ruler to measure the radius of each spool in your model. Record these measurements in the data table for Part A.

Name _____ Class _____ Date _____

DATA TABLE: PART A

Pedal Spool Radius (cm)	Revolutions of Pedal Spool	Wheel Spool Radius (cm)	Revolutions of Wheel Spool	IMA
	5			
	5			
	5			

4. The pedal spool represents the pedals and the gears attached to them. The wheel spool represents the rear wheel and its gears. Using the reference marks, observe the wheel spool as you turn the pedal spool through five complete revolutions. In the data table, record the number of revolutions of the wheel spool.

5. Replace the wheel spool with a spool of a different diameter. Repeat Steps 2 through 4 for each diameter of wheel spool.

6. **Calculating** The ideal mechanical advantage (IMA) of a bicycle is equal to the distance the pedals move divided by the distance the rear wheel moves. For your model,

$$IMA = \frac{5 \times Pedal\ radius}{(Revolutions\ of\ wheel) \times (Wheel\ radius)}$$

Calculate the mechanical advantage of each spool combination that you used. Record these values in the data table.

Part B: Analyzing Bicycle Gears

7. **Measuring** Work in groups of three. Use a meter stick to measure the radius of the pedals and the rear wheel, as shown in Figure 2. Record these measurements in the data table for Part B.

DATA TABLE: PART B

Size of Pedal Gear	Smallest	Smallest	Largest
Size of Rear Wheel Gear	Largest	Medium	Smallest
Pedal Radius (cm)			
Revolutions of Pedal	5	5	5
Rear Wheel Radius (cm)			
Revolutions of Rear Wheel			
IMA	The mechanical advantage of a typical multispeed bicycle gear train can vary from approximately 0.7 to 4.0.		

8. One person should hold the bicycle with its rear wheel slightly off the floor. While a second person turns the pedals, a third person should use the bicycle's gear shifters to place the chain on the smallest pedal gear and the largest rear wheel gear. **CAUTION:** *Keep your hands out of the spokes, chain, and gears.*

9. One person should put on a heavy leather glove, while a second person holds the bicycle with its rear wheel slightly off the floor.

Rear-wheel radius

Pedal radius

Figure 2

10. The third person should slowly turn the pedals through five complete revolutions. The person who is wearing the glove should gently hold the rear tire tread so that the wheel turns only as fast as the pedals force it to move. This person should also observe the position of the valve stem to count the number of revolutions of the rear wheel. In the data table, record the number of revolutions of the rear wheel.

11. Repeat Steps 8 through 10, once using the smallest pedal gear and a mid-sized rear-wheel gear, and then again using the largest pedal gear and the smallest rear-wheel gear.

12. **Calculating** Use the equation in Step 6 to calculate the mechanical advantage of the bicycle for each gear combination you used. Record these values in the data table.

Analyze and Conclude

1. **Analyzing Data** Which combination of pedal and rear-wheel gears provided the greatest mechanical advantage? The least mechanical advantage?

   The largest pedal gear and the smallest rear-wheel gear provided the greatest mechanical

   advantage. The smallest pedal gear and the largest rear-wheel gear provided the least

   mechanical advantage.

   _____

   _____

   _____

   _____

2. **Applying Concepts** To ride quickly on a level road, would you select a gear combination with a large mechanical advantage or a small one? Explain your answer.

   A large mechanical advantage would be best for riding quickly on a level road because it

   would produce the greatest number of turns of the rear wheel for each turn of the pedals.

   _____

   _____

   _____

   _____

   _____

3. **Drawing Conclusions** To decrease the force needed to ride a bicycle up a steep hill, would you select a gear combination with a large mechanical advantage or a small one? What size rear-wheel gear would you use to race on a flat road? Explain.

   A gear combination with a large mechanical advantage would be best for riding up a steep

   hill because it would exert the greatest force on the rear wheel. A small rear-wheel gear would

   be best for racing on a flat road because it would cause the rear wheel to turn fastest and

   therefore cause the bicycle to move fastest. A large rear-wheel gear would be best for uphill

   mountain biking because it would exert the greatest force on the rear wheel.

   _____

   _____

   _____

   _____

   _____

Chapter 15   Energy

Investigating a Spring Clip

*There are many ways to use potential energy. A spring clip is a device
used to hold weights on a barbell. The spring clip stores energy when you
compress it. In this lab, you will determine how the distance you compress
a spring clip is related to the force you apply and to the spring's potential
energy.*

Problem How does the force you apply to a spring clip affect its
elastic potential energy?

Materials

- clamp
- spring clip
- masking tape
- metric ruler
- 50-newton spring scale
- graph paper

Skills Measuring, Using Tables and Graphs

Procedure 🔧 📊

1. Using the clamp, firmly attach one
   handle of the spring clip to a tabletop,
   with the other handle facing up and
   away from the table, as shown.
   CAUTION: *Be careful not to pinch your
   fingers with the clamp or spring clip.*

2. Remove the plastic cover from the
   upper handle of the spring clip. Hook
   the spring scale to the spring clip
   handle, as shown, and use masking
   tape to secure it. Have your teacher
   check your setup for safety before
   proceeding.

3. Have a classmate hold the ruler next
   to the spring clip, as shown. Record
   the starting position of the handle.
   (The reading on the spring scale
   should be zero.)

4. Slowly pull the spring scale down at a right angle to the upper
   handle until the handle moves 0.1 cm. In the data table, record the
   force and the position of the upper handle. Slowly release the scale
   back to the starting position.

DATA TABLE Sample data are shown.

Force (N)	Position of Upper Handle (cm)	Total Distance Moved (cm)
3.5	6.5	0.1
5.0	6.4	0.2
7.0	6.3	0.3
9.0	6.2	0.4
12.0	6.1	0.5

5. Repeat Step 4, this time pulling the handle 0.2 cm from the starting position.

6. Repeat Step 4 a few more times, pulling the handle 0.1 cm farther each time. Continue until the spring scale reaches its maximum force.

7. Calculate the distance the handle moved each time you pulled it and record these values in the data table. Graph your data. Place the distance the handle moved on the vertical axis and the force that was applied on the horizontal axis.

Analyze and Conclude

1. **Using Graphs** What is the approximate relationship between the total distance you compressed the spring clip and the force you applied to it?

As the distance increased, the force increased. The relationship between force and distance is

directly proportional.

2. **Classifying** What type of energy transfer did you use to compress the spring clip? What type of energy did the spring clip gain when it was compressed?

Students did work to compress the spring clip. This action increased the elastic potential energy of

the spring clip.

3. **Drawing Conclusions** What relationship exists between the distance the spring clip was compressed and its potential energy? (*Hint:* The elastic potential energy of the spring clip equals the work done on it.)

The greater the distance the spring clip was compressed, the greater was its elastic potential energy.

Chapter 16   Thermal Energy and Heat   Design Your Own Lab

Using Specific Heat to Analyze Metals

See page 493 in the Teacher's Edition for more information.

In this lab, you will determine the specific heat of steel and aluminum. Then, you will use specific heat to analyze the composition of a metal can.

Problem How can you use specific heat to determine the composition of a metal can?

Materials
- 10 steel bolts
- balance
- 50-cm length of string
- clamp
- ring stand
- boiling water bath (shared with class)

- thermometer
- 500-mL graduated cylinder
- ice water
- foam cup with lid
- aluminum nails
- crushed can

Skills Calculating, Designing Experiments

Procedure 🔬🧤🔪⚒

Part A: Determining Specific Heat

1. Measure and record the mass of 10 steel bolts.

Ten bolts with a mass of 100 g will raise the temperature of 200 mL of water by about 5°C. The same mass of aluminum nails will raise the temperature by about 9°C.

DATA TABLE

	Water	Steel Bolts	Aluminum Nails
Mass (g)			
Initial temperature (°C)			
Final temperature (°C)			
Specific heat (J/g • °C)	4.18		

2. Tie the bolts to the string. Use a clamp and ring stand to suspend the bolts in the boiling water bath. **CAUTION:** *Be careful not to splash boiling water.* After a few minutes, record in the data table the water temperature as the initial temperature of the bolts.

3. Use a graduated cylinder to pour 200 mL of ice water (without ice) into the foam cup. Record the mass and temperature of the ice water. (*Hint:* The density of water is 1 g/mL.)

4. Use the clamp to move the bolts into the cup of ice water. Cover the cup and insert the thermometer through the hole in the cover.

5. Gently swirl the water in the cup. Record the highest temperature as the final temperature for both the water and the steel bolts.

6. Calculate and record the specific heat of steel. (*Hint:* Use the equation $Q = m \times c \times \Delta T$ to calculate the energy the water absorbs.)

7. Repeat Steps 2 through 6 with aluminum nails to determine the specific heat of aluminum. Use a mass of aluminum that is close to the mass you used for the steel bolts.

Part B: Design Your Own Experiment

8. **Designing Experiments** Design an experiment that uses specific heat to identify the metals a can might be made of.

9. In the space below, construct a data table in which to record your observations. After your teacher approves your plan, perform your experiment.

Analyze and Conclude

1. **Comparing and Contrasting** Which metal has a higher specific heat—aluminum or steel?

   The specific heat of aluminum (about 0.90 J/g°C) is higher than the specific heat of steel

   (about 0.45 J/g°C).

2. **Drawing Conclusions** Was the specific heat of the can closer to the specific heat of steel or of aluminum? What can you conclude about the material in the can?

   The specific heat of the can was very close to the specific heat of steel. This is evidence that the

   can is not made of aluminum and may be made of steel.

3. **Evaluating** Did your observations prove what the can was made of? If not, what other information would you need to be sure?

   The observations support the idea that the can is made of steel, but do not prove it; other metals

   may have similar specific heats. A list of the specific heats of various metals for comparison would

   be helpful, as would other kinds of evidence, such as the densities and chemical properties of

   the metals.

4. **Inferring** The can you used is often called a tin can. The specific heat of tin is 0.23 J/g°C. Did your data support the idea that the can was made mostly of tin? Explain your answer.

   The specific heat of the can is close to that of steel, not tin. This suggests that the can is not made

   primarily of tin.

Chapter 17   Mechanical Waves and Sound

See pages 524 and 525 in the Teacher's Edition for more information.

Exploration Lab

Investigating Sound Waves

Sound is produced when a vibrating source causes a medium to vibrate. In this lab, you will investigate how the vibrating source affects characteristics of the sound produced.

Problem What determines the frequency and amplitude of the sound produced by a vibrating object?

Materials
- meter stick
- 2 cardboard tubes
- scissors or scalpel
- 2 rubber bands
- wax paper
- balloon
- small mirror
- transparent tape
- flashlight

Skills Observing, Inferring, Drawing Conclusions, Controlling Variables

Procedure 🔧 ✂️
Part A: Investigating How Length Affects Pitch

1. Hold one end of a meter stick down firmly on a table so that 20 centimeters of the meter stick extends past the edge of the table. Pluck the end of the meter stick that extends past the table to produce a vibration and a sound. Observe the vibration and sound of the meter stick.

2. Repeat Step 1, but this time allow 40 centimeters of the meter stick to extend past the edge of the table. Observe and record how the length of the vibrating part of the meter stick affects the pitch.

   Increasing the length of the overhang lowers the pitch.

   _____

   _____

   _____

3. Repeat Step 1, but this time allow 60 centimeters of the meter stick to extend past the edge of the table. Record your observations.

   Increasing the length of the overhang to 60 cm lowers the pitch even further.

   _____

   _____

   _____

4. Investigate the relationship between length and frequency for a vibrating column of air, as you did with the vibrating meter stick. Make a kazoo by cutting a hole in the middle of one of the cardboard tubes. Make the hole approximately 1 centimeter in diameter. Use a rubber band to fasten the piece of wax paper over one end of the tube. **CAUTION:** *Be careful when cutting with sharp instruments; always cut away from yourself and away from nearby people.*

5. Make a second kazoo by cutting the second tube 10 centimeters shorter than the first tube. Using the short tube, repeat Step 4.

6. Hold the shorter kazoo in front of your mouth and hum into the open end, keeping your pitch steady. Repeat this action with the longer kazoo, making sure to hum exactly as you did before. Observe and record how the length of the kazoo affects the pitch of the sound.

The longer kazoo makes a lower-pitch sound.
_____
_____
_____
_____
_____
_____
_____

Part B: Investigating How Frequency Affects Pitch and How Amplitude Affects Loudness

7. Cut the neck off of the balloon. Replace the wax paper on the longer kazoo with the cut-open balloon. Wrap the rubber band several times around the end of the cardboard tube. The rubber band should hold the balloon tightly stretched over the end of the tube. Use tape to attach the small mirror onto the balloon on the end of the tube.

8. Have a classmate shine a flashlight on the mirror, as shown, while you hum into the kazoo. Your classmate should position the flashlight so that a spot of light is reflected on the wall. It may be necessary to darken the room. Observe how the spot of light moves when you hum into the kazoo. Make a note of your position and the position and angle of the kazoo and the flashlight.

Students should make a sketch or carefully describe their position and the position and angle
of the kazoo and flashlight.
_____
_____
_____
_____
_____

9. Without changing how loudly you hum, use your voice to raise the pitch of your humming. Observe and record how the movement of the spot of light differs from your observations in Step 8. Make sure you do not change your distance from the wall or the angle at which the light from the flashlight strikes the mirror attached to the kazoo.

   The spot will vibrate more rapidly when the pitch increases.
   _____
   _____
   _____

10. Repeat Step 9, but this time hum at a lower pitch than you did in Step 8.

    The spot will vibrate more slowly when the pitch decreases.
    _____
    _____

11. Repeat Steps 9 and 10, but this time vary the loudness of your humming while keeping the pitch constant.

    The amplitude of vibration of the spot decreases when volume decreases, and it increases

    when volume increases.
    _____

Analyze and Conclude

1. **Observing** What happened to the frequency of the meter stick's vibration when you made the overhanging part longer?

   The frequency was reduced.

2. **Inferring** How did the frequency of the meter stick's vibration affect the pitch of its sound?

   The pitch became lower as the frequency was reduced.

3. **Inferring** How did the kazoo's length affect its pitch?

   The longer kazoo had the lower pitch.

4. **Analyzing Data** When you changed the pitch of your humming, how did it affect the frequency of vibration of the mirror?

   Humming at a higher pitch increased the frequency of the mirror's vibration.

5. **Analyzing Data** How is the amplitude of the kazoo's vibration related to its loudness?

   Increasing the loudness increased the amplitude of the kazoo's vibration.

6. **Controlling Variables** Explain why it was important to keep loudness constant when you changed the pitch of your humming in Step 9.

   Keeping the loudness constant ensured that any change in the frequency of the mirror's vibration

   was caused by the change in pitch.

Chapter 18   The Electromagnetic Spectrum and Light   **Exploration Lab**

Mixing Colored Lights

See page 563 in the Teacher's
Edition for more information.

*What is color? How many different colors can be formed from a combination
of only three colors? In this exploration, you will examine what happens
when lights of three different colors are mixed.*

Problem How can you produce a range of colors from three lights
of different colors?

Materials
- sources of red, blue, and green light
- tape
- large sheet of white paper

Skills Observing

Procedure 🔦 🧤

1. Tape a large sheet of white paper to the wall.

2. Dim the room lights. Turn on the red light source and shine it on
   the large sheet of white paper. In the data table, record the colors
   you observe on the paper. **CAUTION:** *Do not touch lamps when they
   are on. They may be hot.*

DATA TABLE

Light Sources	Colors of Lights	Colors of Shadows
Red only		
Blue only		
Green only		
Red and blue		
Red and green		
Blue and green		
Red, blue, and green		

3. Place your hand between the light source and the paper. Record the
   color of your hand's shadow.

4. Repeat Steps 2 and 3 with the blue and then with the green light
   source.

5. Now turn on the red and blue light sources and allow their beams to overlap. Record your observations in the data table.

6. Place your hand in the overlapping beams of light. Note the colors of any shadows that your hand makes. Record your observations in the data table.

7. Repeat Steps 5 and 6 with the red and green light sources. Then repeat Steps 5 and 6 with the blue and green light sources.

8. Turn on all three light sources and allow their beams to overlap. Record your observations in the data table.

9. Place your hand in the overlapping red, green, and blue beams. Note the colors of any shadows that your hand makes on the white paper. Record your observations in the data table.

Analyze and Conclude

1. **Observing** What happened when two colored lights overlapped?

Two colors combined to make a new color.

2. **Analyzing Data** How did the combination of two colored lights produce the shadows you observed?

Because there were two light sources, there were two overlapping shadows. In areas on the paper

where the hand blocked only one beam of light, the other area was lit by the other beam of light.

Therefore, each shadow was the color of one beam of light.

3. **Applying Concepts** Explain how combining three colored lights produced the colors you observed.

Overlapping two beams of primary-colored light produced secondary colors. Combining all three

primary colors in equal intensity produced white light.

4. **Drawing Conclusions** From the shadows you observed when using three colored lights, what can you conclude about how colors of light combine? Explain your answer.

The colors of the shadows show how colors of light combine. In areas where the hand blocked one

beam, the shadow was lit by the two other lights. Therefore, these areas were secondary colors of

light. For example, where the hand blocked only the blue beam, the shadow was lit by red and green

light, producing a yellow shadow. Similarly, red and blue light combined to produce a magenta

shadow, and blue and green light combined to produce a cyan shadow.

Chapter 19   Optics   **Consumer Lab**

Selecting Mirrors

See page 593 in the Teacher's Edition for more information.

In this lab, you will compare several mirrors and select the type that is best for a specific use.

Problem What mirror shape is best for magnifying images? For providing a wide view?

Materials
- plane, convex, and concave mirrors
- 2 metric rulers
- roll of string
- protractor

Skills Observing, Measuring

Procedure
Part A: Comparing Magnification

1. Place the plane mirror on a tabletop with its mirror side facing up. Position a metric ruler horizontally across the center of the mirror.

2. Hold the other metric ruler horizontally against your nose, just below your eyes, as shown below. Make sure the ruler's markings face away from you. Look down at the mirror.

Figure 1

3. Use the ruler resting on the mirror to measure the actual length of the image of a 3-cm-long portion of the ruler you are holding. In the data table, record the size of the image.

DATA TABLE

Mirror	Size of Image	Magnification	Field of View
Plane	A typical concave hand mirror magnifies by a factor of 2 to 3, and a plane mirror produces an image that is reduced by approximately one-third. Typical fields of view for concave, plane, and convex mirrors are 70°, 80°, and 140°, respectively.		
Concave			
Convex			

4. Repeat Steps 1 through 3, using concave and convex mirrors. Observe each image from the same distance.

5. Divide each image size you measured by 3 cm to determine its magnification. Record the magnification in the data table.

Part B: Comparing Fields of View

6. Tie a string to a ruler. Hold the protractor, mirror, and free end of the string. Have a classmate hold the ruler vertically off to one side of the mirror. Position a third classmate (the observer) directly in front of and about 2 meters away from the mirror, as shown in Figure 2.

7. Have the classmate holding the ruler slowly move toward the observer while keeping the string tight. The observer should look directly into the mirror and say "Stop!" as soon as the reflection of the ruler can be seen.

8. Measure the angle the string makes with the protractor. Multiply this angle by 2 and record it as the field of view in the data table.

9. Repeat Steps 6 through 8, using concave and convex mirrors. Observe each mirror from the same distance.

Figure 2

Analyze and Conclude

1. **Observing** Which mirror provided the greatest magnification? The widest view?

   The concave mirror provided the greatest magnification, and the convex mirror produced the

   widest field of view.

2. **Applying Concepts** Which mirror shape would work best for a dentist who needs to see a slightly magnified image of a tooth? Explain your answer.

   A concave mirror is best for a dentist because it magnifies the most.

3. **Drawing Conclusions** Could one of the mirrors be used both to view a wide area and to magnify? Explain your answer.

   None of these mirrors could be used to observe both a wide area and a magnified view of

   small details because increasing the magnification reduces the width of the field of view,

   and increasing the width of the field of view reduces the magnification.

Chapter 20   Electricity   Forensics Lab

Evaluating Electrical Safety   See page 623 in the Teacher's Edition for more information.

Electric appliances must be safely insulated to protect users from injury. In this lab, you will play the role of a safety engineer determining whether an electric power supply is safely insulated.

Problem How much resistance is needed in series with a known resistance to reduce the voltage by 99 percent?

Materials
- 9-volt battery
- battery clip
- multimeter
- 3 alligator clips
- 4 resistors: 1-ohm, 10-ohm, 100-ohm, 1000-ohm

Skills Calculating, Using Tables

Procedure
1. Attach the battery clip to the battery.
   CAUTION: *The circuit may become hot.*

2. Use an alligator clip to attach one wire of the 1-ohm resistor to one of the battery clip's wires, as shown in Figure 1.

3. Clip one wire of the 1000-ohm resistor to the free end of the 1-ohm resistor. Clip the other wire of the 1000-ohm resistor to the free wire of the battery clip.

4. The 1-ohm resistor represents the current-carrying part of the appliance. The 1000-ohm resistor represents the insulation for the current-carrying part. Place one of the multimeter's electrodes on each wire of the 1-ohm resistor. Record the voltage difference.

Resistors

Figure 1

Data Table

Resistance (ohms)		Voltage difference (volts)	
Current-Carrying	Insulating	Current-Carrying	Insulating
1	1000	0.01	8.6
1	100	0.09	8.5
10	1000	0.09	8.5
10	100	0.9	7.7

5. Place the multimeter's electrodes on the wires of the 1000-ohm resistor. Record the voltage difference.

6. To model a reduction in the resistance of the insulation, repeat Steps 4 and 5, replacing the 1000-ohm resistor with a 100-ohm resistor. Disconnect the resistors from the battery clip.

7. **Predicting** Record your prediction of how increasing the resistance of the current-carrying part of the appliance will affect the voltage difference across the insulating part.

   Sample prediction: Increasing the current-carrying resistance will decrease the voltage difference

   across the insulating part.

8. To test your prediction, repeat Steps 2 through 6, using a 10-ohm resistor to represent the current-carrying part of the appliance.

Analyze and Conclude

1. **Calculating** When the resistance of the current-carrying part was 1 ohm and the resistance of the insulating part was 100 ohms, what was the ratio of the voltage differences across the current-carrying part and the insulating part?

   The ratio of the voltage differences was 0.01 (1/100).

2. **Drawing Conclusions** In the circuit you built, what is the voltage difference across each resistor proportional to?

   The voltage difference across each resistor was proportional to its resistance.

3. **Applying Concepts** You know the resistance of the current-carrying part of an appliance. What should the resistance of the insulation be to reduce the voltage by 99 percent?

   The resistance of the insulation should be 100 times the resistance of the current-carrying part.

Chapter 21   Magnetism

Investigating an Electric Generator

See pages 648 and 649 in the
Teacher's Edition for more information.

*All generators have two main parts—a magnet and a wire that is wrapped
into a coil. The arrangement of these parts varies, depending on the size and
power of the generator and whether it produces direct or alternating current.
In this lab, you will determine how several variables affect the current
produced by a simple generator.*

Problem How do the direction in which the magnet moves and the
number and direction of the turns in the coil affect the current that a
generator produces?

Materials
- cardboard tube
- 5-m length of insulated wire
- metric ruler
- multimeter
- bar magnet
- graph paper

Skills Observing, Using Graphs

Procedure 🖎🔧
Part A: Changing the Number of Turns

1. Slip the wire between your hand and the tube so that 15 cm of wire
   extends from the tube. Use your other hand to wrap the long end
   of the wire around the tube 10 times in a clockwise direction, as
   shown in Figure 1. Make sure all the turns are within 10 cm of the
   end of the tube. **CAUTION:** *Be careful not to cut yourself on the sharp
   ends of the wire.*

Figure 1

2. Connect both ends of the wire to the multimeter. Set the multimeter
   to measure current.

3. Hold the bar magnet by its south pole. Observe the multimeter
   as you quickly insert the bar magnet into the open end of the
   cardboard tube that is wrapped with the wire coil. Repeat this
   step if necessary as you adjust the scale of the multimeter.
   Record the maximum current in the data table.

DATA TABLE

Number of Turns	Direction of Turns	Pole Inserted	Current (mA)
10	Clockwise	North	
20	Clockwise	North	
30	Clockwise	North	
30	Clockwise	South	
30	Counterclockwise	South	

4. Disconnect the multimeter from the end of the wire that is farther from the turns.

5. **Predicting** Record your prediction of how increasing the number of turns in the coil will affect the current.

Sample prediction: Increasing the number of turns increases the current.

_____

_____

6. To test your prediction, wrap the wire around the end of the tube 10 more times in the same direction that you wound it previously—clockwise. You should now have a total of 20 turns. Reconnect the wire to the multimeter.

7. Repeat Step 3.

8. Again, disconnect the multimeter from the same end of the wire. Wrap the wire clockwise around the tube 10 more times for a total of 30 turns. Reconnect the wire to the multimeter.

9. Repeat Step 3 and then disconnect the multimeter from the same end of the wire.

Part B: Changing Other Properties of the Generator

10. **Predicting** Record your prediction of how reversing the direction of the magnet will affect the current.

Sample prediction: Reversing the direction of the magnet will reverse the direction of the current.

_____

_____

11. To test your prediction, reconnect the wire to the multimeter exactly as you did before. Repeat Step 3, but this time, hold the magnet by its north pole.

12. **Predicting** Record your prediction of how reversing the direction of the turns in the coil will affect the current if you hold the magnet by its south pole.

Sample prediction: Reversing the direction of the turns will reverse the direction of the current.

_____

_____

13. To test your prediction, remove the wire from the tube. Now wrap 30 turns of wire in the opposite direction—counterclockwise.

14. Repeat Step 3, holding the magnet by its south pole.

15. Construct a graph using the data from the first three rows in the data table. Plot the number of turns on the horizontal axis and the current on the vertical axis.

Analyze and Conclude

1. **Inferring** What caused a current in the wire?

   A current flowed in the wire because the moving magnetic field exerted a force on the electrons

   in the wire, causing them to move.

   _____

   _____

2. **Using Graphs** Based on your graph, what is the relationship
   between the number of turns and the amount of current?

   The graph indicates that the number of turns are in direct proportion to the amount of current.

   _____

   _____

   _____

   _____

3. **Analyzing Data** Explain the effect that reversing the direction of
   the magnet or the direction of the turns had on the direction of
   the current.

   Reversing the direction of the magnet or the turns reversed the direction of the force of the

   magnetic field on the electrons in the wire. This change in direction caused the charges to move

   in the opposite direction.

   _____

   _____

   _____

4. **Predicting** Explain whether a generator could be built with a
   stationary magnet and a coil that moved.

   Yes, it is possible for such a generator to be built. It is only necessary that the magnetic field

   in the wire coils change. It does not matter which part moves to accomplish this task.

   _____

   _____

   _____

   _____

   _____

5. Evaluating and Revising Did your observations support your predictions? If not, evaluate any flaws in the reasoning you used to make the predictions.

Correct predictions should state that an increase in the number of turns in the coil increases

the strength of the current, and that reversing the direction of the turns or the magnet will

reverse the direction of the current. Errors in reasoning may involve assuming that the

direction of the coil or magnet motion does not affect current direction. If a current is too

weak to observe, students may fail to realize that the speed of the magnet's motion may

account for a weak induced current, and that increasing the number of turns may not provide

the right results if the change in the magnetic field is not kept fairly constant throughout the

experiment.

_____

_____

_____

_____

_____

_____

_____

_____

_____

_____

Name _____ Class _____ Date _____

Using Earthquakes to Map Plate Boundaries

See page 697 in the Teacher's Edition for more information.

In this lab, you will analyze data from several earthquakes to determine how the plates in the northwestern United States are moving.

Problem   How can you use earthquake data to infer the movement of tectonic plates?

Materials
• graph paper

Skills   Inferring, Analyzing Data

Procedure

1. Examine the map of Oregon and Washington states. Earthquakes occur in the western parts of these states as a result of the movements of two plates—the Juan de Fuca Plate, which lies under the Pacific Ocean, and the North American plate.

2. Examine the table of earthquake data. Record any patterns that you observe.

_____

_____

DATA TABLE

Year	Location of Epicenter	Distance From Coast (km)	Depth of Focus (km)
1949	Olympia	116	53
1965	Seattle-Tacoma	141	63
1999	Satsop	58	41
2001	Nisqually	108	52
2001	Matlock	60	41

3. Draw a diagram showing how the edges of the Juan de Fuca and North American plates would move if they formed a convergent boundary. Use Figure 30 on page 682 of your textbook to help you draw this diagram.

4. Draw a diagram showing how the edges of the two plates would move if they formed a transform boundary. Use Figure 30 again to help you draw this diagram.

5. Use the information in the data table to construct a graph showing the location and depth of earthquakes. Plot the distance from the coast on the horizontal axis and the depth of the focus on the vertical axis. Label the vertical axis with zero at the top and maximum depth at the bottom.

6. Draw a curve as close as possible to all the points you plotted on your graph. The curve shows the shape and position of the boundary between the Juan de Fuca and North American plates. Compare your graph to the two diagrams you drew in Steps 3 and 4.

Analyze and Conclude

1. **Using Graphs** What kind of boundary do the Juan de Fuca and North American plates form? Explain how your graph supports your answer.

   The curve slopes down to the right, indicating that the border between the two plates slopes down

   to the East under the North American Plate as a convergent boundary.

2. **Inferring** What does your graph suggest about the direction in which the Juan de Fuca and North American plates are moving?

   The graph suggests that the North American Plate is moving west, over the Juan de Fuca Plate.

3. **Predicting** In California, the Pacific plate and the North American plate meet along a transform boundary called the San Andreas fault. Would you expect to observe a similar curve in a graph of the earthquake data from the San Andreas fault? Explain your answer.

   No, in a transform boundary, the plates form a vertical boundary that would appear as a vertical

   line on the graph.

4. **Drawing Conclusions** Based on your data, how is earthquake depth related to distance from a convergent plate boundary? Explain your answer.

   The depth of the earthquakes increases with distance from the boundary because the earthquake

   foci are located along the upper surface of the subducting plate.

Chapter 23   Earth's Surface   **Exploration Lab**

Modeling Erosion   See page 739 in the Teacher's Edition for more information.

Moving water is the major cause of erosion on Earth. In this lab, you will investigate some factors that affect the rate of erosion by moving water.

Problem   What are some of the factors that affect the rate of water erosion?

Materials

- metric ruler
- large sheet of cardboard
- plastic wrap
- newspaper
- soil

- blocks
- pencil
- paper cup
- scissors

- drinking straw
- modeling clay
- paper towels
- small rocks

Skills   Using Models, Inferring

Procedure 🔗 🏠 ✋ 🔧

1. Measure and record the length of the cardboard in centimeters. Wrap the cardboard with plastic wrap to keep it dry.

2. Put several sheets of newspaper on a flat surface. Place cardboard on the newspaper and spread a thin layer of soil over the cardboard.

3. To model a hillside, raise one end of the cardboard about 5 cm from the flat surface by placing blocks under one end.

4. Using a pencil, make a hole in a paper cup 1 cm from the bottom.

5. Cut the straw in half with the scissors and insert the end of one of the halves 2 cm into the hole in the cup.

6. Use modeling clay to seal the hole around the straw. Make sure that the clay forms a tight seal around the straw.

7. Place the cup in the middle of the raised end of the cardboard so that the straw is pointing downhill, as shown.

8. Place your finger over the straw's opening as another student fills the cup with water.

9. Remove your finger. Record your observations in the data table.

DATA TABLE

Elevation of Cardboard	Slope of Cardboard	Rocks	Observations

10. Clean the cardboard with paper towels and cover it again with soil. Put used soil in the trash.

11. Now use blocks to raise the end of the cardboard 15 cm above the flat surface. Repeat Steps 7 through 10.

12. Lower the end of the cardboard to 5 cm above the flat surface. Repeat Steps 7 through 10 again, but this time place a small rock on the cardboard directly in front of the straw. In the data table, record your observations about how water moves around the rock.

13. Repeat Step 12, but this time place a pile of several small rocks on the cardboard directly in front of the straw. In the data table, record your observations about how water moves around the rocks.

Analyze and Conclude

1. **Observing** Does water erosion create smooth curves or sharp angles?

   Water erosion produces smooth curves.

2. **Analyzing Data** How did increasing the elevation of the cardboard affect the speed of the water?

   Increasing the elevation of the cardboard increased the speed of the water.

3. **Calculating** The slope of a hillside is equal to its height divided by the horizontal distance it covers. Using the length of the table under the cardboard and the height it was raised, calculate and record the slope of the model hillside in each row of the data table.

   The slope equals the height the cardboard is raised divided by the length of the table under the

   cardboard. If the table under the cardboard is 100 cm long, the slope is 0.05. Note that the length

   of the table under the cardboard decreases slightly as the elevation of the cardboard is increased.

4. **Inferring** What is the relationship between the slope of a hillside and the rate of erosion?

   The steeper the hillside, the greater is the rate of erosion.

5. **Analyzing Data** Compare the movement of the water with one rock and several rocks in front of the straw. Explain any differences you observed.

   Increasing the number of rocks caused the stream of water to spread out more widely and to move

   more quickly than was the case with one rock.

Chapter 24   Weather and Climate   Exploration Lab

Determining Relative Humidity

See page 783 in the Teacher's Edition for more information.

To measure relative humidity, you can use a sling psychrometer. This device contains two thermometers. An absorbent wick keeps the bulb of one thermometer wet. As you spin the psychrometer, air flows over the wet bulb, increasing the rate of evaporation. In this lab, you will discover how a sling psychrometer measures the relative humidity of the surrounding air.

Problem How can you measure the relative humidity of the air?

Materials
- sling psychrometer
- relative humidity chart from Appendix G
- clock or watch with second hand

Skills Using Tables, Formulating Hypotheses

Procedure 🦠 🧤 🔪 ✋ 🧴

1. Wet the cotton wick of the sling psychrometer with water.

2. Observe the temperature of the wet-bulb thermometer. Then, spin the psychrometer for 30 seconds. **CAUTION:** *Take care not to spin the psychrometer near anyone or anything.*

3. Repeat Step 2 until the temperature of the wet-bulb thermometer remains constant. Then, in the data table, record the temperature of both thermometers.

DATA TABLE

Location	Dry Bulb Temp. (°C)	Wet Bulb Temp. (°C)	Relative Humidity (%)
Classroom	Typical data could consist of a dry-bulb reading of 21°C, a wet-bulb reading of 15°C, and a relative humidity of 53%. Data will depend on local conditions. In any case, the wet-bulb reading will be less than or equal to the dry bulb reading.		

4. Calculate the difference between your dry-bulb and wet-bulb temperatures.

5. In the relative humidity chart, find the row and column that list the dry-bulb temperature and the difference in temperature that you calculated. The number located where this row and column meet is the relative humidity of the classroom. Record the relative humidity in the data table.

6. Place the psychrometer on a flat surface. Observe the temperature of the wet-bulb thermometer every 30 seconds until it remains constant. Then, repeat Steps 2 through 5 at a location your teacher indicates.

Analyze and Conclude

1. Analyzing Data Why did the two thermometers have different temperatures?

The temperature of the wet-bulb thermometer is usually lower than the temperature of the dry-bulb

thermometer because evaporation of water from the wet bulb absorbed energy from the

thermometer, which cooled it.

2. Formulating Hypotheses Explain how the relative humidity of the air affected the difference between the temperatures of the two thermometers.

The difference in temperature between the two thermometers depends on the degree to which

evaporation cools the wet bulb. The lower the relative humidity, the greater is the rate at which water

evaporates, cooling the wet bulb. Relative humidity does not affect the temperature of the dry-bulb

thermometer. Therefore, the lower the relative humidity, the cooler the wet bulb will be, and the

greater the difference in temperature between the two thermometers will be.

3. Drawing Conclusions What do you think caused the difference in relative humidity between the two locations?

Factors that are likely to affect the relative humidity in various locations include sources of water,

especially warm water, and variation in the effectiveness of heating and cooling throughout the

school building.

4. Predicting How would the relative humidity change if you cooled the air in the classroom?

Cooling the room would increase the relative humidity. The maximum concentration of water vapor

in air is reduced at lower temperatures. Therefore, as the air in the room is cooled, the same

concentration of water vapor becomes a higher percentage of the maximum concentration, or a

higher relative humidity.

Chapter 25   The Solar System   **Exploration Lab**

Modeling the Solar System

See page 821 in the Teacher's Edition for more information.

You may have seen models and illustrations that compare the sizes of the planets, but do not accurately show their relative distances from the sun. In this lab, you will compare the sizes of the planets to their distances from the sun.

Problem How can you model both the relative sizes and distances of the planets in the solar system?

Materials
• calculator
• large sheet of unlined paper
• meter stick
• scale models of the sun and planets

Skills Calculating, Using Models

Procedure

1. To model the relative sizes of the planets' orbits, convert the distances of the planets from the sun in astronomical units to kilometers, using Figure 3 on pages 792 and 793 of your textbook. Record these distances in scientific notation.

Mercury: 5.8×10^7 km	Mars: 2.2×10^8 km	Uranus: 2.87×10^9 km
Venus: 1.1×10^8 km	Jupiter: 7.8×10^8 km	Neptune: 4.50×10^9 km
Earth: 1.5×10^8 km	Saturn: 1.4×10^9 km	Pluto: 5.91×10^9 km

2. Use the meter stick to draw a straight line down the entire length of the large sheet of unlined paper. Measure and record the length of this line in centimeters.

Sample answer: 42 cm

3. Label one end of the line *sun* and the other end *Pluto*.

4. To calculate the scale of your model, divide the length of the line in centimeters by Pluto's average distance from the sun in kilometers.

The answer will depend on the length given in Step 2. If the line is 42 cm long, the scale is

7.1×10^{-9} cm/km.

5. To determine Neptune's position, multiply Neptune's average distance from the sun by the scale of your model. Mark Neptune's position on the line in your model.

6. Repeat Step 5 for each of the remaining planets in the solar system.

7. Your teacher will provide a set of scale models of the sun and planets. Use a meter stick to measure and record the diameter of the model of Jupiter.

If a ball 17.5 cm in diameter is used for the sun, Jupiter would be about 2.3 cm in diameter.

8. To determine the scale of the planet models, divide the diameter of the model of Jupiter in centimeters by the actual diameter of Jupiter, which can be found in Figure 20 on page 811 of your textbook.

If the Jupiter model is 2.3 cm in diameter, the scale is 2.3 cm/143,000 km = 1.6×10^{-5} cm/km

9. To determine the size of the solar system at the scale of the planet models, multiply the actual distance from Pluto to the sun by the scale of the planet models. Convert the result from centimeters to meters and record this distance.

At the scale of the planet models provided in the answer to Step 7, the solar system model

would be approximately 983 m long.

Analyze and Conclude

1. **Using Models** How big would a model of the solar system be at the scale of the planet models you used? Explain your answer.

Answers should be twice the distance from Pluto to the sun given as an answer to Step 9,

which represents about half the major axis of Pluto's orbit.

2. **Analyzing Data** What difficulty would you have including the relative sizes of the planets on the paper model you made in Steps 1 through 6?

The orbits of the inner planets would be too small to draw or observe.

3. **Drawing Conclusions** Explain why it is difficult to model the sizes and distances of the planets at the same scale.

The distances among the planets and between the planets and the sun are many times greater

than the sizes of the planets.

Chapter 26   Exploring the Universe   **Exploration Lab**

Investigating Parallax
See pages 856 and 857 in the Teacher's Edition for more information.

Astronomers use parallax to measure the distances to nearby stars. In this lab, you will investigate the effect of distance on parallax. You will observe how an object appears to move against a distant background as you look at it first through one eye, and then through the other.

Problem How is parallax related to the distance to a star?

Materials
- unlined paper
- tape
- marker
- pencil
- meter stick
- index card
- graph paper

Skills Measuring, Using Models

Procedure

Figure 1

1. Tape three sheets of unlined paper to the wall horizontally, at eye level. Use a marker to draw 11 vertical marks 5 centimeters apart on the paper, as shown in Figure 1. The marks represent a distant background against which you will view a closer star. Label the marks in multiples of five from left to right, starting with 0 and ending with 50.

2. Facing the sheets of paper, stand directly in front of the 25-cm mark. Then, use a meter stick to measure a perpendicular distance of 7 m from the mark. Move to that spot and face toward the 25-cm mark. You must remain at this position until you have finished collecting all data.

3. Have a partner hold a pencil vertically at your eye level, as shown in Figure 1. The pencil should be 1 m in front of you. Your partner should use a meter stick to measure this distance. The pencil represents a nearby star.

4. Hold an index card over your left eye and look at the pencil with your right eye. Your right eye represents Earth's position at one point in its orbit. Move your head so the pencil lines up with the mark labeled 0.

5. Now, without moving your head, hold the index card over your right eye and look at the pencil with your left eye. Your left eye represents Earth's position at the opposite end of its orbit six months later. Note the number of the mark that lines up with the pencil. If the pencil is between two marks, estimate its position to the nearest whole number. Your partner should record this number in the appropriate place in the data table.

DATA TABLE Sample data are shown.

Distance to Star (m)	Right Eye (cm)	Left Eye (cm)	Parallax (cm) (Difference)
1.0	0	40	40
1.5	0	15	15
2.0	0	7	7
2.5	0	5	5
3.0	0	3	3

6. To determine the parallax, subtract the right-eye measurement (zero, in this case) from the left-eye measurement. Record the parallax in the appropriate place in the data table.

7. **Predicting** How do you and your partner think the parallax will change as your partner moves the pencil away from you? Your partner should record your prediction.

   Sample prediction: Parallax will decrease as the pencil moves.

8. Have your partner use a meter stick to move the pencil 0.5 m toward the marks. Without moving your head, cover your left eye and look at the pencil with your right eye. Your partner should record the number of the mark the pencil lines up with.

9. Without moving your head, cover your right eye and look at the pencil with your left eye. Your partner should record the number of the mark the pencil lines up with.

10. To determine the parallax, subtract the right-eye measurement from the left-eye measurement. Record the parallax in the appropriate place in the data table.

11. Repeat Steps 8 through 10 until the parallax is less than 1 cm.

12. Construct a graph of the distance to the star (pencil) against the parallax you calculated. Plot the parallax on the horizontal axis and the distance on the vertical axis.

Analyze and Conclude

1. **Using Graphs** What does your graph show is the relationship between the distance to the pencil and the pencil's parallax?

   The graph shows that as the distance increases, parallax decreases.

2. **Analyzing Data** Was your prediction in Step 7 correct? Explain your answer.

   If students predicted that the parallax would decrease, they were correct. They should explain

   that the parallax decreases as distance increases.

3. **Drawing Conclusions** Assume that a parallax of less than 1 cm is too small to be measured. What is the maximum distance at which the pencil would still have a parallax you can measure?

   Students should report a maximum distance of 4 to 6 m, depending on their visual acuity, the

   distance between their eyes, and the precision of their measurements.

4. **Applying Concepts** Parallax can only be used to measure the distances to nearby stars. Why can't this method be used to find the distances to far-away stars?

   Parallax of distant stars is too small to be measured using current technology.

5. **Inferring** Astronomers usually make two measurements of the position of a star six months apart, when Earth is at opposite sides of its orbit. How is this useful in determining the star's parallax?

   Making the measurements six months apart allows the points at which the measurements are

   made to be as far apart as possible. This allows parallax to be measured as accurately as

   possible, and thus for the greatest possible distances to be measured.